RT X-Ray Physics Review

RT X-Ray Physics Review

Walter Huda, Ph.D.

Department of Radiology and Radiological Science
Medical University of South Carolina
Charleston, South Carolina

and

Kerry Greene-Donnelly, R.T.(R)(M)(CT)(QM)

Department of Medical Imaging Sciences
SUNY Upstate Medical University
Syracuse, New York

MEDICAL PHYSICS PUBLISHING
Madison, Wisconsin

15 14 13 12 11   1 2 3 4 5 6

Library of Congress Control No.: 2011933323

ISBN 13: 978-1-930524-54-5
ISBN 10: 1-930524-54-4

Medical Physics Publishing
4513 Vernon Boulevard
Madison, WI 53705-4964
Phone: 1-800-442-5778, 608-262-4021
Fax: 608-265-2121
Web: www.medicalphysics.org

Printed in the United States of America

Dedication

Walter Huda dedicates this book to Joyce.

Kerry Greene-Donnelly dedicates this book to Dennis.

Acknowledgments

RT X-Ray Physics Review would not have been possible without the assistance of many colleagues. Kent Ogden, Ph.D., and Marsha Roskopf, R.T.(R) were instrumental in the acquisition of images and creation of graphics, in addition to offering their years of experience and knowledge with the authors. Thank you to the following individuals who offered their clinical expertise and aided in image acquisition: Andrew Smith, Ph.D., Janet Bentley, R.T.(R), Jennifer McBurnie, R.T.(R)(CT), Robyn Ouderkirk, R.T.(R)(CT), Richard Thompson, R.T.(R)(CT), and Donna Fritz.

A special thank you to those who reviewed all or part of the draft manuscript: Dominick DeMichele, R.T.(R)(CT), Charles Drago, R.T.(R)(CT), Colleen Donahue, R.T.(R)(MR), and Rosemary Morin, R.T.(R).

Contents

PART I. BASIC PHYSICS

PART II. IMAGING WITH X-RAYS

PART III. DOSE, QUALITY, AND SAFETY

Preface

I. Radiological Physics

Radiology is an ever-changing field in health care. Since the discovery of x-rays by Roentgen in 1895, many aspects of image production have improved. Advancement in the use of computers and imaging equipment has led to improvement in the detection of disease processes, more efficient patient care, and increased occupational safety. Radiological Physics is involved in every aspect of medical imaging, from image acquisition to display and storage.

Understanding and application of Radiological Physics is essential for the production of quality medical images using Radiography, Fluoroscopy, Mammography, Interventional Radiology, and Computed Tomography. Members of the imaging team include the radiologist, the medical physicist, and the technologist. The imaging team, by working together, provides quality imaging services while maintaining a high level of patient care.

Associated with most imaging modalities is the issue of radiation exposure for both the patient and the operators. Technologists must be aware of the radiation dose to the patient and personnel. One of the most important goals of imaging professionals is to ensure that radiation levels are kept As Low As Reasonably Achievable (i.e., ALARA principle). Exposure levels to operators and patients must also meet regulatory and accreditation limits.

II. Review Book Structure

This review book will assist the student technologist with preparation for the registry/licensing examination. As a review book, it is not intended to cover all Radiological Physics concepts fully, rather, it is to be used as part of a comprehensive registry preparation plan. Use of this review book will complement the student's understanding and application of radiological physics.

This review book is separated in to three units of study. Unit I presents basic concepts in physics, production/interaction of x-rays, and the x-ray tube. Unit II discusses radiographic detectors, the computer in imaging, projection radiography, fluoroscopy, and computed tomography. Unit III concludes the review book with radiation dosimetry, image quality, quality control practices, radiation biology, and protection. Each chapter has 30 questions for content review, and two 100-question comprehensive examinations are included at the end of this book.

The ARRT examination currently uses traditional radiation units, i.e., R, rad, and rem. The radiation quantities provided herein are generally provided using SI units, with traditional units to follow. In the text, the term "exposure" is not used, in favor of "Air Kerma." An Air Kerma of 10 mGy is taken to be approximately equal to an exposure of 1 R.

III. ARRT Exam

The American Registry of Radiologic Technologists (ARRT) oversees imaging-related credentialing examinations in the United States. The ARRT credentialing examinations are available for many modalities, such as Radiography, Mammography, and Computed Tomography. This review book has been produced for those taking the Radiography credentialing examination. The ARRT examination includes the following content areas: (1) radiation protection, (2) equipment operation and maintenance, (3) image production and evaluation, (4) radiographic procedures, and (5) patient care.

ARRT examinations are computer based and given at secure testing centers across the country. The exam contains 200 questions and must be completed in 3.5 hours. A scientific calculator is provided, as well as a writing surface and a pen. As each ARRT examination is unique, a scaled score exam is used, in that examinations are scaled on their level of difficulty to account for any variation.

A (scaled) test score of 75 is required to pass the ARRT exam. Further information on the American Registry of Radiologic Technologists can be obtained at the ARRT web site (www.arrt.org).

PART I. BASIC PHYSICS

Chapter 1

MATTER AND RADIATION

1.1 ENERGY

A. Units

- In the International System (SI), energy in expressed in **joules (J)**.
- At the atomic level, **electron volts (eV)** are commonly used.
- Outer shell electrons are bound to the atom with binding energies of a few eV.
- A thousand eV is 1 keV.
- Inner shell electrons in atoms commonly have binding energies of a few keV or a few tens of keV.
- A thousand keV is 1 MeV, or a million eV.

B. Energy forms

- **Potential energy** is the ability to do work based on an object's position.
- A ball at the top of a cliff has potential energy.
- **Kinetic energy** is the energy related to an object's motion.
- A ball dropped from the top of a cliff converts potential energy into kinetic energy.
- **Heat energy** results from molecules in motion.
- Increasing the amount of heat increases the movement of molecules.
- **Chemical energy** is the resulting energy from any chemical reaction.
- **Electrical energy** is related to electrons moving in a wire.
- Electrical energy can be converted into work using an electric motor.
- **Nuclear energy** is released during nuclear transformation.

C. Energy characteristics

- **Energy** is the ability to do work.
- Potential energy can be converted into kinetic energy and *vice versa*.
- The **law of conservation of energy** states that energy can be neither created nor destroyed.
- Quantum physics and relativity show that matter can be transformed into energy.
- Energy can also be used to create matter.
- The relationship between energy (E) and mass (m) is $E = mc^2$, where c is the velocity of light.
- Energy that moves through space is called **radiation**.

D. Power and work

- **Power** incorporates the time required to perform the work.
- Power is the rate at which work is done.
- Power is measured in **joules/second (J/s)**, which is a **watt (W)**.
- **Figure 1.1** illustrates an increase in energy produced over the time a light bulb is in use.

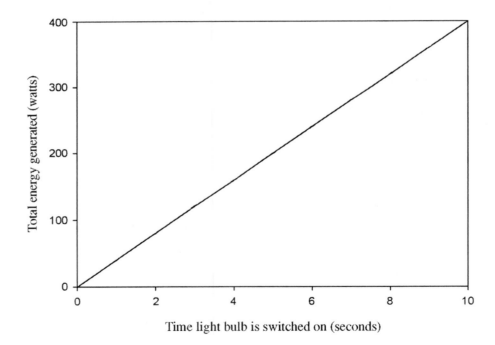

Figure 1.1
Total energy generated by a 40-watt light bulb
plotted against the time the bulb is switched on.

- In radiography, the energy produced increases with longer exposures.
- **Work** is the product of the force applied × the distance over which it is applied.

1.2 MATTER

A. Matter

- **Matter** is composed of atoms.
- Atoms unite to create molecules.
- **Mass** is measured in **kilograms (kg)** and quantifies matter.
- Common states of matter are gas, liquid, or solid.
- Matter can change states.
- The **law of conservation of matter** states that matter can be neither created nor destroyed.
- Matter may be converted into energy, and vice versa.

B. Atomic constituents

- **Atoms** contain electrons, protons, and neutrons.
- **Electrons** have a negative electrical charge.
- Electrons are small in size and have little mass.
- **Electrons are arranged in shells** around a nucleus.
- Protons and neutrons are termed **nucleons** due to their location in the nucleus.
- **Table 1.1** provides examples of energy levels within atoms.
- **Protons** have a positive charge.
- **Neutrons** have no charge and are electrically neutral.
- Protons and neutrons have masses that are ~2000 times larger than the electron mass.
- Atoms generally have the same number of electrons and protons.

Table 1.1
Typical energy levels in an atom

Atomic location	Typical energy levels		
	eV	keV	MeV
Outer shell electrons	5	0.005	0.000005
Inner shell electrons	1,000 to 100,000	1 to 100	0.001 to 0.1
Nucleus	5,000,000	5,000	5

C. Atomic number (Z)

- The **atomic number (Z)** describes the number of protons.
- The **atomic mass (A)** is the number of **protons (Z)** plus **neutrons (N)** in the nucleus.

$$A = Z + N.$$

- The type of **element** is determined by the **number of protons.**
- **Isotopes** are atoms that have the same number of protons but a different number of neutrons.
- Isotopes with the same atomic number (Z) all behave the same way during chemical reactions.

D. Atomic structure

- The structure of atoms is often called the **Bohr model.**
- Bohr's model is a replica of the solar system with the **nucleus as the center** and electrons revolving about it.
- Electrons revolve around the nucleus in specific shells, or energy levels.
- Electron shells are known as the **K shell, L shell, M shell, N shell,** etc.
- The closest shell to the nucleus is the K shell.
- The second closest shell is the L shell, then the M shell.
- Shells are numbered from the nucleus to the periphery of the atom by a shell number (n).
- K shells can contain up to two electrons.
- **Figure 1.2** shows the maximum number of electrons in the K, L, and M shells.
- The maximum number of electrons per shell is equal to $2n^2$.
- The maximum number of electrons in the outer shell is eight.

E. Binding energy

- **Electron binding energy** describes how tightly bound an electron is to the nucleus of its atom.
- The **electron binding energy is required to remove the electron** from an atom.
- The closer an electron is to the nucleus, the more attracted it is.
- **K-shell** electrons have the **highest binding energies.**
- Electron binding energy progressively gets smaller with increasing distance from the nucleus.
- K-shell binding energy is greater than the L-shell binding energy, which in turn is greater than the M-shell binding energy, and so on.
- The more protons in the nucleus, the greater the K-shell binding energy.

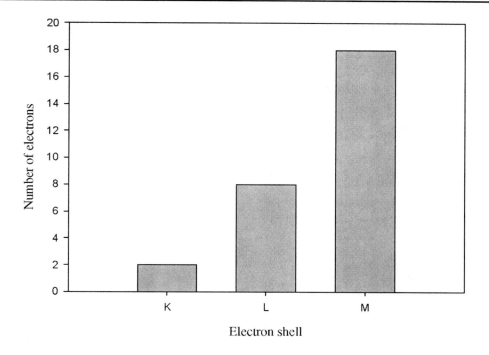

Figure 1.2
Maximum electron capacity in atomic shell structure.

- K-shell binding energy increases very rapidly with increasing atomic number (Z).
- **Table 1.2** lists the Z number and K-shell binding energies of common materials encountered during radiography.
- Calcium K-shell binding energy (i.e., 4 keV) is eight times greater than oxygen K-shell binding energy (i.e., 0.5 keV).
- Outermost shell electrons always have the lowest binding energies.
- The binding energy of outermost electrons is a few electron volts.

Table 1.2
K-shell binding energies for atoms of interest in diagnostic radiology

Atom	Atomic number (Z)	K-shell binding energy (keV)
Oxygen	8	0.5
Calcium	20	4.0
Iodine	53	33
Barium	56	37
Tungsten	74	70
Lead	82	88

1.3 ELECTROMAGNETIC RADIATION

A. Waves

- The number of cycles (oscillations) in a given time period is **frequency**.
- Frequency is usually given as cycles per second.
- **Frequency** is measured in **hertz (Hz)**.
- One hertz is 1 cycle per second.
- The wavelength is the distance between two successive crests of the wave.
- For all waves, **velocity** is equal to the product of **frequency (f)** and **wavelength (λ)**:

$$v = f \times \lambda.$$

B. Electromagnetic waves

- Electromagnetic waves have electric and magnetic fields that are continuously changing in a wavelike manner.
- **Electric fields** are responsible for the interaction of electrostatic charges.
- **Magnetic fields** are responsible for the interaction of magnetic poles.
- Electromagnetic energy travels at the **speed of light (3×10^8 m/s)**.
- The speed of light is a constant velocity for all electromagnetic radiation.
- **Wavelength and frequency of electromagnetic waves are inversely proportional.**
- Increasing the electromagnetic wave frequency reduces the wavelength.
- Decreasing the electromagnetic wave frequency increases the wavelength.

C. Electromagnetic spectrum

- Electromagnetic waves (energy) that pass through space are **electromagnetic radiation**.
- **Electromagnetic spectrum** includes radiowaves, microwaves, ultraviolet light, infrared light, visible light, and x-rays.
- **Radiowaves** have the lowest frequencies and the longest wavelengths.
- Radiowaves used in magnetic resonance (MR) imaging have wavelengths comparable to the size of humans.
- **Visible-light spectrum** covers a range of energies, starting with lower-energy red light and extending to include higher-energy violet radiation light photons.
- The wavelength of visible light is measured in **nanometers (nm)**.
- Visible light interacts with living cells, such as the rods and cones of the eye.

D. Photons

- A **photon** is the smallest quantity of any type of electromagnetic wave.

- A **bundle of energy** may be termed a **photon** or a **quantum**.

- Photons have no mass and travel through space at the speed of light.

- The **energy of a photon is directly proportional to its frequency**, with the constant of proportionality called **Planck's constant (h)**.

- **Figure 1.3** demonstrates the direct relationship between increased photon frequency and increased energy.

- Relationship between energy (E) and frequency (f) is **E = hf**. The greater the frequency, the higher the photon energy.

- Since f is c/λ, the photon energy may also be expressed as **E = h (c/λ)**, and photon energy is inversely proportional to photon wavelength.

- All photons exhibit both types of behavior (**wave-particle duality of electromagnetic energy**).

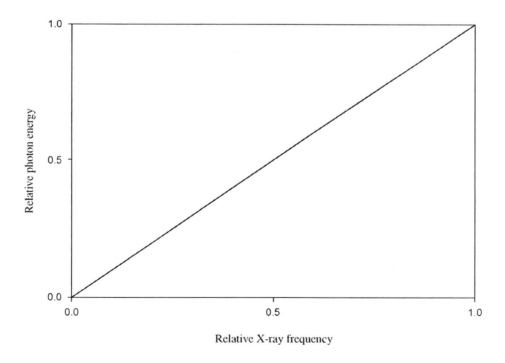

Figure 1.3
Graph showing the linear relationship between
x-ray photon energy and the corresponding x-ray frequency.

- Visible-light photons tend to behave more like waves than particles.
- High-frequency photons, including **x-rays** behave more like particles than waves.

E. Inverse square law

- **Intensity (I)** of electromagnetic waves **decreases with distance from the source.**
- The distance of an object from the source is SID (source-to-image distance).
- Decrease in intensity is inversely proportional to the square of the distance of the object from the source.
- This is called the **inverse square law.**
- Decrease in intensity with increasing distance is a result of the fact that the energy is distributed over a greater area.
- When the distance from the source is doubled, the intensity is only a quarter the intensity at the initial location.
- When the distance from the source is halved, the intensity is four times higher than the intensity at the initial location.
- **Table 1.3** shows various distances and the resulting intensities.
- Inverse square law applies to all electromagnetic radiation, including x-rays.

$$\frac{I_1}{I_2} = \frac{(SID_2)^2}{(SID_1)^2},$$

where I_1 represents the intensity at a source-to-object distance SID_1 and I_2 represents the intensity at a changed source-to-object distance SID_2.

Table 1.3
Variation of x-ray beam intensity with distance
from the x-ray source (inverse square law)

Distance from source (m)	Intensity (Relative to intensity at 1 m)
1/10	100
1/3	9
1	1
3	1/9
10	1/100

1.4 IONIZING RADIATION

A. Ionization

- Loss of an atomic electron is known as **ionization**.

- **Ionizing radiation** removes an electron from an atom.

- Upon losing an electron the remaining atom will possess a positive charge (+).

- Both the positively charged atom and negatively charged electron are **known as ions**. Together they form an **ion pair**, each maintaining an independent charge.

- **Ionizing radiation** is capable of damaging tissues.

- **Figure 1.4** shows the relationship between the energy deposited in tissues (keV), and the corresponding number of ionization events produced.

- A 30 keV electron thus produces about 1000 ionizations.

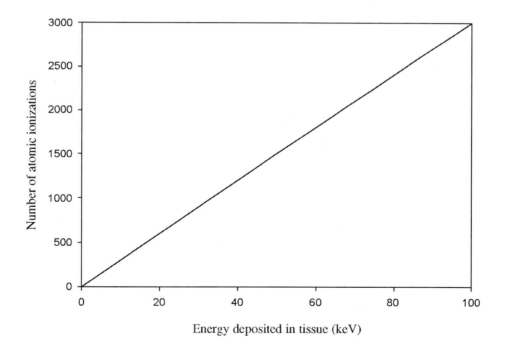

Figure 1.4
Number of atomic ionizations produced plotted against
the amount of energy deposited in tissue.

B. Ionizing radiations

- **Radiowaves, microwaves,** and **visible light** are not ionizing, since the photon energy is insufficient to eject an electron out of any atom.
- **Ultraviolet photons** have (just) sufficient photon energies to eject atomic electrons, and are therefore a **form of ionizing radiation.**
- **X-rays** are ionizing radiations.
- The photon energy of x-rays is sufficient to eject electrons out of atoms.
- **Gamma rays** are the result of a radioactive decay.
- Gamma rays used in nuclear medicine and radiotherapy are ionizing.
- **Gamma rays** are similar to x-rays but originate in nuclear transformations.
- **Particulate radiation (alpha and beta particles)** are also ionizing.
- **Table 1.4** lists typical photon energies of a range of electromagnetic radiations.

C. X-rays

- X-rays are electromagnetic waves that travel at the speed of light (c).
- An **x-ray photon** and a **visible light photon** are similar, except that x-rays have much higher frequency.
- Hence x-rays have a (much) shorter wavelength than visible light.
- **X-rays have high frequencies and short wavelengths.**
- The wavelength of an x-ray is comparable to the size of an atom.
- X-rays are usually characterized by their energy.

Table 1.4

Different types of electromagnetic radiations, typical photon energies,
and whether these radiations are ionizing

Type of radiation	Typical photon energy (keV)	Ionizing radiation
Radiowaves (MR)	0.000000001	No
Microwaves	0.000001	No
Visible light	0.002	No
Ultraviolet radiation	0.02	Yes
Diagnostic x-rays	50	Yes
Gamma rays (Cobalt-60)	1,000	Yes

- **X-ray energies** in diagnostic radiology range from **~20 keV to 150 keV**.
- X-rays cause ionization at a rate of **~100 ion pairs/cm** in air.
- In tissue, x-rays are **attenuated exponentially,** and do not have a finite range.

D. Alpha particles

- **Alpha particles** are given off during radioactive decay of heavy nuclei (e.g., uranium).
- **An alpha particle is a helium nucleus,** and contains two protons and two neutrons.
- Alpha particles generally have **~5 MeV of kinetic energy.**
- A typical **alpha particle** travels about **50 mm in air.**
- In tissues, alpha particles travel no more than 0.1 mm, because tissue has a much higher density than air.
- In air and tissues, an **alpha particle will ionize tens of thousands of atoms.**

E. Beta particles

- **Beta particles** are given off through the decay of unstable nuclei.
- **Beta particles** can be **negative** (i.e., **electrons**) or **positive** (i.e., **positrons**).
- Beta particles have little mass and may travel up to **1 m of air.**
- In tissue, beta particles can travel up to ~10 mm.
- Like alpha particles, **beta particles also generally ionize tens of thousands of atoms** in both air and tissue.
- Photons and beta particles ionize at similar rates in both air and tissue.
- Beta particles remove electrons in tissue, thus depleting their kinetic energy, which causes them to slow down and eventually stop.

QUESTIONS

Chapter 1: Matter and Radiation

1.1   In the SI system, energy is measured in:
A. joules.
B. ergs.
C. calories.
D. BTU.

1.2   When a ball is thrown into the air, the initial kinetic energy is converted into an energy form that is best characterized as:
A. electrical.
B. chemical.
C. nuclear.
D. potential.

1.3   The relationship between energy (E), matter (m), and the velocity of light is _____.
A. $E = mc$
B. $E = m/c$
C. $E = mc^2$
D. $E = m/c^2$

1.4   Power is measured in:
A. joules.
B. watts.
C. voltages.
D. amperes.

1.5   The smallest unit of matter is most likely an:
A. atom.
B. molecule.
C. gram-mole.
D. grain.

1.6   Normal constituents of atoms are least likely to be:
A. neutrons.
B. protons.
C. electrons.
D. photons.

1.7   Chemical properties of atoms are most likely determined by the number of:
A. protons.
B. neutrons.
C. neutrons and protons.
D. protons and electrons.

1.8   The relationship between the atomic mass (A), number of protons (Z), and number of neutrons (N) is _____.
A. $A = Z + N$
B. $Z = A + N$
C. $N = A + Z$
D. None of the above

1.9   The name of the innermost atomic electron shell is _____.
A. A
B. I
C. K
D. Varies with Z

1.10 The electron capacity of the innermost shell of any atom is _____.
A. 1
B. 2
C. 4
D. 8

1.11 Electron binding energies are most likely measured in:
A. watt.
B. joule.
C. eV.
D. horse power.

1.12 The K-shell binding energy (keV) of oxygen is _____.
A. 0.5
B. 4
C. 20
D. 33

1.13 The K-shell binding energy (keV) of lead is _____.
A. 25
B. 33
C. 70
D. 88

1.14 The binding energy (eV) of an outer shell electron of tissue is most likely _____.
   A. 1
   B. 10
   C. 100
   D. 1000

1.15 The speed of light (m/s) is normally taken to be _____.
   A. 3×10^2
   B. 3×10^4
   C. 3×10^6
   D. 3×10^8

1.16 The velocity of an x-ray photon is proportional to the photon:
   A. frequency.
   B. wavelength.
   C. energy.
   D. none of the above.

1.17 Which has the longest wavelength?
   A. Visible light
   B. Microwaves
   C. Radiowaves
   D. X-rays

1.18 Which has the highest frequency?
   A. Radiowaves
   B. Microwaves
   C. Infrared
   D. Gamma rays

1.19 The energy of an electromagnetic photon with frequency (f) is proportional to _____.
   A. f
   B. $f^{0.5}$
   C. f^2
   D. 1/f

1.20 When a photon's energy is doubled, the photon wavelength will be:
   A. the same.
   B. doubled.
   C. quadrupled.
   D. halved.

1.21 The fall-off of intensity of an x-ray source with distance is most likely called:
A. exponential.
B. linear.
C. inverse square law.
D. quadratic.

1.22 Removing an electron from an atom is likely known as:
A. ionization.
B. excitation.
C. isomeric transition.
D. annihilation.

1.23 The charge on an atom that has lost an electron is most likely:
A. negative
B. positive
C. neutral
D. positive or negative

1.24 Which of the following is a form of ionizing radiation?
A. Radiowaves
B. Microwaves
C. Visible light
D. Ultraviolet

1.25 Which of the following is not ionizing radiation?
A. Gamma rays
B. X-rays
C. Visible light
D. Ultraviolet

1.26 The energy of an x-ray photon (keV) in diagnostic radiology is most likely _____.
A. 0.5
B. 5
C. 50
D. 500

1.27 The charge on an alpha particle is _____.
A. −2
B. −1
C. +1
D. +2

1.28 The average distance an alpha particle travels in tissue is most likely _____ mm.
   A. 0.1
   B. 1
   C. 10
   D. 100

1.29 A beta particle is most like a(n):
   A. atom.
   B. proton.
   C. neutron.
   D. electron.

1.30 The distance a beta particle travels in air is most likely _____ m.
   A. 0.01
   B. 0.1
   C. 1
   D. 10

ANSWERS[1]

Chapter 1: Matter and Radiation

1.1	A	The SI unit for energy is a joule (J); however, radiology often uses an electron volt (eV).	*p. 4 Bushong* *p. 22 Carlton/Adler*
1.2	D	Potential energy is the energy of an object due to its position.	*p. 24 Bushong* *p. 28 Carlton/Adler*
1.3	C	$E = mc^2$	*p. 5 Bushong* *p. 22 Carlton/Adler*
1.4	B	P = Energy/t The SI unit for power is joules/second, or a watt (W).	*p. 23 Bushong* *p. 15 Carlton/Adler*
1.5	A	Atoms are the smallest particles.	*p. 38 Bushong* *p. 22 Carlton/Adler*
1.6	D	Atoms are composed of neutrons, protons, and electrons. Photons are not part of an atom.	*p. 40 Bushong* *p. 34 Carlton/Adler*
1.7	A	The number of protons within an atom determines chemical properties, and the number of electrons determines if the atom is electrically neutral.	*p. 41 Bushong* *p. 23 Carlton/Adler*
1.8	A	The atomic mass number (A) represents the number of Protons (Z) + Neutrons (N) in a nucleus.	*p. 46 Bushong* *p. 25 Carlton/Adler*
1.9	C	The electron shells within an atom are labeled, K being the innermost shell.	*p. 42 Bushong* *p. 26 Carlton/Adler*
1.10	B	The maximum number of electrons per shell can be calculated with the following equation: $2n^2$, where n is the shell number ($2 * 1^2 = 2$).	*p. 43 Bushong* *p. 26 Carlton/Adler*
1.11	C	Binding energy is measured in eV or keV.	*p. 44 Bushong* *p. 27 Carlton/Adler*
1.12	A	K-shell binding energy of oxygen is 0.53 keV.	*p. 53 Bushong* *p. 28 Carlton/Adler*

---

[1] As a study aid, page numbers for additional study are given for the following references:
Bushong SC: *Radiologic Science for Technologists,* 9th ed. St. Louis, MO: Mosby, 2008.
Carlton RR, Adler AM: *Principles of Radiographic Imaging: An Art and a Science,* 4th ed. Albany, NY: Delmar Publishing Inc., 2005.

| 1.13 | D | K-shell binding energy of lead is 88 keV. | *p. 53 Bushong* |
| | | | *p. 28 Carlton/Adler* |

| 1.14 | B | Outer shell binding energies of tissue are ~10 eV. | *p. 26 Carlton/Adler* |

| 1.15 | D | All electromagnetic radiation travels at the same velocity (3×10^8 m/s). | *p. 60 Bushong* |
| | | | *p. 34 Carlton/Adler* |

| 1.16 | D | All electromagnetic radiations travel at the same velocity, 3×10^8 m/s. | *p. 60 Bushong* |
| | | | *p. 34 Carlton/Adler* |

| 1.17 | C | Radiofrequency has the longest wavelength and the lowest frequency. | *p. 61 Bushong* |
| | | | *p. 36 Carlton/Adler* |

| 1.18 | D | Gamma rays/x-rays have the shortest wavelength and the highest frequency. | *p. 61 Bushong* |
| | | | *p. 31 Carlton/Adler* |

| 1.19 | A | A photon's energy is directly proportional to its frequency. | *p. 62 Bushong* |
| | | | *p. 33 Carlton/Adler* |

| 1.20 | D | $v = f \times \lambda$, where v = velocity, f = frequency, and λ = wavelength. All photons travel at the same velocity so that wavelength and frequency are inversely proportional. | *p. 60 Bushong* |
| | | | *p. 34 Carlton/Adler* |

| 1.21 | C | The inverse square law may be applied to calculate the effect, $(I_1/I_2) = (d_2/d_1)^2$, where I_1 and I_2 are the radiation intensity and d_1 and d_2 = distance. | *p. 67 Bushong* |
| | | | *p. 40 Carlton/Adler* |

| 1.22 | A | Ionization is the removal of an electron from an atom | *p. 5 Bushong* |
| | | | *p. 25 Carlton/Adler* |

| 1.23 | B | Ionization is the removal of an electron from an atom. The atom is the positively charged ion and the free electron is the negatively charged ion. | *p. 5 Bushong* |
| | | | *p. 25 Carlton/Adler* |

| 1.24 | D | Ionizing radiation includes ultraviolet, x-rays, and gamma rays; all other electromagnetic radiation lacks sufficient energy to ionize. | *p. 63 Bushong* |
| | | | *p. 137 Carlton/Adler* |

| 1.25 | C | Ionizing radiation includes ultraviolet, x-rays, and gamma rays; all other electromagnetic radiation lacks sufficient energy to ionize. | *p. 63 Bushong* |
| | | | *p. 137 Carlton/Adler* |

| 1.26 | C | Diagnostic x-rays are generated at voltages ranging between 50–150 kVp, and the average energy is about 50 keV. | *pp. 144 & 149 Bushong* |
| | | | *p. 130 Carlton/Adler* |

| 1.27 | D | Alpha particles contain 2 protons and 2 neutrons, resulting in a +2 charge. | *p. 49 Bushong* |
| | | | *p. 137 Carlton/Adler* |

1.28   A   Alpha particles can travel only 0.1 mm in tissue.   *p. 53 Bushong*
                                                                        p. 137 Carlton/Adler

1.29   D   Beta emission results in an electron released from the   *p. 49 Bushong*
             nucleus of an atom.   *p. 137 Carlton/Adler*

1.30   C   Beta particles can travel 1 m in air.   *p. 53 Bushong*
                                                                        p. 137 Carlton/Adler

Chapter 2

PHYSICS LAWS

2.1 BASICS

A. Mechanics

- **Mechanics** addresses objects at rest (statics) and objects in motion (dynamics).
- **Velocity** measures how fast an object moves.
- Velocity is also referred to as "speed."
- Velocity is equal to **distance traveled [d] divided by time [t] ($v = d/t$)**.
- **Velocity** is expressed in **meters per second (m/s)**.
- Velocity of an object may change.
- **Acceleration** is used to describe the rate of change in velocity over time.
- Change in velocity divided by time provides an object's acceleration, expressed in **meters per second squared (m/s^2)**.
- The equation for average **acceleration** is change in velocity ($v_{final} - v_{initial}$) **divided by the time** over which the velocity changes from $v_{initial}$ to v_{final}.
- An acceleration of zero describes an object with a constant velocity.

B. Newton's laws of motion

- **First law (inertia)** states that an object will remain at rest or, if in motion, will maintain velocity in a straight line unless an external force is exerted.
- A toy car rolling across the floor will first slow and then stop due to friction, the external force that disrupts the car's constant velocity.
- **Second law (force)** defines **Force (F)** applied to an object as the product of the object's **mass (m)** and the resulting **acceleration (a)**.

$$\text{Force} = \text{mass} \times \text{acceleration} \qquad (F = ma)$$

23

- Sliding an empty box across the floor requires little force due to the relatively low mass of the object, but a full box mass increases, requiring a greater force.
- **Third law (action/reaction)** states that for every action (force), there is an equal force in the opposite direction.

C. Temperature

- **Temperature** is a physical property that expresses the notions of hot and cold in a quantitative manner.
- Objects of low temperature are cold, whereas hot objects have a high temperature.
- Thermometers are used to measure **temperature**.
- Most countries use the Celsius scale for temperature measurements.
- The United States uses the Fahrenheit scale, where water freezes at 32 °F and boils at 212 °F.
- To convert °F to °C, subtract 30 and divide by 2.
- To convert °C to °F, double, then add 30.
- **Figure 2.1** shows that the Celsius and Fahrenheit scales have a direct relationship.

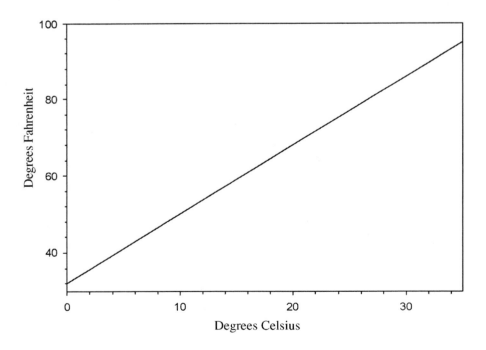

Figure 2.1
Relationship between degrees Celsius and degrees Fahrenheit.

- The Kelvin scale is used in science and engineering, and has the same incremental scaling as the Celsius scale.

- Absolute zero (0 Kelvin) is equal to −273 °C.

D. Heat

- **Heat** is a form of energy.

- The **calorie** is defined as the heat (energy) required to raise the temperature of 1 g of water through 1 °C.

- Heat can be transmitted through conduction, convection, or radiation.

- **Conduction** occurs when objects are **in contact**, allowing the heat of one object to be conducted to the other.

- Over time the temperature of the separate objects will equalize.

- **Convection** allows the molecules of the "hotter" gas or liquid to migrate from one area to another.

- **Thermal radiation** is the release of heat through the **emission of infrared radiation.**

- **X-ray anodes** transfer their heat through **radiation.**

- **Table 2.1** contains examples of heat transfer and the type of transmission.

Table 2.1
Methods of heat transfer

Heat transfer mode	Example
Conduction	Heat flowing up a spoon that is immersed in a hot cup of coffee (metals are good conductors)
Convection	Water in a heated pot rises to the top, and the cooler water at the top sinks to the bottom (macaroni will rise and fall)
Radiation	Sunlight flowing away from the sun without the presence of any intervening matter (solid or fluid)

2.2 ELECTROSTATICS

A. Electrical charges

- **Matter** may have an electrical charge that is either positive or negative.

- The electron has the least electrical charge.

- Electrons and protons have equal charges: one negative and the other positive.

- **Electrons** in the outermost shell of atoms can migrate to other atoms.
- **Protons** are not mobile and remain in the nucleus of an atom.
- Objects become charged when they gain or lose electrons.
- **Friction, induction, or contact** with a battery may charge an object.
- The Earth is referred to as an **electrical ground** because it can receive unlimited electric charges.
- The observation and investigation of charged particles is **electrostatics**.

B. Electrostatic laws

- Individual **electric charges** have an **electric field**.
- The direction of the electric field is from positive charges to negative charges.
- Electric fields are used to characterize forces between electric charges.
- **Laws of electrostatics** explain how charged particles relate to each other.
- Like electrical charges repel each other.
- Unlike electrical charges attract each other.
- Attraction and repulsion of charges is described as **electrostatic force**.
- **Coulomb's law** quantifies the attraction and repulsion of electric charges.
- Electrostatic force is directly proportional to the product of electrostatic charges.
- Electrostatic force is inversely proportional to the square of the distance between electrostatic charges (**inverse square law**).
- **Table 2.2** shows examples of the application of Coulomb's law.

Table 2.2

Illustration of how the force between changes with the number of charges, and the distance between the charges. When A and B have the same polarity (sign), the force is repulsive, and when the charges have opposite polarity, the force is attractive.

Charge on A	Charge on B	Distance between A and B	Relative Force between A and B
+1	+1	1	1
+2	+1	1	2
+2	+3	1	6
+1	+1	2	1/4
+1	+1	1/2	4

C. Electric voltage

- Electric charges contain **potential energy.**
- Similar electric charges have potential energy when positioned near one another.
- When repulsion occurs, the charges gain **kinetic energy** as they move apart.
- **Volt (v)** is the unit of electric voltage, and is also sometimes referred to as a "potential."
- A volt describes potential energy/unit charge, or a **joule/coulomb (1 V = 1 J/C).**
- In the United States, most residential electric voltage is **110V.**
- Most x-ray generators cannot operate at residential voltages.
- **X-ray generators usually use voltages greater than 110V, i.e., 400V.**

2.3 ELECTRICITY

A. Electrodynamics

- **Electric current** is the result of an electric voltage being applied to a wire, which causes electrons to flow along the wire.
- Materials that allow the flow of electrons are **conductors.**
- Metals are generally considered to be good conductors.
- Materials that do not allow the flow of electrons are **insulators.**
- Examples of good insulators are glass or wood.
- Materials that can act as a conductor or as an insulator, depending on conditions, are considered **semiconductors.**
- **Silicon (Si)** and **germanium (Ge)** are examples of semiconductors.
- The flow of electrons is decreased at higher temperatures so that cooling materials allow for the flow of electrons with less **resistance.**
- Specific materials known as **superconductors have no resistance** to the flow of electrons when cooled below a "critical temperature."
- Examples of superconductors are **niobium (Nb)** and **titanium (Ti).**
- The observation and investigation of moving electric charges is **electrodynamics.**

B. Electric circuits

- Conductors connected in a closed arrangement represent an **electrical circuit.**
- **Impeding the flow of electrons,** or **resistance,** reduces the number of electrons available.

- **Coulomb (C)** is used to measure electric charge, $1\ C = 6 \times 10^{18}$ electron charges.
- **Ampere (A)** is used to measure electrical current.
- **1 A** equals the electric charge of **1 coulomb per second (C/s)** flowing through a conductor.
- **Electric voltage** is measured in **volts (V).**
- **Electric resistance** is measured in **ohms (Ω).**
- **Ohm's law** describes the relationship between electric current, voltage, and resistance within an electric circuit.
- Ohm's law states that the potential voltage across the circuit is equal to the current $\times$ the resistance.
- **V = IR, where V is the potential in volts, I is the current in amperes, and R is the resistance in ohms.**
- **Figure 2.2** shows Ohm's law graphically.

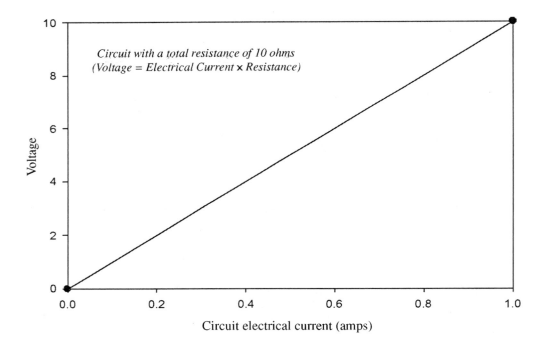

Figure 2.2
Relationship between electrical current and voltage in a circuit
illustrating Ohm's law (V = I $\times$ R).

C. AC/DC electricity

- **Applying a voltage** in an electrical circuit **causes electrons to move.**
- The positive region of an electrical circuit is called the **anode,** and negative region is called the **cathode.**
- Electrons are repelled from cathodes and attracted to anodes.
- The flow of electrons in one direction is termed **direct current (DC).**
- The flow of electrons in one direction, then the opposing direction is termed **alternating current (AC).**
- In a U.S. domestic home, every 1/60 of a second a complete cycle—start of flow in one direction, stop, start of flow in opposite direction, stop—occurs.
- Alternating current is said to have a **60 Hz current,** since there are 60 complete cycles every second.

D. Single-phase/Three-phase electricity

- Power supplies to homes in the United States have a minimum of two wires and are known as **single phase.**
- **Single-phase** power supplies have one wire that has an oscillating voltage, with the other carrying no voltage.
- If there is a third wire, this is an "earth" for reasons of safety.
- U.S. electricity is an **alternating current (AC)** that oscillates at **60 cycles per second (60 Hz).**
- **Three-phase** power supplies have **three lines of voltage.**
- **Figure 2.3** depicts **three-phase power,** each 120° out of phase with the others.
- Three-phase power supplies provide more power than single phase.

E. Electric power

- **Watt (W)** measures electrical power.
- **1 W = 1 A flowing through 1 V.**
- **Power (W) = voltage (V) × current (A).**
- $P = IV$, where P is the power in watts, I is the current in amperes, and V is the electric potential in volts.
- **Alternatively, $P = I \times V = I \times (IR) = I^2R$, where R is resistance in ohms.**
- **Table 2.3** lists power levels of electrical systems.
- Standard radiographic equipment requires much greater power levels (e.g., 100 kW) than is used in household appliances, such as microwaves (e.g., 1 kW).

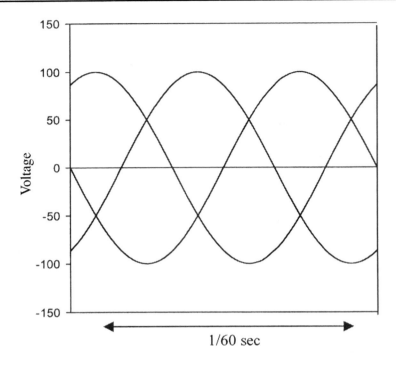

Figure 2.3
Variation in voltage over time in each of three wires
in a three-phase power supply.

Table 2.3
Power requirements of electrical equipment

Electrical equipment	Typical electrical power use (watts)
Bright flashlight	10
Bright light bulb	100
High capacity microwave	1000
Large domestic home	5000
X-ray generator	100,000

2.4 MAGNETISM

A. Magnetism

- Matter may exhibit **magnetism.**
- **Magnetic fields** may be displayed through an intensity line drawing.
- Electrons rotate on an axis, which is termed "electron spin."
- **Rotation of electrons** on their axis **creates a magnetic field.**
- Electrons found in pairs cancel out each other's magnetic field.
- Magnetic field lines are closed loops; the fields are termed **dipoles.**
- The SI unit **tesla (T)** is currently used to describe magnetic field strength.
- The unit **gauss (G)** had historically been used to describe magnetic field strength.
- The Earth has a magnetic field of ~50 µT at the equator, with a maximum of ~100 µT at the poles.
- Common household magnets have magnetic fields of ~100,000 µT, (i.e., 0.1 T).
- **Table 2.4** compares magnetic field strengths and commonly encountered sources.

Table 2.4
Examples of magnetic field strengths

Type of magnet	Approximate strength (µT)
Earth's magnetic field (equator)	50
Earth's magnetic field (North or South Pole)	100
Common household magnet	100,000
Magnet in MR scanner	1,500,000 (i.e., 1.5 T)

B. Magnetic materials

- Atoms with an **even number of electrons** generally have **no magnetic field.**
- Atoms having an **odd number of electrons** will possess a magnetic field.
- Materials composed of atoms with magnetic fields may function like a **magnet** if the individual atomic **dipoles** align.
- Materials composed of atoms with nonaligned magnetic fields are capable of acting like a magnet when placed in a strong external magnetic field.
- Magnetic susceptibility describes the ease with which materials can be magnetized.
- **Ferromagnetic materials** are susceptible to magnetic fields and include **iron, cobalt, and nickel.**

C. Magnets

- Magnets may be naturally occurring.
- The Earth is a **natural magnet** due to its rotation on an axis.
- Magnets may also be artificially induced, permanent, and electromagnets.
- Man-made **permanent magnets** place iron in a strong electromagnetic field, which aligns the atomic dipoles in the same direction.
- When individual magnetic dipoles fall out of alignment, the material loses its magnetic properties.
- **Electromagnets** are created when an electrical current is allowed to flow through a coil of wire.
- A **core of iron** placed within the coil of wire can **increase the intensity** of the magnetic field.
- Electromagnets have the advantage of being turned on or off.

D. Magnetic laws

- Magnets possess two poles known as "north" and "south."
- **Magnetic field lines** run from the magnet north pole to its south pole.
- Magnetic poles are analogous to positive and negative electrostatic charges.
- Like poles repel.
- Unlike poles attract.
- The force between magnets is proportional to the product of magnetic pole strengths divided by the square of the distance between them (**inverse square law**).
- **Figure 2.4** illustrates graphically the inverse square law.

E. Electromagnetism

- **Moving charged particles,** such as electrons, form a **magnetic field** that is perpendicular to the flow of the particle.
- Perpendicular magnetic fields are the result of flowing electrons in a closed section of wire.
- **Electric current can be induced through modulating magnetic fields.**
- A magnetic field alone cannot induce an electric current.
- The magnetic field must change to induce a current.

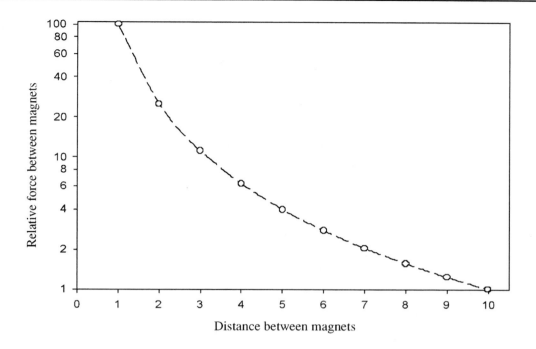

Figure 2.4
Relative force between magnets plotted against the distance between the magnets.

2.5 GENERATORS/TRANSFORMERS

A. Generators

- Creation of electric current is accomplished by a **generator.**

- Mechanical motion can create current in a coil of wire.

- A coil of wire is placed with strong magnetic poles on each side.

- The coil is mechanically rotated within the magnetic field, and an **electric current** is induced within the coil.

- The current will not be constant, but will vary with the coil position relative to the **magnetic fields.**

- The current is initially induced in one direction, and changes to the opposite direction as the coil rotates.

- This change in direction is termed **alternating current (AC).**

- The level of induced current is dependent on the magnetic field strength.

- Induced currents also depend on the speed of the magnetic field change, the angle at which the field crosses the conductor, and the number of turns within the coil.

B. Electromechanical devices

- **Electric motors** provide mechanical motion from electric current.
- X-ray tubes rely on **induction motors** for **movement of the rotor shaft.**
- **Rotors** in x-ray tubes are composed of copper and iron, allowing for movement through attraction to strong external magnetic fields.
- The strong magnetic fields are located about the rotor shaft and are known as **stators.**
- Rotors use induction motors and there is no current supplied to the rotor assembly.
- Induction is used to create current within the rotor.
- The stator assemblies, **electromagnets,** are turned on to create a moving magnetic field.
- The changing magnetic field induces a current in the rotor winding, generating its own magnetic field, resulting in continuous motion.

C. Transformers

- A **transformer** is used to vary the voltage intensity of **AC electricity.**
- A continuous loop of **ferromagnetic** material is bound on each side with independent coils of wire, a primary coil and a secondary coil.
- The **magnetic fields** created in the primary coil will influence the secondary coil.
- Modulating the current in the primary coil will affect the current in the secondary coil.
- The change in **voltage** is **directly proportional** to the turns ratio of the **number of turns** in the **secondary coil (N_s)** to the number of turns in the **primary coil (N_p).**
- The **turns ratio** of a transformer is represented as N_s/N_p.
- The turns ratio is proportional to the change in voltage within the transformer.
- Turns ratios greater than 1 are termed **step up transformers**, due to the increase in voltage in the secondary coil.
- A turns ratio of less than 1 is considered a **step down transformer**, with a decrease in voltage in the secondary coil.
- **Table 2.5** provides examples of step up and step down transformers and the effects on voltage and amperage.
- **Voltage** and **current** are inversely related so that when one increases, the other decreases.
- Doubling the voltage in a transformer would normally halve the output current.

Table 2.5
Output current and voltage for an ideal transformer where the input current is 1 amp
and the input voltage is 100 volts (i.e., 100–watt power transformer)

Turns ratio	Output voltage (volts)	Output current amps (A)	Output current milliamps (mA)
0.1	10	10	10,000
1[a]	100	1	1000
10	1,000	0.1	100
100	10,000	0.01	10

[a]Known as an isolation transformer

D. Rectification

- In the United States, electrical current is supplied as **alternating current (AC)**, which oscillates at 60 Hz.

- A 60-Hz alternating current changes direction twice per cycle, or 120 times per second.

- **X-ray tubes** require **direct current (DC)**, so that electrons always travel in the same direction from the **cathode** (filament) to the **anode** (target).

- Alternating current (AC) can be redirected to form DC current in a process known as **rectification**.

- **Rectification** circuits contain diodes.

- **Diodes** are electronic devices that allow electrons to flow in one direction only.

- **Figure 2.5** illustrates a rectification circuit.

- Because transformers require alternating current (AC), rectification occurs in the **high voltage section after** the secondary side of the **transformer**.

- After rectification, the cathode is always negative and the diode is always positive.

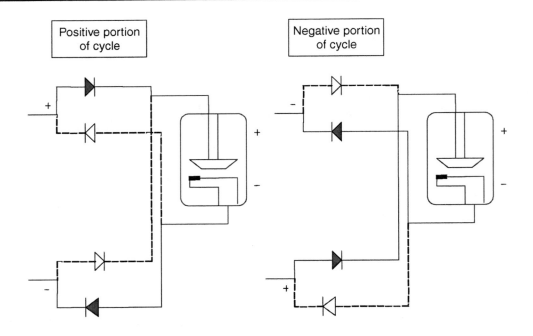

Figure 2.5
Full-wave rectified circuits utilize two diodes to redirect flow,
allowing for use of both the positive and negative portions of the cycle.

QUESTIONS

Chapter 2: Physics Laws

2.1   When an object travels a distance d in a time t, the velocity is _____.
A. d/t
B. t/d
C. d^2/t
D. t^2/d

2.2   An acceleration of zero implies that the velocity of an object is:
A. increasing.
B. decreasing.
C. constant.
D. indeterminate.

2.3   The relationship between a Force (F), mass (m), and acceleration (a) is:
A. $F = m \times a$.
B. $M = F \times a$.
C. $a = m \times F$.
D. $F = m + a$.

2.4   90 °F on the centigrade scale is approximately _____.
A. 10
B. 20
C. 30
D. 40

2.5   Transmission of heat is least likely to involve:
A. conduction.
B. convection.
C. radiation.
D. transmutation.

2.6   Observation and investigation of charged particles is known as:
A. mechanics.
B. electrostatics.
C. electrodynamics.
D. statics.

2.7   How would doubling one of the charges affect the size of the electrostatic force?
    A. Have no effect
    B. Double it
    C. Quadruple it
    D. Halve it

2.8   Units of electric voltage are:
    A. joules/coulomb.
    B. joules/second.
    C. coulomb/joule.
    D. coulomb/second.

2.9   Observation and investigation of moving electric charges is known as:
    A. electrodynamics.
    B. electrostatics.
    C. induction.
    D. electromagnetism.

2.10 Which of the following is most likely an insulator?
    A. Copper
    B. Oil
    C. Silver
    D. Tungsten

2.11 When 10 coulombs flow through a circuit in 0.1 second, the electrical current (A) is _____.
    A. 0.1
    B. 1
    C. 10
    D. 100

2.12 Electrical resistance is measured in:
    A. coulombs.
    B. ohms.
    C. amperes.
    D. hertz.

2.13 The relationship between the voltage (V), electric current (I), and resistance (R) in an electrical circuit is:
    A. $V = IR$.
    B. $V = I^2R$.
    C. $V = I/R$.
    D. $V = R/I$.

2.14 Domestic AC electricity in the United States has a frequency (Hz) of _____.
  A. 30
  B. 60
  C. 90
  D. 120

2.15 The phase difference in degrees of a 3-phase power supply is _____.
  A. 0
  B. 45
  C. 90
  D. 120

2.16 What is the power dissipation (kW) when a current of 10 A flows in a circuit with a voltage of 100 V?
  A. 1
  B. 10
  C. 100
  D. 1000

2.17 What is the non-SI unit of magnetic field strength?
  A. Gauss
  B. Hertz
  C. Ohm
  D. Candela

2.18 The earth's magnetic field (μT) is most likely _____.
  A. 0.5
  B. 5
  C. 50
  D. 500

2.19 An electromagnet most likely requires the application of:
  A. electric currents.
  B. magnetic fields.
  C. mechanical forces.
  D. moving objects.

2.20 Which type of magnet is easiest to turn on and off?
  A. Natural magnet
  B. Permanent magnet
  C. Temporary magnet
  D. Electromagnet

2.21 How would doubling pole strength of each of two magnets affect the size of the magnetic force?
    A. Have no effect.
    B. Double it.
    C. Quadruple it.
    D. Halve it.

2.22 How would doubling the distance between magnetic poles affect the size of the magnetic force?
    A. Halve it.
    B. Reduce to a quarter.
    C. Double it.
    D. Quadruple it.

2.23 To induce an electric current, a magnetic field needs to:
    A. change.
    B. exceed 0.1 T.
    C. last >1 second.
    D. remain constant.

2.24 A rotor shaft of an x-ray tube is most likely moved by use of a(n):
    A. induction motor.
    B. rectifier.
    C. transformer.
    D. generator.

2.25 Electrical power is most likely produced by a:
    A. generator.
    B. rectifier.
    C. transformer.
    D. none of the above.

2.26 Transformers are most likely used to change the magnitude of electrical:
    A. voltage.
    B. resistance.
    C. frequency.
    D. power.

2.27 Transformers require _____ current to operate.
   A. DC
   B. AC
   C. rectified
   D. constant

2.28 If a transformer increases the voltage 100%, the change in electrical current is most likely:
   A. +100%.
   B. +50%.
   C. 0% (no change).
   D. −50%.

2.29 A rectification circuit is most likely to consist of:
   A. diodes.
   B. resistances.
   C. coils.
   D. electromagnets.

2.30 A rectification circuit is most likely found in an x-ray:
   A. electrical generator.
   B. tube housing.
   C. control panel.
   D. collimator assembly.

ANSWERS[1]

Chapter 2: Physics Laws

2.1   A $v = d/t$, where v = velocity, d = distance traveled, and t = time.

p. 19 Bushong
p. 34 Carlton/Adler

2.2   C   Acceleration is the rate of change in velocity within a specific time period.
$a = (v_f - v_o)/t$, where a = acceleration, v_f = final velocity, v_o = original velocity, and t = time.

p. 20 Bushong
p. 34 Carlton/Adler

2.3   A   Newton's second law states that the mass of an object multiplied by the acceleration produced equals the force applied. $F = ma$, where F = force, m = mass of object, and a = acceleration.

p. 21 Bushong
p. 34 Carlton/Adler

2.4   C   Conversion from °F to °C can be calculated by subtracting 30 and dividing by 2, i.e., (90 – 30)/2 equals 30 °C.

n/a Bushong
n/a Carlton/Adler

2.5   D   Heat is transferred via conduction, convection, and radiation, but not transmutation.

p. 25 Bushong
p. 46 Carlton/Adler

2.6   B   The study of static electric charges is known as electrostatics.

p. 73 Bushong
p. 39 Carlton/Adler

2.7   B   Doubling one charge will double the force.

n/a Bushong
n/a Carlton/Adler

2.8   A   Voltage represents the electric potential, measured as joules/coulomb (J/C).

p. 77 Bushong
p. 15 Carlton/Adler

2.9   A   The study of electric charges in motion is known as electrodynamics.

p. 78 Bushong
p. 39 Carlton/Adler

2.10   B   Oil is used as an insulator in x-ray tubes. Most metals are good conductors, not insulators.

p. 90 Bushong
p. 45 Carlton/Adler

2.11   D   100 A of current is created when 10 coulombs flow in 0.1 second (1 A = 1 coulomb/s).

p. 78 Bushong
na Carlton/Adler

---

[1] As a study aid, page numbers for additional study are given for the following references:
Bushong SC: *Radiologic Science for Technologists,* 9th ed. St. Louis, MO: Mosby, 2008.
Carlton RR, Adler AM: *Principles of Radiographic Imaging: An Art and a Science,* 4th ed. Albany, NY: Delmar Publishing Inc., 2005.

2.12	B	Electrical resistance is measured in ohms.	*p. 79 Bushong* *p. 48 Carlton/Adler*
2.13	A	V = IR, where V = electrical potential in volts, I = electric current in amperes, and R = resistance in ohms.	*p. 79 Bushong* *p. 47 Carlton/Adler*
2.14	B	Alternating current (AC) operates at 60 Hz in the United States.	*p. 81 Bushong* *p. 91 Carlton/Adler*
2.15	D	Each phase of energy is one-third a cycle different from the next, such that they are at 120 degrees difference between each phase.	*p. 113 Bushong* *p. 93 Carlton/Adler*
2.16	A	1 kW (1000 W) is the result of the equation Power = IV or (10 * 100 = 1000 W, or 1 kW).	*p. 116 Bushong* *p. 98 Carlton/Adler*
2.17	A	Gauss is the traditional unit for magnetic field strength. Tesla is the SI unit.	*p. 88 Bushong* *p. 60 Carlton/Adler*
2.18	C	The earth's magnetic field is 50 µT at the equator.	*p. 88 Bushong* *p. 62 Carlton/Adler*
2.19	A	An electromagnet is a coil of wire wrapped about an iron ore core. When a current flows through the wire, a magnetic field results.	*p. 85 Bushong* *p. 60 Carlton/Adler*
2.20	D	Electromagnets have the advantage of being turned on or off as required.	*p. 90 Bushong* *p. 60 Carlton/Adler*
2.21	C	Doubling the pole strength of each of two magnets would quadruple the force between them.	*n/a Bushong* *n/a Carlton/Adler*
2.22	B	Doubling the distance between magnets would reduce the force between them to a quarter.	*n/a Bushong* *n/a Carlton/Adler*
2.23	A	An electric current is induced if the circuit is placed in a changing magnetic field.	*p. 91 Bushong* *p. 66 Carlton/Adler*
2.24	A	The rotating anode in diagnostic x-ray tubes is controlled through the use of an induction motor. Induction motors allow for rotor motion while maintaining a vacuum x-ray tube.	*p. 127 Bushong* *p. 73 Carlton/Adler*
2.25	A	Generators convert mechanical energy into electrical energy.	*p. 91 Bushong* *p. 68 Carlton/Adler*
2.26	A	Transformers are used to change the magnitude of voltage in an alternating current.	*p. 94 Bushong* *p. 74 Carlton/Adler*

2.27 B An electric current is induced if the circuit is placed in a changing magnetic field. AC current creates a changing magnetic field, thus inducing a current in the secondary coil.

p. 91 Bushong
p. 74 Carlton/Adler

2.28 D Power = IV, or Power = current × potential. Voltage and current are inversely proportional, so that when the voltage increases, the current must decrease.

p. 116 Bushong
p. 74 Carlton/Adler

2.29 A Rectification circuits contain diodes. Modern rectifiers are solid-state diodes, which replaced valve tubes.

p. 110 Bushong
p. 79 Carlton/Adler

2.30 A Rectification occurs in the generator after the high voltage transformed, but prior to the x-ray tube.

p. 100 Bushong
p. 78 Carlton/Adler

Chapter 3

X-RAY PRODUCTION

3.1 X-Ray Generators
3.2 Physics of X-Ray Production
3.3 X-Ray Quantity
3.4 Tube Heating

3.1 X-RAY GENERATORS

A. X-ray transformers

- Radiography equipment is generally manufactured to work with **220 V** of incoming electrical power.

- Special radiography may require 110V or 440V, i.e., mammography and interventional suites.

- Incoming line voltage varies. **Line compensation** ensures the correct voltage is available for image production.

- **Generators** must produce a **high voltage** to be applied across the x-ray tube.

- High voltages are applied between the **cathode** (filament) and the **anode** (target).

- A low voltage also needs to be obtained to apply across the **filament**.

- Input voltages from the power company are changed to those required by the use of **transformers**.

- **Autotransformers** increase or decrease voltages **in the low voltage range**.

- Autotransformers have **a single winding** and core with selections for primary and secondary connections.

- More turns in the secondary results in the autotransformer functioning as a **step up transformer**, which **increases the voltage**.

- Autotransformers are capable of doubling the voltage.

- Once the autotransformer has adjusted voltage, a **step up transformer** increases the voltage to kilovolts (kV).

- The ratio of secondary to primary turns is known as the **turns ratio**.

- **Typical turns ratios are between 500:1 and 1000:1**.

B. Rectifiers/Waveform ripple

- The **alternating current (AC)** supplied by the power company also needs to be converted into a **direct current (DC)** before being applied across the x-ray tube.
- AC is changed to DC by the use of **rectification circuits.**
- The key component of a rectification circuit is a **diode.**
- **Diodes** are electrical items that only permit electrical currents to flow in one direction.
- The variation voltage across the x-ray tube with time is known as the **voltage ripple.**
- When the voltage varies from zero to some peak value (i.e., kVp), the ripple is 100%.
- A **constant voltage** over time has a waveform **ripple of 0%.**
- Table **3.1** shows common x-ray generators and representative waveform.
- Reducing the waveform/voltage ripple increases x-ray production.
- Reducing the waveform/voltage ripple results in a reduced mAs and patient exposure.
- **Modern high-quality generators** in radiology generally **have low voltage ripples.**

Table 3.1

Typical voltage ripples on x-ray generators

Power Supply	Generator type	Waveform ripple (%)
Single phase	Half-wave (self) rectified	100
Single phase	Full-wave rectified	100
Three phase	Six pulse	~13
Three phase	Twelve pulse	~3
Three phase	High frequency	~1

C. Single-phase generators

- **Single-phase generators** use a single-phase power supply.
- In **half-wave rectification,** only one half of the wave is being utilized.
- Depending on the manufacturer, half-wave rectified units may have 0, 1, or 2 diodes.
- **Half-wave rectified units** use only one-half of the 120 alternating peaks and valleys and **produce 60 pulses per second.**
- **Full-wave rectified** systems utilize all 120 alternating peaks and valleys and **produce 120 pulses per second.**
- Full-wave rectified units are much more efficient when compared to half-wave rectified units.

- Full-wave and half-wave generators have a voltage ripple of 100%.
- **Single-phase generators** have low output and limited time stations.
- Single-phase generators are rarely encountered in modern radiology departments.
- Most dental offices make use of single-phase generators.

D. Three-phase and high-frequency generators

- Modern radiography systems have either **three-phase** or **high-frequency generators**.
- **Three-phase generators** use a three-phase power supply.
- **Three-phase six-pulse** has a voltage ripple of ~13%.
- **Six-pulse** and **twelve-pulse generators** are available.
- **Three-phase twelve-pulse** has a voltage ripple of ~3%, and is more efficient than a six pulse.
- Three-phase equipment has a higher quality and quantity when compared to single phase.
- **High-frequency generators** use a single phase of power and alter the number of hertz at which the unit operates.
- Alternating current (AC) functions at 60 Hz normally; however high-frequency generators often convert this up to 25,000 Hz.
- **Inverter circuits** are used to alter DC power into square pulses of energy.
- **High-frequency generators** have a voltage ripple of ~1%.
- High-frequency generators are appealing due to their small size and nearly absent voltage ripple.
- High-frequency generators are capable of producing up to 100 kW.
- **Table 3.2** shows various combinations of kVp and mA stations and total power produced on a high-frequency generator.

Table 3.2
Nominal power generated by a high-frequency generator

Tube voltage (kVp)	Tube current (mA)	Power produced (kW)
50	400	20
60	600	36
80	800	64
100	1000	100

E. Capacitor discharge and constant potential generators

- **Portable radiography** equipment may also use **high-voltage generators** to charge **nickel-cadmium (NiCd) batteries**.
- Such portable units use silicon-controlled rectifiers to form DC voltage.
- **Charge is stored at very high voltage**.
- During exposure, the charge is released, providing current to the x-ray tube.
- **Capacitor discharge** systems decrease the **voltage** over exposure at a rate of 1 kV/mAs.
- Decreasing kVp over the exposure time will also limit the mAs available for image production.
- **Constant potential generators** are a specialized x-ray unit.
- The voltage ripple is less than 2%.
- **Three-phase voltage** is required.
- Constant potential generators have **no autotransformer**.
- Modulation of the kVp occurs on the secondary side of the high-voltage transformer.

3.2 PHYSICS OF X-RAY PRODUCTION

A. Electron target interactions

- The **x-ray tube current** generates **projectile electrons**.
- These electrons cross the x-ray tube from cathode to anode.
- **Projectile electrons** directed at the target will interact at the surface, **losing some or all of their kinetic energy**.
- Upon losing their kinetic energy, the electrons are conducted through the anode and back to the high-voltage generator.
- **Projectile electrons** are influenced by nuclear fields or collide with outer shell electrons of the target atom.
- Electrons normally travel ~0.5 mm into the x-ray tube target.

B. Bremsstrahlung radiation

- **Bremsstrahlung radiation** is produced as projectile electrons loose kinetic energy due to the attraction of the positive **nuclear field**.
- As the projectile electron slows and changes direction, the **loss of energy** is given off as **ionizing radiation**.

- **The closer the projectile electron comes to the nucleus,** the increased attraction will slow or stop the electron, **the greater the resulting x-ray energy.**

- For example, an 80 keV electron that courses closely to the nuclear field may lose all of its energy, resulting in an 80 keV photon.

- An electron that barely interacts with the nuclear field may slow down slightly, resulting in a photon of 10 keV.

- **Bremsstrahlung radiation** results in a range of x-ray photon energies, from zero to kVp applied to the x-ray tube (keV of the projectile electrons).

- Bremsstrahlung radiation is the **majority of an x-ray beam (>90%).**

- Bremsstrahlung radiation **may be produced at any energy level.**

- Average energy is generally between one-half and one-third of the maximum energy (kVp).

- **Figure 3.1** shows typical average photon energies as a function of x-ray tube voltage (kVp).

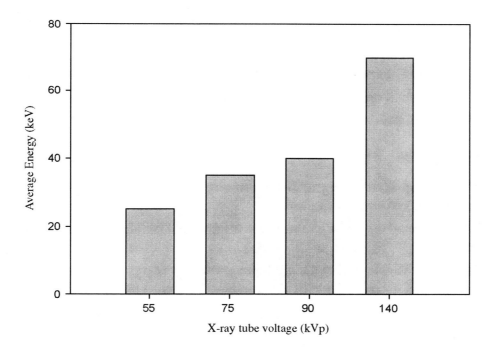

Figure 3.1
Approximate values of the average photon energy for various kVp settings.

C. Characteristic radiation

- **Characteristic radiation** results from the interaction of projectile electrons with inner shell electrons of the target atom (tungsten).
- The **projectile electrons** must possess enough **kinetic energy** to remove an **inner shell electron.**
- With the removal of an inner shell electron, the **atom is unstable** because of a vacancy in the electron shell.
- As a result, an **outer shell electron** will drop down and fill in the vacancy.
- Electrons will continue to fill inner shells until a vacancy exists in the outermost shell, known as **characteristic cascade.**
- When the electron moves between shells (energy levels), **a characteristic x-ray will result.**
- The characteristic x-ray energy is the difference between the outer shell and inner shell electrons' binding energy.
- **Characteristic x-ray** photons have predetermined energies, based on the shell of the removed electron and that which fills the vacancy.
- Any of the outer shells can fill a K-shell vacancy, resulting in a variety of possible x-ray energies.
- **Only K-shell characteristic interactions are of importance in diagnostic radiology.**
- Characteristic x-rays make up a **small portion of the total beam.**
- **Tungsten K-shell** characteristic x-rays require a tube voltage of at least 70 kVp.

D. X-ray spectra

- The **x-ray spectrum** is a graphical representation of the **energies within a beam** and the **quantity at each energy level.**
- The position of the curve on the x-axis is representative of the beam's **energy level** or **quality.**
- The farther the curve is to the right, the greater the energy.
- The numerical value where the curve crosses the horizontal x-axis is the kVp value.
- **Characteristic x-ray spectrum** is shown as **peaks on an emission graph,** due to the discrete energy level of characteristic radiation.
- The lines or peaks are drawn in clusters, such that each cluster represents the possible characteristic x-rays produced for each shell.
- In diagnostic imaging, **one peak at 69 keV is drawn to represent characteristic radiation,** as K-shell interactions are the only useful characteristic interactions.
- **Bremsstrahlung radiation** is created from **zero to the maximum kVp selected.**

- Bremsstrahlung spectrum resembles a bell-shaped curve.
- Few x-rays created at the extremes of the spectrum and the majority about one-third to one-half of the maximum.

3.3 X-RAY QUANTITY

A. Exposure/Air Kerma

- The quantity of the x-ray beam is described as its **intensity**.
- Historically, the **intensity** of an x-ray beam has been measured in **roentgens (R)**.
- 1 R is 1000 milliroentgens (mR).
- **Exposure** is measured in **mR/min** or **mR/mAs**.
- The unit of exposure is currently being replaced by **Air Kerma**.
- Kerma stands for Kinetic Energy Released per unit Mass.
- **Air Kerma** is measured in **gray (Gy)**.
- 1 Gy is 1000 mGy.
- 1 R is approximately 10 mGy.
- **Table 3.3** lists Air Kerma values (intensities) incident on a patient for common examinations.

Table 3.3

Typical entrance Air Kerma values in diagnostic radiology

Examination	Projection	Entrance Air Kerma (mGy)	Exposure (mR)
Chest	PA	0.2	200
Skull	Lateral	1.5	150
Abdomen	AP	3.0	300

B. Target/Waveform

- The **target material** affects both the **quantity** and **quality** of the resulting beam.
- An increased **atomic number** will increase the efficiency and the resulting energy of x-ray production.
- **Tungsten (Z = 74)** is the target material in diagnostic imaging for the production of higher energy x-rays.

- **Molybdenum (Z = 42)** and **rhodium (Z = 45)** are target elements used for mammography resulting in a softer x-ray beam.
- **Table 3.4** shows K-shell binding energy of x-ray target materials.
- The more efficient the generator type, the more efficient X-ray production.
- This is demonstrated in the **emission spectrum** as an increase in amplitude (intensity).
- The increased efficiency in the three-phase units is equivalent to a 12% increase in kVp or a doubling in mAs for the same technique used in a single-phase unit.
- Emission spectrum of a **three-phase unit** has a **greater amplitude** and will be **shifted to the right**, compared with a single-phase spectrum at the same technical factors.

Table 3.4
Key characteristics of target materials used in radiography tubes. For each target, the characteristic x-rays have energies that are just below the K-shell binding energy (e.g., for Mo, the average characteristic x-ray energy is ~18 keV)

Material	Atomic number (Z)	K-shell binding energy (keV)	Application
Molybdenum (Mo)	42	20	Mammography
Rhodium (Rh)	45	23	Mammography
Tungsten (W)	74	70	Radiography, Fluoroscopy, CT

C. mAs

- A doubling of the **mA** will double the number of **electrons** available to the anode, and thus double the number of **x-rays** created.
- A doubling of **time** will result in the same situation as described with a doubling of mA.
- An increase in **mAs** will result in an increase in **amplitude** or a taller emission spectrum, with no change to the shape.
- **Figure 3.2** shows the effect of changing mAs on the resultant x-ray spectrum.
- For diagnostic x-ray beams, intensities are typically **0.05 mGy/mAs** (~5 mR/mAs) at 100-cm SID.
- The number of x-rays produced is directly proportional to the number of electrons crossing the x-ray tube.
- **X-ray quantity is proportional to mAs.**
- Increasing **mAs** does not increase x-ray production efficiency.

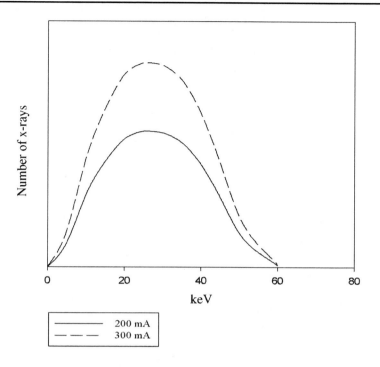

Figure 3.2
Increasing mA results in an increased amplitude
of the emission spectrum; no change in shape.

D. kVp

- An increase in **kVp** causes both an increase in the beam's **energy**, and an increase in the **number of electrons** available to the anode.

- An increase in kVp causes an increase in the area under the **emission spectrum**.

- In addition to the **quantity** increase, the **quality** increases, or the curve shifts to the right.

- Increasing the kVp will cause a decrease in low-energy photons, and an increase in high-energy photons.

- Increasing the kVp **increases the amplitude** and **shifts the emission spectrum to the right**.

- **Figure 3.3** shows how adjusting kVp affects the x-ray spectrum.

- X-ray quantity is (approximately) proportional to the kVp^2.

- Small changes in **kVp** result in considerable changes in x-ray quantity.

- **Figure 3.4** shows how x-ray tube output varies with x-ray tube voltage (kVp).

- Increasing the **kVp** increases the **efficiency** of x-ray production.

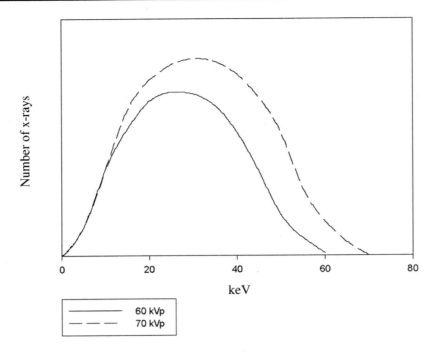

Figure 3.3
Increasing kVp results in an increased amplitude
of the emission spectrum and a shift to the right.

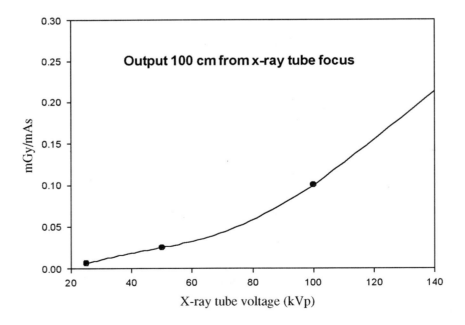

Figure 3.4
X-ray tube output.

E. kVp vs. mAs

- **A 15% increase in kVp is equivalent to a doubling of mAs in the diagnostic energy range.**

- This equivalent is based on the slight increase in quantity and the increase in quality realized with increased kVp.

- The increased quality and quantity realized with a 15% increase in kVp is similar to a 100% increase in mAs when comparing intensity at the image receptor.

- Unlike the relationship of mAs and quantity, a doubling of kVp has quadrupling effect on quantity.

- Increasing **kVp** results in more **transmission** through the patient and less **absorption** due to the increased penetrability of the beam.

- If kVp is increased 15%, the mAs must be decreased by 50% to maintain intensity at the image receptor (**15 percent rule**).

3.4 TUBE HEATING

A. Heat production

- **Heat** is created after projectile electrons interact with outer shell electrons, raising the electron to a higher energy level.

- When the electron returns to its normal energy level, the **excess energy materializes as heat**.

- Within the x-ray tube, 99% of the **electrical energy** results in **heat** production.

- Only the remaining **1% of deposited energy** is transformed into **x-ray energy**.

- Heat in the **target** is rapidly conducted to the x-ray tube **anode**.

- The anode temporarily stores the heat energy.

- **Anode heat capacity** is finite, which places a limitation on the **x-ray techniques** that can be used in x-ray imaging.

B. Anode energy deposition

- Radiography equipment systems are often described by their **generators' power (kW)**.

$$\text{Watts} = \text{Amperes} \times \text{Volts.}$$

- **High-voltage generator power rating (kW) is (mA $\times$ kVp)/1000.**

- Single-phase generators are less productive.

- To account for that decreased production, the power rating formula has an additional factor or constant (0.7).

- **Single-phase generator power rating (kW) is $0.7 \times (mA \times kVp)/1000$.**
- Basic radiography generators have a power of ~40 kW.
- Advanced radiography generators range between 80 and 100 kW.
- **Heat units (HU)** are used to describe thermal changes in the anode.
- The product of 1 kVp, 1 mA, and 1 s is 1 heat unit.
- **Single-phase** $HU = kVp \times mA \times s.$
- Three-phase/high-frequency $HU = 1.4 \times kVp \times mA \times s.$
- Joule can also be used to describe heat storage in an anode.
- **1 J is approximately equal to 0.7 HU.**

C. Anode heating

- Most energy is deposited as heat in the anode, and very little energy is converted to x-rays.
- Radiation production **is increased** by increases in voltage (**kVp**).
- At 50 kVp, ~0.5% of electron kinetic energy is converted to x-rays.
- At 100 kVp, ~1% is converted to x-rays.
- Excessive exposures can cause pitting or surface melting of the focal track, resulting in reduced output.
- **X-ray tube failure is the result of excessive or prolonged heating of the tube.**
- Exposing a cool anode causing rapid temperature increase will cause rapid expansion and often cracking, causing immediate tube failure.
- An extended period of anode heating causes bearings to heat and warp.
- Exceeding the **anode heat capacity** would damage the x-ray tube.
- Modern x-ray tubes have computers that prevent the **anode heat capacity** to be exceeded.

D. Anode cooling

- The x-ray tube cools through radiation by means of **infrared radiation**.
- **Conduction** of heat is from the surface of the anode to the disk and shaft.
- **Convection** occurs through the use of oil or air that is circulated about the tube's surface.
- Anode cooling is significant in the initial minutes after exposure, and the cooling rate decreases with time.
- Cooling of the tube housing will occur at **twice the normal rate if a fan is used** for circulation.

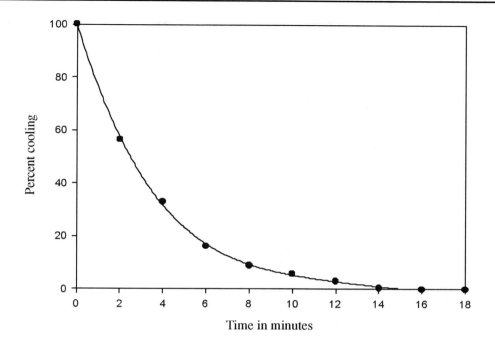

Figure 3.5
Anode cooling curve represents percent cooling from maximum over time.

- The **anode cooling chart** is a graphical representation of the heat load and cooling times of the anode.
- Similar to the anode cooling chart, the **housing cooling chart** provides a means of selecting appropriate technical factors for an x-ray tube.
- **Figure 3.5** shows a typical anode cooling curve where it can take several minutes to achieve significant anode cooling.

QUESTIONS

Chapter 3: X-Ray Production

3.1   The voltage (V) input to an x-ray transformer is most likely _____.
   A. 60
   B. 220
   C. 660
   D. >660

3.2   A typical turns ratio in a step up transformer is most likely _____.
   A. 7:1
   B. 70:1
   C. 700:1
   D. 7000:1

3.3   Variation of x-ray tube voltage with time is best described as the:
   A. ripple.
   B. pulse frequency.
   C. uniformity.
   D. nonlinearity.

3.4   The % ripple of a high-frequency generator is most likely _____.
   A. 1
   B. 5
   C. 10
   D. >10

3.5   The number of pulses per cycle of a half-wave rectified single-phase generators is _____.
   A. ½
   B. 1
   C. 2
   D. 6

3.6   Which generator has the lowest ripple?
   A. Single phase
   B. Six pulse
   C. Twelve pulse
   D. High frequency

3.7   Which generator is most likely to reduce the kVp during an exposure?
A. Portable
B. Dedicated chest
C. R/F unit
D. Interventional radiology

3.8   The maximum distance (mm) energetic electrons travel into the x-ray tube tungsten target is most likely _____.
A. 0.05
B. 0.5
C. 5
D. 50

3.9   The maximum bremasstrahlung energy (keV) produced at 80 kVp is _____.
A. 100
B. 80
C. 70
D. 35

3.10 The percentage (%) of bremasstrahlung radiation at 120 kVp is most likely _____.
A. 1
B. 10
C. 50
D. 90

3.11 The average bremsstrahlung energy (keV) produced at 100 kVp is most likely _____.
A. 100
B. 70
C. 55
D. 40

3.12 Tungsten characteristic K-shell x-rays have an energy (keV) of _____.
A. 85
B. 65
C. 35
D. 18

3.13 The percentage (%) of K-shell characteristic x-rays at 55 kVp in a tungsten target is _____.
A. 0
B. 5
C. 10
D. >10

3.14 An x-ray spectrum shows a graph of the number of photons on the vertical axis against _____ on the horizontal axis.
A. kVp
B. keV
C. mAs
D. mA

3.15 The highest intensity in a spectrum from a tungsten target is most likely at the:
A. low energies.
B. middle energies.
C. high energies.
D. low and high energies.

3.16 1 roentgen is approximately equal to _____ (mGy).
A. 0.1
B. 1
C. 10
D. 100

3.17 Which target will result in the most x-rays, assuming a constant x-ray tube kVp?
A. Mo
B. Rh
C. W
D. No difference (all the same)

3.18 An x-ray tube current is a flow of:
A. electrons.
B. protons.
C. neutrons.
D. ionized atoms.

3.19 Doubling the x-ray tube current, and quadrupling exposure time, increases x-ray tube output by _____.
A. 2×
B. 4×
C. 8×
D. 16×

3.20 The most likely x-ray tube output (mGy/mAs) 100 cm from the x-ray tube focus is most likely _____.
A. 0.05
B. 0.5
C. 5
D. 50

3.21 Doubling the mAs increases x-ray production efficiency by _____%.
A. 0
B. 10
C. 50
D. 100

3.22 Increasing the x-ray tube voltage (kVp) will increase the number of photons with:
A. low energies.
B. average energies.
C. high energies.
D. all energies.

3.23 Doubling the x-ray tube voltage would likely increase the x-ray tube output by _____ %.
A. 50
B. 100
C. 200
D. 400

3.24 Which peak voltage (kVp) is likely most efficient for x-ray production (% electrical power converted to x-rays)?
A. 55
B. 75
C. 90
D. 120

3.25 Doubling the x-ray tube mAs is equivalent to increasing the x-ray tube voltage by _____ %.
A. 5
B. 15
C. 50
D. 100

3.26 Which x-ray component is most likely to store the heat generated during an x-ray?
A. Anode
B. Cathode
C. Target
D. Filament

3.27 The formula for computing the generator power is:
A. Voltage + Current
B. Voltage × Current
C. Voltage/Current
D. $(\text{Voltage/Current})^{-1}$

3.28 Anode heat capacity is most likely expressed in terms of:
A. heat units.
B. watts.
C. temperature.
D. specific heat.

3.29 How many heat units is 1 J?
A. 0.35
B. 0.7
C. 1.35
D. 1.7

3.30 Which of the following is not a method for heat dissipation?
A. Conduction
B. Radiation
C. Convection
D. Spallation

ANSWERS[1]

Chapter 3: X-Ray Production

3.1   B   Commercial line voltages are 220V.

p. 103 Bushong
p. 90 Carlton/Adler

3.2   C   Turns ratio in a high-voltage transformer is approximately 500:1 to 1000:1.

p. 109 Bushong
p. 74 Carlton/Adler

3.3   A   The change in voltage or the pulsing of the current is described as voltage ripple.

p. 115 Bushong
p. 93 Carlton/Adler

3.4   A   A high-frequency voltage would have a 1% variation in voltage.

p. 115 Bushong
p. 96 Carlton/Adler

3.5   B   Single-phase half-wave rectified has 1 pulse/cycle.

p. 115 Bushong
p. 96 Carlton/Adler

3.6   D   High-frequency generators have a 1% or less voltage ripple, or approximately constant potential.

p. 115 Bushong
p. 98 Carlton/Adler

3.7   A   Portable units that use batteries may have a falling voltage during exposure that limits the mA available.

p. 115 Bushong
p. 98 Carlton/Adler

3.8   B   A projectile electron will travel ~0.5 mm into the target material during the production of radiation.

n/a Bushong
p. 127 Carlton/Adler

3.9   B   An electron may lose all, some, or none of its KE when entering the anode. If the kVp is 80 and an electron loses all its KE, the resulting x-ray has an energy of 80 keV.

p. 142 Bushong
p. 127 Carlton/Adler

3.10   D   Only a small portion of the x-ray beams are characteristic, with the majority of the beams consisting of bremsstrahlung, ~90%.

p. 145 Bushong
p. 127 Carlton/Adler

3.11   D   The average of a 100 kVp beam is ~40 (i.e., approximately one-third to one-half the kVp).

p. 145 Bushong
p. 127 Carlton/Adler

[1] As a study aid, page numbers for additional study are given for the following references:
   Bushong SC: *Radiologic Science for Technologists,* 9th ed. St. Louis, MO: Mosby, 2008.
   Carlton RR, Adler AM: *Principles of Radiographic Imaging: An Art and a Science,* 4th ed. Albany, NY: Delmar Publishing Inc., 2005.

3.12	B	The K-shell binding energy of tungsten is 70 keV and K-shell characteristic x-rays are slightly less than 70 keV, approximately 65 keV.	*p. 142 Bushong* *p. 129 Carlton/Adler*
3.13	A	The K-shell binding energy of tungsten is 70 keV, so a projectile electron needs a keV of 70 or higher to create a K-shell interaction. No K-shell interactions take place at energies less than 70 keV.	*p. 142 Bushong* *p. 131 Carlton/Adler*
3.14	B	An emission spectrum is a graphic representation of the x-ray beam, displaying the number of x-rays at each energy level, keV.	*p. 147 Bushong* *p. 131 Carlton/Adler*
3.15	B	The average or most x-rays are produced at the middle energy levels.	*p. 145 Bushong* *p. 130 Carlton/Adler*
3.16	C	The conversion factor to calculate R to Gy is 0.01, such that 1 R × 0.01 = 0.01 Gy, or 10 mGy.	*Front pages Bushong* *p. 139 Carlton/Adler*
3.17	C	The efficiency of production and the resulting energy of those x-rays will increase with increasing atomic number of the target. Tungsten (W) is the highest atomic number target given.	*p. 148 Bushong* *p. 110 Carlton/Adler*
3.18	A	X-ray tube current is the number of electrons flowing in the filament circuit.	*p. 124 Bushong* *p. 1061 Carlton/Adler*
3.19	C	mAs is the product of mA and time of exposure. mAs controls the quantity of the x-ray beam; any change in mA or time has a proportional change in quality or output (2X × 4X = 8X).	*p. 246 Bushong* *p. 173 Carlton/Adler*
3.20	A	An average output of an x-ray tube at 70 kVp is 0.05 mGy/mAs, or 5 mR/mAs.	*p. 152 Bushong* *n/a Carlton/Adler*
3.21	A	mAs has no effect on efficiency of production.	*p. 246 Bushong* *p. 173 Carlton/Adler*
3.22	D	Increasing the kVp will increase the number of x-rays produced at all energy levels.	*p. 147 Bushong* *p. 172 Carlton/Adler*
3.23	D	The increased output of an x ray tube is approximately proportional to a square of the ratio of change in kVp, so a doubling of kVp increases output by 4 times, or 400%.	*pp. 155 & 254 Bushong* *p. 177 Carlton/Adler*
3.24	D	X-ray production efficiency increases with increasing kVp, so 120 kVp is the most efficient.	*p. 140 Bushong* *p. 130 Carlton/Adler*

3.25	B	A 15% increase in kVp is equivalent to a doubling of mAs in respect to optical density of an image.	*p. 154 Bushong* *p. 177 Carlton/Adler*
3.26	A	The anode is responsible for dissipating the heat that results from x-ray tube use.	*n/a Bushong* *pp. 132 & 109 Carlton/Adler*
3.27	B	Power = Current × Potential or Amperes × Voltage.	*p. 116 Bushong* *p. 96 Carlton/Adler*
3.28	A	The thermal state of the anode is described using heat units.	*p. 134 Bushong* *p. 108 Carlton/Adler*
3.29	C	1 joule = 1.35 HU for a three-phase or high-frequency generator.	*p. 136 Bushong* *p. 121 Carlton/Adler*
3.30	D	The anode dissipates heat through conduction, convection, and radiation. Spallation is not a form of heat dissipation.	*p. 132 Bushong* *p. 1061 Carlton/Adler*

Chapter 4

X-RAY INTERACTIONS

4.1 **X-Ray Interactions**
4.2 **Scatter**
4.3 **Grids**
4.4 **Beam Attenuation**
4.5 **X-Ray Beam Quality**

4.1 X-RAY INTERACTIONS

A. Coherent scattering

- In **coherent scattering**, an x-ray photon is incident on an atom.
- The incident x-rays excite the target atom.
- The target atom **emits the excess energy** immediately as a **photon** of the same energy, but in a different direction.
- Other names for **coherent scattering** are **classical scattering** and **Thompson scattering**.
- In coherent scattering there is **no ionization**.
- Coherent scatter is of little importance in the **diagnostic energy range**.
- **Less than 5%** of all x-ray interactions in patients are coherent scatter interactions.

B. Compton effect

- **Compton scatter** is of great importance in the diagnostic energy range.
- Incident x-rays interact with the **outer shell electrons** of the target atom, resulting in a scattered lower energy x-ray and an electron being removed from the target atom.
- The **Compton scatter photon has less energy** than the incident photon and **travels in a different direction**.
- The remaining energy can be accounted for in the electron binding energy and the electron's kinetic energy upon ejection from the target atom.
- A scatter photon may have **additional Compton interactions** before absorption or exit from the patient.

71

C. Compton scatter characteristics

- Scatter can occur in any direction.
- Scatter that is **180° from the incident path** is termed backscatter.
- **Backscatter radiation** is approximately two-thirds the energy of the incident photon.
- **Table 4.1** shows the energy of backscatter photons in the diagnostic energy range.
- Compton scatter is inversely proportional to the energy of the incident photon, **1/E**.
- The relationship between photon energy and probability of a Compton scatter is shown in **Figure 4.1a**.
- Increasing the kVp will therefore always decrease the likelihood of Compton scatter.
- The **atomic number** of a material **has little effect on Compton scatter.**
- In diagnostic radiology, the amount of Compton scatter is **directly proportional to tissue density.**
- Denser materials like bone have more Compton interactions than soft tissues.
- Lung has fewer Compton interactions than soft tissues.

Table 4.1
Energy of a Compton photon that is backscattered (i.e., scattering angle of 180°).
The difference between the incident photon energy and the backscattered photon energy
is primarily transferred to the Compton electron

Incident photon energy	Energy of x-ray scattered through 180° (backscattered)
50	42
100	72
150	95

D. Photoelectric effect

- The absorption of radiation is termed the **photoelectric effect (PE)**.
- Photoelectric effect occurs when incident photons interact with **inner shell electrons** in the target atom.
- The **incident photon** interacts with and ejects an **inner shell electron**.
- The incident photon's energy is split between the **binding energy**, to remove the electron from orbit, and the **kinetic energy** the ejected electron receives.

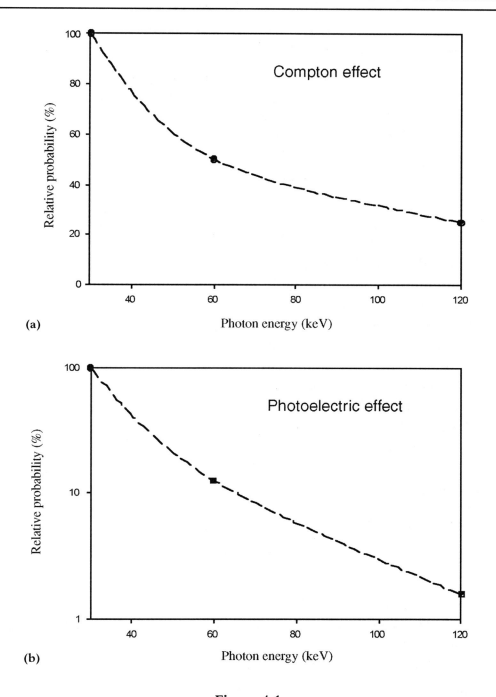

Figure 4.1
Graphs showing interaction probabilities in soft tissue with changing
photon energy. (a) Compton interactions on a *linear scale* and
(b) photoelectric absorption on a *logarithmic scale.*

- Low atomic number materials, soft tissue, result in **photoelectrons** maintaining the bulk of the incident photon's energy.
- These **photoelectrons** travel about 0.02 mm and deposit all their energy within the patient.

E. PE characteristics

- **Photoelectric interactions** are both **energy** and **atomic number dependent.**
- The incident photon must have sufficient energy, equal to or greater, to **ionize** the target atom.
- Above the K-edge, as the **energy** of **incident photon** increases, the likelihood of absorption decreases.
- **Probability of experiencing a photoelectric effect** decreases with the third power of the photon energy $(1/E^3)$.
- **Figure 4.1b** shows the relationship between photon energy and probability of the photoelectric effect.
- Maximum PE occurs when the energy of the incident photon is slightly higher than the binding energy of the target atom K-shell.
- **Probability of experiencing a photoelectric effect** is directly proportional to the third power of the atomic number of the absorbing material $(\mathbf{Z^3})$.
- Small changes in target material atomic number result in large increases in absorption.

4.2 SCATTER

A. Scatter radiation

- **Remnant radiation** is that exiting the patient.
- **Remnant radiation** contains both **transmitted** and **scattered radiation.**
- Radiation that interacts with the image receptor is termed **image-forming radiation.**
- **Scatter radiation** provides exposure to the image receptor in the form of **fog,** and contains no useful information.
- **Image contrast is reduced with increasing scatter**, so decreasing scatter is desirable.
- **Table 4.2** describes the factors that influence scatter.

B. Field size

- The greater the area irradiated, the greater the scatter produced.
- **Scatter is directly proportional to the x-ray beam area.**

Table 4.2
Important factors that affect scatter production in radiography

Factor	Effect on image
Field size	Scatter directly proportional to field size. Increasing field size increases scatter reaching image receptor.
Patient thickness	Scatter directly proportional to patient thickness. Multiple scatter interactions are more likely, and scatter angle increases.
X-ray tube voltage	As voltage increases, percentage of interactions that are Compton scatter increases.

- **Collimation** reduces the area irradiated and production of scatter.
- **Scatter radiation** increases the density of an image (exposure at the image receptor).
- If **scatter** is reduced, a corresponding increase in **mAs** is necessary.
- Narrow beam geometry minimizes scatter.
- For example, narrow beams in CT (<4 cm) result in minimal scatter.
- Collimation reduces the area of patient exposed, as well as the amount of scatter.

C. Patient thickness

- Any increase in **tissue irradiated** increases production of scatter.
- Increased thickness allows for multiple scatter interactions to take place.
- The angle of scatter increases with increased part thickness.
- **Types of tissue within a body part also affect scatter.**
- Bone results in more absorption, and therefore less scatter.
- Soft tissues will result in (much) more scatter than bone.
- **Figure 4.2** illustrates the relationship between increasing part thickness in typical radiographic exams and resulting scatter production.
- Remnant radiation from an extremity is about half scatter, whereas the **abdomen is almost all scatter.**
- Decreasing thickness is generally not a practical option for a radiographer.
- **Compression**, however, is used in **mammography**, which can **reduce scatter**.

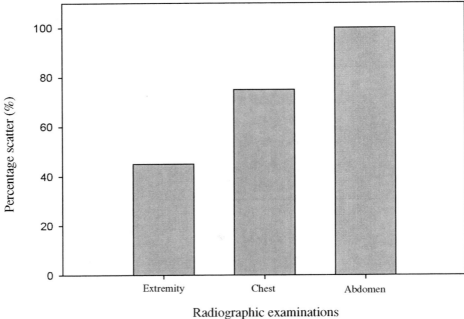

Figure 4.2
Percentage of remnant radiation that is scatter for common
radiographic examinations.

D. X-ray tube voltage (kVp)

- As **kVp increases**, the percentage of the beam **absorbed decreases** (beam is more penetrating).
- As the **kVp increases**, the percentage of the beam **scattered increases**.
- A greater fraction of interactions at high kVp are scatter than occurs at lower kVp.
- Lower kVp will therefore reduce scatter.
- Use of **high kVp** techniques will also **decrease dose because the beam is more penetrating**.

E. Scatter removal

- **Grids are used to reduce the amount of scatter reaching the image receptor.**
- Grids are generally placed on top of the image receptor to absorb scatter radiation.
- Grids are composed of alternating strips of absorbing and transmitting materials.
- **Lead** is the most common material for **grid strips**.

- Scatter radiation travels at an angle to the primary beam and the **radiopaque grid lines**, resulting in absorption.
- The high atomic number of lead provides for maximum absorption of scatter radiation.
- **Primary photons** are (unfortunately) **absorbed** in the grid, as well as scattered photons.
- **The percent of a beam absorbed by the grid is the (grid line width)/(grid line width + interspace width).**
- The **interspace material** allows for transmission of the primary beam through the grid with little interaction.

4.3 GRIDS

A. Construction

- **Interspace** materials are generally **aluminum** or **plastic**.
- Aluminum will absorb slightly more radiation than plastic.
- Aluminum is less susceptible to moisture and warping.
- A **stationary grid** produces visible grid lines on an image.
- To reduce the appearance of grid lines, the grid may be moved, in an effort to blur the grid lines.
- Grids may **reciprocate**, move side to side, or **oscillate**, move in a circular pattern.
- Grid motion during exposure causes blurring of the strips and renders them practically invisible.
- **Moving grids** are Potter-Bucky diaphragm, or **"Bucky"**.

B. Grid properties

- A grid consists of **grid strips** and **interspace material**.
- The thickness of the **grid strips (T)**, the **height of the strips (h)**, and the thickness of the **interspace material (D)** are used to calculate grid ratio.
- **Grid ratio** may be calculated by dividing the grid height by the width interspace **(h/D)**.
- **Grid ratio** is used to describe a grid's ability to absorb scatter.
- Higher grid ratios are achieved by increasing the height of the grid strips, increasing the probability that the photon will be absorbed.
- **Increasing grid ratios increases the amount of scatter that is absorbed.**
- Grid ratios used in radiography are 4:1, 8:1, and 12:1.
- **Figure 4.3** shows typical grid performance.

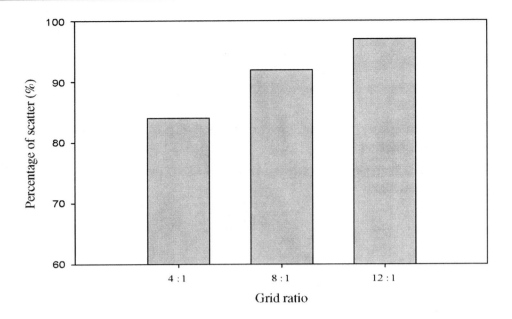

Figure 4.3
Percentage of scatter removed by commonly used radiographic grids.

- Increased **grid ratios** require increased **mAs** and will result in an increased **patient dose**.
- **Grid frequency** is the number of grid lines per centimeter.
- **Grid frequency** is obtained by dividing the thickness of one line pair **(T+D)**, measured in μm, into 10,000 μm (i.e., 1 cm expressed in microns).
- **The higher the frequency, the less obvious the grid lines on the image.**
- High-frequency grids have additional grid lines and generally absorb more scatter radiation and require greater exposure.
- Grid frequency is typically between **25–45 lines per centimeter**.

C. Grid types

- A **parallel grid** consists of alternating strips of radiolucent and radiopaque materials.
- Grid strips generally run with the long axis of an image receptor.
- **Crossed grids** are composed of two parallel grids set at right angles to one another.
- Parallel grids absorb scatter in one direction, where a **crossed grid will absorb scatter in two directions**.
- **Crossed grids** are more effective at scatter reduction.
- Crossed grids require precise positioning and increased technical factors.

- **Focused grids** have radiopaque strips that are aligned with the **divergence of the x-ray beam.**

- **Focused grids** must be used at a specific SID, or range of SID, known as **focal distance.**

- Focused grids have less grid cutoff when positioned appropriately.

D. Bucky factor

- The use of a grid does have the disadvantage of increased patient dose, described as **Bucky factor (B).**

- **Bucky factor,** or **grid conversion factor,** describes the increase in mAs needed based on the grid's effectiveness.

- Higher performing grids require higher technical factors.

- A 5:1 grid ratio has an average Bucky factor of 2.

- An 8:1 grid ratio has a Bucky factor of about 4, which increases to 5 for a 12:1 grid and to 6 for a 16:1 grid.

- **The higher the grid ratio, the higher the Bucky factor.**

- Increasing the x-ray tube voltage generally increases the Bucky factor.

- An 8:1 grid has a Bucky factor of 3 at 79 kVp but 4 at 120 kVp.

E. Grid problems/Artifacts

- **Grid cutoff** results in abnormal absorption of the x-ray beam due to an error, such as improper SID, tilting of the grid, or angling of the tube.

- **Poor positioning** of the grid, such as tilt or off centering of the x-ray tube, will result in **significant grid cutoff.**

- If the central ray is angled or the grid is tilted such that the central ray enters the grid at an angle, **grid cutoff** will occur across the entire image.

- If using a **focused grid,** it must be at the proper **SID** indicated on the grid.

- Upside-down focused grid results with only the center of the radiograph exposed; severe grid cutoff is seen on both sides.

- The higher the **grid ratio,** the greater the **probability of cutoff**; as higher ratio grids are more sensitive to positioning errors.

- Having both **off-center** and **off-focus** grid error is seen in mobile radiography, resulting in an uneven exposure across an image.

- **Table 4.3** lists common grid errors.

Table 4.3
Common focused grid errors and the effect on image quality

Name	Cause	Effect on image
Off level	Tube angled or grid angled such that CR is not perpendicular to grid plane	Loss of OD across image
Off center	CR is not aligned with the center of the grid	Loss of OD across image
Off focus	Inappropriate SID used with a focused grid, either too long or short	Loss of OD at periphery
Upside down	Focused grid place upside down	Extreme loss of OD increasing from image center towards periphery

CR – Central Ray; OD – Optical Density; SID – Source to Image Receptor Distance.

4.4 BEAM ATTENUATION

A. Differential absorption

- The combination of **Compton scatter** and **photoelectric absorption** within the patient results in varying amounts of radiation intensity at the image receptor.
- Images are the result of ~0.5% of the incident beam reaching the image receptor.
- The difference in what is transmitted through different body parts is termed **differential absorption**.
- Areas where radiation is transmitted will appear dark.
- Areas of absorption are generally white.
- **Differential absorption** is important because it results in **image contrast**.

B. kVp

- At low kVp, the **photoelectric effect** is the most important.
- **Photoelectric effect** is also important for **high-Z materials** such as bone, iodine, and barium.
- **As kVp increases, the probability of interactions, whether PE or Compton, decreases.**
- With increasing kVp, PE falls much more rapidly than Compton scatter.
- In soft tissues, **Compton interactions** are equal to those of **photoelectric absorption at 25 keV.**

- Above **25 keV, Compton interactions** are the most important for soft tissues.
- At higher kVp, Compton predominates and PE is less likely.

C. Mass density

- **Mass density** relates to how closely atoms are located within a material.
- As the mass density increases, the space between the atoms decreases.
- Potential for **interactions** increases.
- **X-ray transmission is reduced as the mass density increases.**
- This is true for all types of interactions, Compton, and PE.
- Increasing the tissue density will increase the whiteness in a normal radiographic image.
- Decreasing the tissue density will increase the blackening on a radiographic image.
- X-ray **attenuation coefficients** are generally directly proportional to the **mass density**.
- Doubling mass density will double x-ray attenuation coefficients.

D. Exponential attenuation

- **Attenuation** is the absorption or scatter of a beam as it travels through a target material.
- As the thickness of tissue increases and radiation travels through it, more is attenuated.
- **Attenuation is exponential.**
- A constant fraction of x-rays are attenuated when traveling a given distance.
- If the **attenuation coefficient** is 0.1 cm^{-1}, 10% of **the incident photons** are lost in traveling 1 cm.
- 100 photons incident on a 1-cm attenuator (attenuation coefficient of 0.1 cm^{-1}) would transmit 90 photons through 1 cm.
- 81 photons would be transmitted through the second centimeter because they lose 10% of the incident photons (90 photons $\times$ 0.1 transmission).
- Transmission is incident $\times$ $e^{-\mu t}$, where μ **is the linear attenuation coefficient** and **t is the thickness of the absorber**.
- t is expressed in cm and μ is expressed in cm^{-1}.
- **Table 4.4** shows how soft tissue attenuation varies with x-ray energy.

Table 4.4
X-ray attenuation and transmission in soft tissue (water) as a function of photon energy

Photon energy (keV)	Linear attenuation coefficient μ cm^{-1}	Photons transmitted through 1 cm (%)	Photons lost in 1 cm (%)
30	0.38	73	27
50	0.22	85	15
100	0.17	89	11

E. Contrast agents

- Blood vessels are not visible in soft tissue because blood attenuates x-rays as much as soft tissue.

- To visualize a blood vessel requires the addition of a material that attenuates more (or less) than soft tissues.

- **Iodine attenuates x-rays much more than soft tissues,** and is used to permit visualization of the patient vasculature.

- **Iodinated contrast** results in blood vessels appearing whiter than the surrounding tissues.

- **Carbon dioxide** is sometimes used to visualize the patient vasculature.

- Since **carbon dioxide attenuates less than soft tissue,** the blood vessels normally appear darker.

- **Barium** has excellent x-ray **absorption properties,** which are very similar to those of **iodine.**

- **Barium** has an atomic number of 56 (K-edge of 37 keV) which is similar to that of iodine (Z = 53; K-edge of 33 keV).

- Addition of iodine/barium to the GI tract permits visualization of the esophagus, stomach, intestines, and colon.

- Air can also be administered to the GI tract (double contrast).

- **Contrast agents generally result in very high image contrast.**

4.5 X-RAY BEAM QUALITY

A. X-ray penetration

- Increasing **kVp** results in a stronger, more penetrating beam.

- Penetration describes the ability of x-rays to transverse tissue.

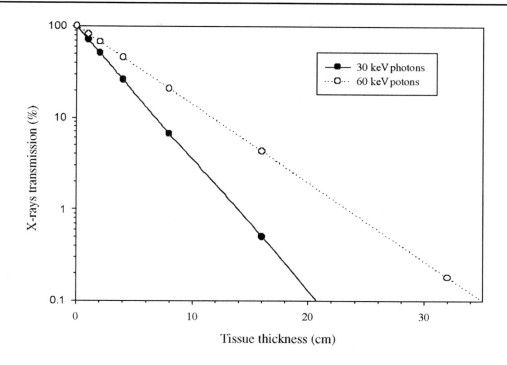

Figure 4.4
X-ray transmission through soft tissue showing exponential attenuation
for monoenergetic photons, with very few x-rays getting through
a typical adult abdomen of ~25 cm.

- **Increased beam quality** implies an **increase in the ability to penetrate tissues.**
- Increased quality, kVp, results in increased penetration of tissue.
- **Figure 4.4** illustrates the increased penetrating power of higher energy photons.
- kVp is the controlling factor in beam penetrability.
- **mAs and distance do not affect beam quality.**

B. Half-value layer

- **Absorption** and **scattering** of the beam decrease intensity, known as **attenuation.**
- The higher the **kVp**, or beam quality, the greater the **penetrating power**.
- At 60 keV, ~20%/cm is attenuated as compared to 30%/cm at 30 keV (**Figure 4.4**).
- The **half-value layer (HVL)** is used to describe beam quality.
- HVL is defined as the thickness of a material that will reduce the intensity to one-half its original value.

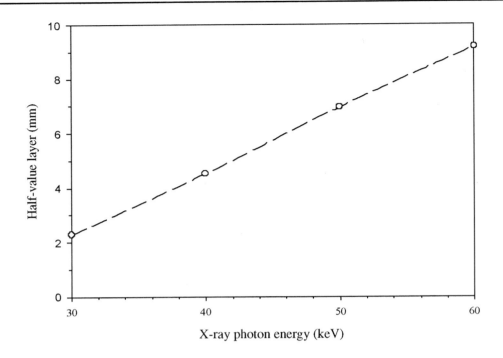

Figure 4.5
Aluminum half–value layer (HVL) for monoenergetic x–ray photons.
Note that 35 keV photons have an HVL of ~3 mm Al.

- The HVL is measured with a dosimeter and varying thicknesses of an attenuator, usually aluminum.
- **Figure 4.5** depicts the relationship between increasing HVL and photon energy.

C. HVL and kVp

- Increasing kVp results in more x-ray photons, and an increase in the maximum photon energy.
- As the x-ray tube voltages increases, there is a shift of the emission spectrum to the right.
- As a result, the average photon energy increases with increasing kVp.
- The higher average photon energy will result in increased penetration through patients.
- Photons with energy of 30 keV have a HVL of 1.9 mm Al.

- Increasing the photon energy to 40 and 50 keV increases the HVL to 4.1 mm Al and 6.8 mm Al, respectively.

- Increases in **kVp always** result in an increase in **beam quality, because the HVL will increase.**

- **At 80 kVp the HVL should be no less than ~2.5 mm Al.**

D. HVL and filtration

- **Filtration absorbs the very-low-energy x-rays produced.**

- The low-energy photons are of no diagnostic value and only serve to increase patient dose if allowed to exit the tube housing.

- **Filtration decreases** the total **number of photons** within the beam and **increases its average keV.**

- **Aluminum** is most often used as a **filter material.**

- Average photon energy in an x-ray beam increases with increasing filtration.

- The **emission spectrum** will decrease on the left or low end of the energy spectrum, and the amplitude will decrease overall, with a shift of the average to the right.

- **Filtration always reduces the beam intensity.**

- **Table 4.5** provides a summary of representative HVL in mammography, radiography, and CT.

Table 4.5
Representative half-value layers in diagnostic radiology

Imaging modality	Filtration	Tube voltage (kVp)	Half-value layer (mm Al)
Mammography	30 μm Mo	26	0.3
Radiography	3 mm Al	80	3
CT	6 mm Al (+ bowtie)	120	8

QUESTIONS

Chapter 4: X-Ray Interactions

4.1   The most likely amount of energy an x-ray photon loses in a coherent scatter interaction is _____ %.
   A. 0
   B. 5
   C. 25
   D. >25

4.2   Compton interactions are most likely to occur with:
   A. outer shell electrons.
   B. K-shell electrons.
   C. electrons in all shells.
   D. atomic nuclei.

4.3   Backscatter is the term used to describe a photon deflected through an angle of _____ degrees.
   A. 90
   B. 180
   C. 270
   D. 360

4.4   When the density of an absorber is doubled, the number of Compton interactions is most likely to increase by _____ %.
   A. 25
   B. 50
   C. 100
   D. 200

4.5   A 50 keV photon absorbed in soft tissue is most likely to produce an electron with an energy of about _____ keV.
   A. 50
   B. 25
   C. 5
   D. 0

4.6   To be absorbed by a K-shell electron in an iodine atom, an x-ray photon must have a minimum energy of _____ keV.
A. 4
B. 25
C. 33
D. 70

4.7   The probability of a photoelectric interaction with an x-ray photon of energy E varies as _____.
A. E^3
B. E
C. 1/E
D. $1/E^3$

4.8   Attenuation by lead (Z = 82) is greater than in soft tissue (Z ~ 8) by a factor of about:
A. 10.
B. 100.
C. 1000.
D. 10,000.

4.9   Remnant radiation is the radiation that:
A. enters the patient.
B. exits the patient.
C. is back scattered.
D. is scattered through 90°.

4.10 When the x-ray beam area doubles, the amount of scatter produced in the patient is most likely to increase by _____%.
A. 10
B. 25
C. 50
D. 100

4.11 Which x-ray examination is likely to result in the greatest amount of scatter radiation?
A. Abdomen (AP)
B. Chest (PA)
C. Extremity
D. Skull

4.12 Which would likely be the best interspace material in an x-ray scatter removal grid?
   A. Aluminum
   B. Copper
   C. Silver
   D. Tungsten

4.13 If a grid has strip thickness, T, and an interspace thickness, D, the grid frequency is:
   A. T/D.
   B. D/T.
   C. 1/(D + T).
   D. 1/(D − T).

4.14 The percentage of scatter absorbed by an x-ray grid is most likely _____ %.
   A. 5
   B. 20
   C. 50
   D. 90

4.15 A grid frequency is most likely _____ lines per cm.
   A. 0.3
   B. 3
   C. 30
   D. 300

4.16 Using a focused grid (80 to 100 cm) at an SID of 120 cm would likely increase:
   A. grid cutoff.
   B. primary transmission.
   C. focal blur.
   D. scatter radiation.

4.17 An abdomen radiograph exposed using 25 mAs results in excessive scatter. Using a grid with a Bucky factor of 5, what is the mAs required to maintain image quality?
   A. 5 mAs
   B. 50 mAs
   C. 75 mAs
   D. 125 mAs

4.18 Grid cutoff is most likely to increase with increasing:
   A. SID.
   B. grid ratio.
   C. grid frequency.
   D. interspace thickness.

4.19 The percentage of the x-ray beam in a skull radiograph that reaches the image receptor is most likely _____%.
A. 0.01
B. 0.1
C. 1
D. 10

4.20 In soft tissue, at which photon energy (keV) are photoelectric and Compton interactions equally likely?
A. 15
B. 25
C. 45
D. 65

4.21 More scatter is likely to be produced when a 120 kVp x-ray beam travels 1 cm through:
A. air.
B. soft tissue.
C. lung.
D. bone.

4.22 If the attenuation coefficient is 0.1 cm^{-1}, the percentage of x-rays lost in a distance of 1 cm is most likely _____%.
A. 0.01
B. 0.1
C. 1
D. 10

4.23 Which is least likely to be used as a contrast agent in patients?
A. Iodine
B. Barium
C. Carbon dioxide
D. Water

4.24 Increasing which factor is likely to increase the percentage of x-rays transmitted through a patient?
A. Tube current
B. Exposure time
C. X-ray voltage
D. SID

4.25 The material most likely used to specify an x-ray beam half-value layer is:
   A. aluminum.
   B. copper.
   C. molybdenum.
   D. tungsten.

4.26 The relationship between kVp and HVL is most likely:
   A. directly proportional.
   B. indirectly proportional.
   C. sinusoidal.
   D. none.

4.27 The minimum HVL at 80 kV is most likely _____ mm Al.
   A. 0.5
   B. 1.5
   C. 2.5
   D. 4.5

4.28 Which x-ray photons are most likely to be attenuated by an x-ray beam filter?
   A. Low energy
   B. Average energy
   C. High energy
   D. Characteristic x-rays

4.29 Addition of x-ray beam filtration is primarily done to:
   A. improve spatial resolution.
   B. decrease image noise.
   C. reduce patient exposure.
   D. increase exposure time.

4.30 Addition of x-ray beam filters will most likely shift an x-ray spectrum:
   A. upward.
   B. downward.
   C. leftward.
   D. rightward.

ANSWERS[1]

Chapter 4: X-Ray Interactions

4.1   A   Coherent scatter results from an incident x-ray exciting an atom, the atom releasing the excess energy as an x-ray with the *same* energy.   *p. 163 Bushong*   *p. 189 Carlton/Adler*

4.2   A   Compton interactions occur between incident x-ray photons and outer shell electrons.   *p. 164 Bushong*   *p. 189 Carlton/Adler*

4.3   B   Backscatter is scatter radiation that travels back towards the direction of the incident beam, or at 180° to the incident beam.   *p. 165 Bushong*   *p. 190 Carlton/Adler*

4.4   C   Compton's interactions are proportional to the mass density of a tissue, so that when one double the mass density, the interactions double (i.e., 100% increase).   *p. 165 Bushong*   *p. 245 Carlton/Adler*

4.5   A   Soft tissue has a K-shell binding energy of ~0.5 keV, so that the photoelectrons will leave the atom with almost all of the incident photons energy, or ~50 keV.   *p. 167 Bushong*   *p. 187 Carlton/Adler*

4.6   C   The K-shell binding energy of iodine is 33 keV, so an x-ray photon needs at least this level of energy to knock the electron out of the atom.   *p. 166 Bushong*   *p. 187 Carlton/Adler*

4.7   D   The probability of a PE interaction is inversely proportional to the third power of the energy, $1/E^3$.   *p. 166 Bushong*   *p. 188 Carlton/Adler*

4.8   C   The probability of a PE interaction is directly proportional to the third power of the materials atomic number. A ratio may be used to find the difference in probability based on atomic number, i.e., $(82/8)^3$, ~1000.   *p. 167 Bushong*   *p. 187 Carlton/Adler*

4.9   B   Remnant radiation is that which exits the patient and reaches the image receptor.   *p. 228 Bushong*   *p. 185 Carlton/Adler*

4.10   D   Doubling field size increases the amount of scatter radiation by 100%.   *p. 228 Bushong*   *p. 230 Carlton/Adler*

---

[1] As a study aid, page numbers for additional study are given for the following references:
Bushong SC: *Radiologic Science for Technologists*, 9th ed. St. Louis, MO: Mosby, 2008.
Carlton RR, Adler AM: *Principles of Radiographic Imaging: An Art and a Science*, 4th ed. Albany, NY: Delmar Publishing Inc., 2005.

4.11 A   The thicker the body part, the more scatter will be produced, and the abdomen is the thickest body part.

p. 225 Bushong
p. 205 Carlton/Adler

4.12 A   Aluminum is a common interspace material because it transmits most incident x-rays.

p. 234 Bushong
p. 257 Carlton/Adler

4.13 C   Grid frequency can be calculated by adding the width of the grid strip and the interspace into one centimeter, $1/(D + T)$.

p. 234 Bushong
p. 259 Carlton/Adler

4.14 D   High-quality grids will remove about 90% of scatter.

p. 233 Bushong
p. 262 Carlton/Adler

4.15 C   Commonly used grids in diagnostic radiography have grid frequencies of ~30 lines/cm.

p. 233 Bushong
p. 259 Carlton/Adler

4.16 A   Focused grids must be used at the specified focal length to minimize the likelihood of grid cut off.

p. 239 Bushong
p. 265 Carlton/Adler

4.17 D   Bucky factor is equal to the mAs with a grid divided by the mAs without a grid, so that 125 mAs would be required when using a grid with a Bucky factor of 5.

p. 235 Bushong
p. 263 Carlton/Adler

4.18 B   The higher the grid ratio, the greater the care must be taken to prevent misalignment and the resultant grid cutoff.

p. 242 Bushong
p. 259 Carlton/Adler

4.19 C   Only about 1% of the incident beam will reach the image receptor.

p. 224 Bushong
p. 165 Carlton/Adler

4.20 B   Compton and photoelectric interactions are equal in soft tissue at 25 keV.

p. 171 Bushong
p. 195 Carlton/Adler

4.21 D   At high photon energies, where Compton scatter is dominant, bone will generate most scatter because it has the highest density (most atoms).

p. 165 Bushong
p. 190 Carlton/Adler

4.22 D   The attenuation coefficient describes the percentage of the beam attenuated in a given distance within a tissue type. A 0.1 cm^{-1} attenuation coefficient would be equivalent to 10% attenuation.

p. 175 Bushong
p. 239 Carlton/Adler

4.23 D   Air, iodine, and barium are commonly used contrast agents in radiography. Water is rarely used as a contrast agent in radiography due to its close attenuation with that of soft tissue.

p. 167 Bushong
p. 187 Carlton/Adler

4.24   C   At the higher x-ray voltages (kVp) there will be *less* attenuation and *more* transmission.

p. 165 Bushong
p. 175 Carlton/Adler

4.25   A   HVL is a measure of beam quality and is generally measured in mm of Al equivalent.

p. 155 Bushong
p. 165 Carlton/Adler

4.26   A   As kVp increases, the HVL will also increase.

p. 157 Bushong
p. 166 Carlton/Adler

4.27   C   The minimum HVL for an 80 kVp beam is ~2.5 mm Al.

p. 307 Bushong
p. 166 Carlton/Adler

4.28   A   Lower energy photons are most likely to be absorbed by a filter.

p. 165 Bushong
p. 165 Carlton/Adler

4.29   C   Additional filtration decreases the low-energy x-rays in the beam that add no diagnostic value, so filtration decreases patient exposure.

p. 155 Bushong
p. 205 Carlton/Adler

4.30   D   Addition of filters will shift the emission spectrum to the right.

p. 147 Bushong
p. 133 Carlton/Adler

Chapter 5

X-RAY TUBES

5.1 Cathode/Anode
5.2 Housing/Mountings
5.3 Collimation/Filtration
5.4 Performance

5.1 CATHODE/ANODE

A. Filament (cathode)

- The negative electrode in the x-ray tube is the **cathode**.
- The cathode is composed of a **focusing cup** that holds a **filament**.
- The **filament** is a ~2 mm in diameter and 1–2 cm in length coil of wire.
- Most diagnostic x-ray tubes have two filaments, one for each of the two focal spot sizes.
- As current flows through the filament, it heats allowing outer shell electrons to be released.
- The process is known as **thermionic emission**.
- **Tungsten** metal combined with 1% **thorium (Th)** is used to increase thermionic emission.
- The focusing cup houses the filament.
- The **focusing cup is negatively charged** as to repel the electrons created at the filament into a finely focused beam.
- The focusing cup also functions as the grid in a grid-controlled tube.
- The **focusing cup** can be used as the **exposure switch** to allow for rapid control of the x-ray tube.
- **Figure 5.1** shows a dual filament within a focusing cup.

B. Filament current

- The **filament current** is controlled through the tube current selected on the operating console.
- Filament currents in radiography tubes operate at between **3 A** and **6 A**.
- The **filament transformer** is a **step down transformer** having more windings in the primary than the secondary.
- **Table 5.1** shows typical current and voltage values in a filament (step down) transformer.

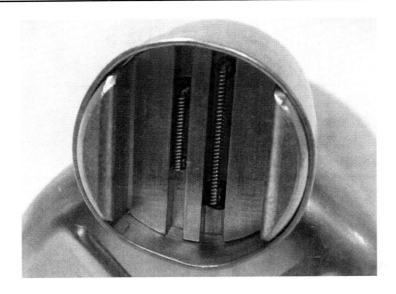

Figure 5.1
Dual filament focusing cup.

Table 5.1
Voltages and currents on the primary and secondary sides
of a typical x-ray tube filament transformer

Filament transformer	Current (Amp)	Voltage (V)
Primary	1	150
Secondary	6	12

- Filament current controls the filament temperature and, therefore, the number of electrons released through thermionic emission.

- As the **temperature** is increased, increased **mA**, the emission of **electrons** increases.

- As the filament heats and releases electrons, a cloud is formed with a negative electrical charge.

- The occurrence is known as **space charge**.

- **Space charge effect occurs when the negative cloud is strong enough to deter continued emission.**

- A **correction circuit** prevents the space charge effect.

- **Figure 5.2** show how the x-ray tube **current** varies with x-ray tube **voltage**, and identifies the space charge limited and emission limited voltages.

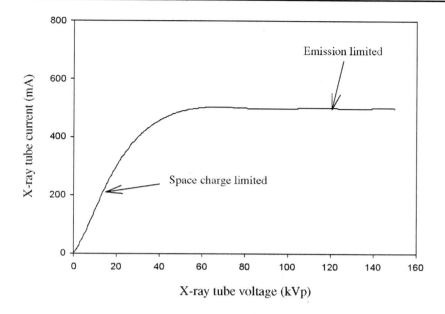

Figure 5.2
Variation of x–ray tube current (mA) with voltage (kVp) showing
a saturation current of 500 mA at voltages >60 kVp.

C. Target

- The **positive electrode** within the x-ray tube is the recipient of the electron beam emitted by the cathode.
- **Positive electrodes** conduct electrons via cables back to the **high voltage generator.**
- The area bombarded by electrons on the anode is the **target.**
- An electron beam is focused at a precise spot on the **target, the focal spot.**
- **Target material** selection is based on the resulting beam energies, thermal conductivity, and melting point.
- **Tungsten** is selected for diagnostic tubes due to its high atomic number (74), efficient dissipation of heat, and **high melting point (3400 °C).**
- A **tungsten rhenium alloy** is used for **focal tracks** due to its increased strength and thermal properties.
- Anodes may be composed of **molybdenum** and **graphite** for increased heat dissipation and rotation times.
- **Molybdenum** is often used for mammography x-ray tube target material due to the lower energy K-characteristic x-rays created.
- **The target is embedded in an anode,** which temporarily stores the heat generated during the x-ray production process.

D. Anodes

- **Stationary anodes** have a specific target location, or **focal spot**, usually composed of a tungsten alloy within a copper anode.
- **Rotating anodes** are slightly different in design, in that a **focal track** is embedded in a molybdenum or graphite **anode**.
- Rotating anodes provide a much larger area for interaction due to the continual movement of the focal spot.
- Because the anode rotates, the actual area on the anode is only bombarded with electrons for a brief period, before it is rotated away to cool.
- **Rotating anodes** allow for increased **mA** and shorter **exposure time**.
- **Anodes rotate between 3600–10,000 rpm.**
- The anode is rotated via an **electromagnetic induction motor.**
- Induction motors have two components, namely the **stator** and the **rotor**.
- The **rotor** is a ferromagnetic rod within the x-ray tube, whereas the **anode** is mounted on the rotor.
- The **stator** is composed of electromagnets outside the x-ray tube about the rotor.
- The stator's electromagnets are turned on in sequence, causing it to rotate within the x-ray tube.
- **Figure 5.3** shows an example of a rotating anode.

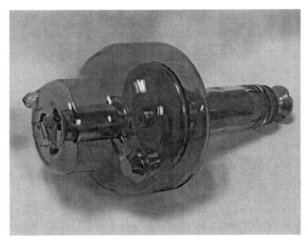

(a)

(b)

Figure 5.3
Glass envelope x-ray tube (a) and a rotating anode (b).

5.2 HOUSING/MOUNTINGS

A. Glass/Metal enclosure

- X-ray tubes are **vacuum tubes**, meaning they contain no air or gases.
- An x-ray tube is also known as a **Coolidge tube**.
- **Figure 5.3** shows a photograph of a glass envelope.
- X-ray tubes are composed of **Pyrex® glass** or **metal** to withstand the high thermal loads created during x-ray production.
- **Table 5.2** lists examples of materials used for the x-ray tube envelope.
- Within the vacuum tube are two electrodes, the **cathode** and the **anode**.
- If the vacuum within the tube is breached and gases enter, x-ray production decreases and tube failure is possible.
- Metal vacuum tubes are preferable to glass envelopes, due to their reduced failure rates.
- In a **glass envelope**, tungsten that is vaporized from the cathode will coat the inside of the tube.
- Coated glass envelopes provide a contact for current other than the anode (arcing).
- **Arcing occurs and leads to tube failure.**

Table 5.2
Commonly used x-ray tube types in diagnostic imaging

Envelope material	Comments
Pyrex® glass	Limited tube loading, used for mammography and radiography tubes
Metal/Glass	Grounded metal housing provides increased stability at high kVp, CT tubes
Metal/Ceramic	Highest tube loading, faster cooling, Interventional Radiography tubes

B. Protective housing

- X-ray production occurs in all directions, or **isotropically**.
- Radiography makes use of only those x-rays that are directed to the **window**.
- X-ray tube **windows** are made of **low attenuating glass or metal**, allowing for maximum transmission.
- Area of x-ray tube **windows is ~5 cm^2**.

- The **useful beam** is that which exits the tube through the window.
- **Leakage radiation** is any radiation that exits the protective metal housing of the tube.
- **Leakage radiation** is not image producing and only serves to increase **patient dose.**
- The **protective tube housing** is required to limit leakage radiation to **1 mGy/h (100mR/h) at 1 m.**
- The protective housing also protects the tube from damage through daily use.
- The **protective housing** contains a layer of **insulating oil** used to prevent electric shock and to aid in heat dissipation.

C. X-ray tube mountings

- A **ceiling-mounted tube** allows for maximum flexibility of tube movement.
- The tube is suspended from the ceiling, and allowed to move both longitudinally and transversely.
- In addition, the tube height is adjustable, providing variable SID.
- A **floor-to-ceiling tube-mounted system** consists of a movable tube support attached to the ceiling and floor.
- A popular design for an operating room system, interventional suites, and digital radiography (DR) systems is a **C-arm system.**
- Detector and tube are located on an arm in the shape of a C that can be ceiling mounted, or independently mounted on wheels.

5.3   COLLIMATION/FILTRATION

A. Aperture/Cones

- **Beam restriction** will reduce the production of **scatter.**
- The simplest form of beam restriction is the **aperture diaphragm.**
- A lead sheet with an open area, circle, square, or rectangle is placed on the tube housing.
- The diaphragm is designed to leave a 1 cm border of nonirradiated image receptor.
- A **cone** is an extension of a **diaphragm.**
- **Cones are no better or worse at reducing the field size when compared with a diaphragm.**
- A **cylinder** may be added to the diaphragm, which may be extendable.

- **Cylinders restrict the field size more than cones or diaphragms alone.**
- Size of the distal opening and the distance from the source determine the size of the irradiated area.
- Cylinders do require accurate alignment with the image receptor and the source to prevent "cutting off" of anatomy.

B. Variable aperture collimator

- Modern radiography equipment has a **variable aperture collimator**.
- Most commonly used as a beam restrictor.
- A **variable collimator** has two parts: a **fixed collimator** is closest to the focal spot, is stationary, and absorbs most of the off-focus radiation.
- A second set is controlled by the technologist, is **variable**, and is after the stationary collimator.
- Variable parts of the collimator are **~3 mm of lead**, and create a square or rectangular field of irradiation.
- Along with beam restriction, the collimator is equipped with a **light source**.
- A **light field** representative of the **irradiated field** is created using a **light source** and **mirror system**.
- Many radiography units have **positive beam limitation (PBL)**.
- **PBL** uses a sensor in the **Bucky tray** to relay the size of the image receptor to the collimator.
- The collimators will adjust their position to irradiate only the **imaging receptor area**.
- The automated PBL may be turned off on most equipment.

C. Inherent/Additional filtration

- Inherent filtration consists of the **x-ray tube window, insulating oil, and tube housing**.
- **Over time, the vaporized** tungsten will deposit within the x-ray tube and increase the inherent filtration.
- **Inherent filtration is ~0.5 mm Al equivalent.**
- **Additional filtration** is added to inherent to produce the desired total filtration for patient safety.
- Filtration also occurs because of the **collimator/light/mirror** within the x-ray tube.
- **Additional filtration of ~1 mm Al equivalent is added,** supplemental to the collimator apparatus, providing ~1 mm Al equivalent.

Table 5.3
Typical filters used in radiography, fluoroscopy, and mammography

Application	Filter Type	Comments
Radiography and Fluoroscopy	Al	Most common filter material
	Cu	May be used with aluminum in compound filters
Mammography	Mo	Used for lower density breast tissue
	Rh	Used for denser breast tissue
	Ag	Novel filter used in digital units

- **Table 5.3** lists typical filters used in radiography, fluoroscopy, and mammography.
- **Total filtration** in a diagnostic x-ray tube is generally required to be **2.5 mm Al equivalent**.
- **Figure 5.4** shows typical filtration levels in radiographic x-ray tubes.

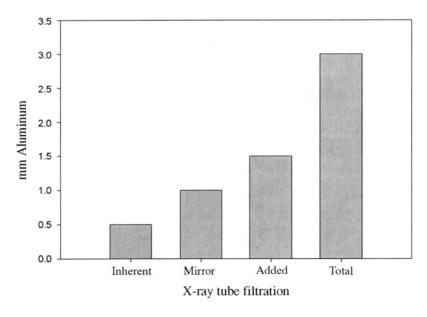

Figure 5.4
Typical filtration values for a diagnostic x-ray tube.

D. Variable/Compensating filters

- Some units are provided with **variable filtration**, which is controlled by the technologist.

- **Variable filtration** is used in addition to the standard 2.5 mm Al equivalent in the tube.

- **Compensating filters** are used for examinations containing considerable changes in anatomy thickness or density.

- Compensating filters are manufactured in various shapes, i.e., wedge filter.

- **Compensating wedge filters** can be used for foot images.

- The foot has a very thick/dense tarsal region with a thin, less dense toe region.

- The thick portion of the wedge is placed over the thin portion of the anatomy.

- **Compensating filters** result in an image with approximately equal intensity at the image receptor across the varying part.

- Compensating filters prevent overexposure of the toe region and underexposure of the tarsal bones when used for foot imaging.

5.4 PERFORMANCE

A. Focal spot

- **Diagnostic x-ray tubes** usually have two **focal spot sizes** available that correspond to the different size filaments.

- **Small focal spots are ~0.6 mm.**

- **Small focal spot** size is limited to **~300 mA** due to heat concerns and potential tube failure.

- **Large focal spots are typically ~1.2 mm.**

- **Large focal spot** size allows for maximum **mA (400 mA+)**.

- The larger the focal spot, or area, the greater its heat capacity and power loading.

- **Table 5.4** shows typical **focal spot** loading values in radiography.

- The **line focus principle** allows for a large actual focal spot, with a smaller effective focal spot.

- The **line focus principle** is based on **angling the target** in a way that results in the focal spot appearing smaller from the patient's perspective.

- The angle is measured off of the vertical axis, such that a target angle of 7° will provide a smaller effective focal spot as compared to a 15° angle.

- **Angles** between **5°–20°** are typically used in diagnostic tubes.

Table 5.4
Maximum power loadings on an x-ray tube focal spot

Focal spot size (mm)	Nominal values of maximum power loading (kW)	Comment
0.1	0.8	Mammography (small)
0.3	2.5	Mammography (large)
0.6	25	Radiography (small)
1.2	100	Radiography (large)

B. kVp/mA

- **Diagnostic imaging** exams utilize a **kVp between 25–150**.
- A **kVp meter** is located on the autotransformer for safety and reads the voltage.
- The current within the x-ray tube is measured in milliamperes (mA).
- **Tube current** is not freely selectable, rather, resistors with specific stations set tube currents between **50–1200 mA** in most units.
- **Falling load generators** select the maximum mA at the start of exposure and drop mA stations as the anode heats.
- An **mA meter** is used to monitor the current in the tube circuit, which is on **the low voltage side of the circuit**.
- The combination of **tube current (mA)** and **exposure time (s)** is termed **mAs**.
- mAs is also known as electrostatic charge (C).
- The highest mA station with the least exposure time is generally selected by an mAs timer.
- **Falling load** and **capacitor discharge** system use an **mAs timer**.
- **Figure 5.5** shows the maximum tube currents as a function of x-ray tube voltage.

C. Timers

- A timer is required to terminate the production of x-rays.
- Radiography **timer circuits** provide for the **initiation** of exposure by the technologist and **termination** by the timer mechanism.
- For the safety of the patient and x-ray tube, a **timer is limited to ~6 seconds of exposure**.
- **Synchronous timers** are very simplistic, motor-driven devised.

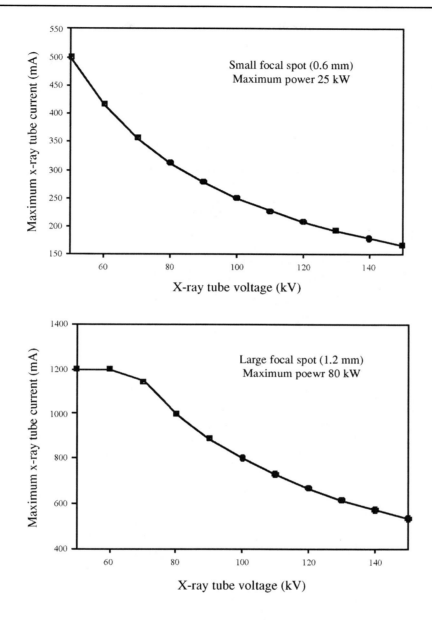

Table 5.5

Typical maximum tube currents for an 80 kW generator.

- Synchronous timers rotate 60 times, a full 360° per second, and can be detected when time stations are multiples of 60, i.e., 1/30 s or 1/10 s.
- Synchronous timers are not capable of serial imaging.
- **Electronic timers** are highly accurate and allow for exposure times as low as 1 ms.
- A **microprocessor** is used to operate the electronic timer.

D. Heel effect

- A disadvantage of the **line focus principle** is **varying intensity** across the irradiated field.
- This results from attenuation in the **anode** as the beam exits, resulting in decreased intensity at the anode and increased intensity at the **cathode** end of the field.
- The resulting effect is known as **anode heel effect**.
- **Anode heel effect** intensifies with smaller **anode angles**, decreased **SID**, and large **field sizes**.
- **Table 5.5** describes factors affecting visualization of the heel effect.
- Intensity of the field varies by as much as 45%.
- Radiographers use the anode heel effect to their advantage, by placing the cathode side of the field over the thicker end of the part being imaged.
- **Applying the anode heel effect** to anatomical parts of varying thickness **improves exposure** at the image receptor.

Table 5.5
Important factors that affect the heel effect

X-ray tube parameter	Heel effect increases when parameter	Comment
Anode angle	Decreases	Results in more target attenuation
SID	Decreases	Includes peripheral regions of the x-ray beam
Field size	Increases	Includes the peripheral regions of the x-ray beam

E. Off-focus radiation

- **Off-focus** radiation is the result of electron interaction with something other than the focal spot.
- **Off-focus** radiation should be limited as it degrades image quality.
- A **fixed collimator** is located adjacent to the window and acts to prevent off-focus radiation from exiting the tube.
- **Off-focus radiation** that exits through the tube window **is capable of creating images** at the edge of primary beam collimation.

- Off-focus radiation can cast a shadow of the soft tissues of the face outside of the primary beam area on lateral nasal bones.

F. Rating charts

- **Radiographic rating charts** are used to determine safe techniques and unsafe techniques for specific radiography generator/tube combinations.
- Most modern radiography units incorporate a **microprocessor** that will prevent unsafe exposures.
- Charts are provided for small and large focal spot use.
- When viewing the **rating chart**, at a selected mA all selections of time and kVp below the curve are safe and those above the curve are not.
- The use of the lowest kVp, mA, and exposure time to produce quality images will prolong tube life.
- **Anode cooling curves** are used to determine **anode heat load** and time requirements for **cooling**.
- Anode cooling curves are used to determine time needed between exposures to prevent overheating of the anode.

QUESTIONS

Chapter 5: X-Ray Tubes

5.1 The length of an x-ray tube filament is most likely _____ cm.
A. 0.15
B. 1.5
C. 15
D. 150

5.2 X-ray tube filaments are most likely made of:
A. molybdenum.
B. silver.
C. tungsten.
D. lead.

5.3 The most likely x-ray tube filament current is _____ A.
A. 0.04
B. 0.4
C. 4
D. 40

5.4 The melting point of tungsten targets in x-ray tubes is most likely _____ °C.
A. 34
B. 340
C. 3400
D. 34,000

5.5 The material added to tungsten targets in x-ray tubes is most likely:
A. rhenium.
B. silver.
C. thorium.
D. iron.

5.6 The target of a mammography x-ray tube is most likely:
A. molybdenum.
B. silver.
C. aluminum.
D. copper.

5.7   X-ray tube targets are most likely embedded in the:
   A. anode.
   B. cathode.
   C. housing.
   D. focusing grid.

5.8   The most likely rotation speed of an anode in a chest radiographic x-ray tube is _____ rpm.
   A. 50
   B. 500
   C. 5000
   D. 50,000

5.9   The type of gas in an x-ray tube is most likely:
   A. air.
   B. oxygen.
   C. nitrogen.
   D. none (vacuum).

5.10   Vaporized tungsten coated on the x-ray tube glass envelope is most likely to result in:
   A. arcing.
   B. leakage radiation.
   C. gas leaks.
   D. secondary radiation.

5.11   X-ray production in an x-ray tube is most likely to be emitted (towards):
   A. anode.
   B. cathode.
   C. filament.
   D. isotropically.

5.12   The area of an x-ray tube window is most likely _____ cm^2.
   A. 5
   B. 50
   C. 500
   D. 5000

5.13   Radiation that escapes through the protective housing is most likely called:
   A. primary.
   B. secondary.
   C. leakage.
   D. scatter.

5.14 The most likely material between the protective housing and x-ray tube is:
   A. oil.
   B. water.
   C. air.
   D. acrylic.

5.15 The shape of an aperture diaphragm is least likely to be a(n):
   A. circle.
   B. square.
   C. rectangle.
   D. ellipse.

5.16 Field size is most severely restricted by use of a(n):
   A. cylinder.
   B. cone.
   C. diaphragm.
   D. alignment mirror.

5.17 The lead thickness of collimator leaves is most likely _____ mm.
   A. 0.003
   B. 0.03
   C. 0.3
   D. 3

5.18 The minimum filtration required in a diagnostic x-ray tube is most likely _____ mm Al.
   A. 1.0
   B. 1.5
   C. 2.5
   D. 4.0

5.19 Added filtration is most likely made of:
   A. molybdenum.
   B. rhenium.
   C. aluminum.
   D. silver.

5.20 The inherent aluminum equivalence of light mirror is most likely _____ mm.
   A. 0.01
   B. 0.3
   C. 1
   D. 3

5.21 The small focal spot size in a conventional (W target) x-ray tube is most likely _____ mm.
   A. 0.1
   B. 0.3
   C. 0.6
   D. 1.2

5.22 The limiting tube current on a small focal spot size is most likely _____ mA.
   A. 3
   B. 30
   C. 300
   D. 3000

5.23 The maximum tube current for a typical diagnostic x-ray tube is most likely _____ mA.
   A. 100
   B. 1000
   C. 10,000
   D. 100,000

5.24 The maximum tube voltage for a typical diagnostic x-ray tube is most likely _____ kV.
   A. 15
   B. 150
   C. 1500
   D. 15,000

5.25 The most likely exposure time (s) for a synchronous timer would be _____ second.
   A. 1/50
   B. 1/60
   C. 1/70
   D. 1/80

5.26 The lowest exposure time of an electronic timer is most likely _____ second.
   A. 0.001
   B. 0.003
   C. 0.010
   D. 0.030

5.27 The most important factor affecting the heel effect is most likely the anode:
   A. angle.
   B. rotation.
   C. size.
   D. density.

5.28 Which field size (cm × cm) is likely to show the highest heel effect?
   A. 35 × 43
   B. 30 × 35
   C. 24 × 30
   D. 18 × 25

5.29 Off-focus radiation is best controlled by the use of:
   A. high kVp.
   B. high mA.
   C. collimators.
   D. a grid.

5.30 X-ray tubes that are used with reduced techniques are most likely to have:
   A. longer lives.
   B. off-focus radiation.
   C. microprocessor failures.
   D. repeat rates.

ANSWERS[1]

Chapter 5: X-Ray Tubes

5.1	B	Diagnostic x-ray tubes are ~2 mm in diameter and 1.5 cm in length.	*p. 122 Bushong* *p. 106 Carlton/Adler*
5.2	C	Filaments are made of thoriated tungsten.	*p. 122 Bushong* *p. 106 Carlton/Adler*
5.3	C	Filament currents is ~4 amperes.	*p. 124 Bushong* *p. 95 Carlton/Adler*
5.4	C	The melting point of tungsten is ~3400 degrees Celsius.	*p. 127 Bushong* *p. 106 Carlton/Adler*
5.5	A	A tungsten rhenium alloy is the material of choice in diagnostic x-ray targets, for added mechanical strength.	*p. 122 Bushong* *p. 108 Carlton/Adler*
5.6	A	Molybdenum is a target material used in mammography due to the lower atomic number and softer, lower energy x-ray beam.	*p. 127 Bushong* *p. 611 Carlton/Adler*
5.7	A	Most x-ray systems use a rotating anode with tungsten focal track embedded within.	*p. 126 Bushong* *p. 111 Carlton/Adler*
5.8	C	Rotating anodes in radiography systems operate between 3500 and 10,000 rpm, so 5000 rpm is a reasonable average value.	*p. 126 Bushong* *p. 116 Carlton/Adler*
5.9	D	Radiography tubes use a vacuum for increased efficiency.	*p. 122 Bushong* *p. 118 Carlton/Adler*
5.10	A	Vaporized tungsten causing arcing within the x-ray tube is the most common cause of tube failure.	*p. 133 Bushong* *p. 119 Carlton/Adler*
5.11	D	X-rays are produced isotropically, requiring proper shielding of the x-ray tube to limit leakage radiation.	*p. 121 Bushong* *p. 118 Carlton/Adler*
5.12	A	Typical x-ray tube windows measure 5 cm^2.	*p. 122 Bushong* *p. 118 Carlton/Adler*

---

[1] As a study aid, page numbers for additional study are given for the following references:
Bushong SC: *Radiologic Science for Technologists,* 9th ed. St. Louis, MO: Mosby, 2008.
Carlton RR, Adler AM: *Principles of Radiographic Imaging: An Art and a Science,* 4th ed. Albany, NY: Delmar Publishing Inc., 2005.

5.13	C	Any radiation that exits the tube, other than at the window, is considered leakage radiation.	*p. 121 Bushong* *p. 118 Carlton/Adler*
5.14	A	A layer of oil is located between the x-ray tube and housing, which is used for heat dissipation and electrical insulation.	*p. 122 Bushong* *p. 118 Carlton/Adler*
5.15	D	Aperture diaphragms are most likely square, rectangular, or circular in shape, but not elliptical.	*p. 233 Bushong* *p. 230 Carlton/Adler*
5.16	A	Cylinders allow for the most beam restriction as the end of the cylinder is farther from the focal spot.	*p. 230 Bushong* *p. 232 Carlton/Adler*
5.17	D	Collimator leaves in diagnostic x-ray systems are ~3 mm of lead.	*p. 232 Bushong* *p. 229 Carlton/Adler*
5.18	C	Diagnostic x-ray systems must have a minimum of 2.5 mm Al equivalent filtration.	*p. 158 Bushong* *p. 163 Carlton/Adler*
5.19	C	Added filtration of 1.0 mm Aluminum is common.	*p. 158 Bushong* *p. 166 Carlton/Adler*
5.20	C	Diagnostic x-ray systems with a mirror collimator system provide 1.0 mm Al equivalent filtration.	*p. 158 Bushong* *p. 166 Carlton/Adler*
5.21	C	Diagnostic radiography small focal spots are ~0.6 mm.	*pp. 124 & 232 Bushong* *p. 114 Carlton/Adler*
5.22	C	Small FSS are limited to ~300 mA to prevent overheating of the anode.	*p. 124 Bushong* *n/a Carlton/Adler*
5.23	B	Diagnostic radiography equipment maximum mA station is generally 1000 mA.	*p. 124 Bushong* *p. 88 Carlton/Adler*
5.24	B	Diagnostic x-ray systems are manufactured to provide a maximum of 150 kV.	*p. 101 Bushong* *p. 88 Carlton/Adler*
5.25	B	Synchronous timers are based on a 60-Hz system and generally have times in derivatives of 1/60 s.	*p. 108 Bushong* *p. 95 Carlton/Adler*
5.26	A	Electronic timers are the most accurate and provide times as low as 0.001 second (1 ms).	*p. 108 Bushong* *p. 95 Carlton/Adler*
5.27	A	Anode heel effect is increased with decreasing anode angles.	*p. 129 Bushong* *p. 114 Carlton/Adler*
5.28	A	Anode heel effect is increased with large film sizes and will therefore be greatest for a field size of 35 × 43 cm.	*p. 129 Bushong* *p. 114 Carlton/Adler*

5.29   C   First-stage fixed collimators along with second stage variable *p. 231 Bushong*
collimators work together to prevent off-focus radiation *p. 232 Carlton/Adler*
from leaving the tube housing.

5.30   A   Decreasing the load on an x-ray system will allow for longer *p. 108 Bushong*
use due to less wear on the filament and decreased heating *p. 123 Carlton/Adler*
issues in the anode, i.e., warped bearings.

PART II. IMAGING WITH X-RAYS

Chapter 6

DETECTING X-RAYS

6.1 Film
6.2 Film Processing
6.3 Screens/Cassettes
6.4 Digital Detectors

6.1 FILM

A. Base

- **Film base** is a passive device that provides a **structure for emulsion**.
- A base is used to provide stability.
- The base is generally made of **polyester**.
- Base must be resistant to shrinkage or stretching, but be flexible for use in processors.
- **A base must transmit most of the light that emerges from a light box** (i.e., be lucent).
- A **blue dye** may be added to film bases for ease of viewing.
- It is believed that a blue tinge will help to relieve radiologist eyestrain.
- Active **image-forming materials are applied** on one or both sides of a base.

B. Emulsion

- The **emulsion (gelatin)** is attached to one or both sides of the base.
- Emulsions are adhered to the base.
- Emulsion layers are thin, typically ~**5 to 10 μm**.
- **Protective coating** is used over the emulsion to provide resistance to mishandling.
- Film emulsion may contain **silver halide crystals**.
- **Silver halide crystals** are embedded in a layer of **gelatin** for uniform distribution.
- Silver halide crystals may have a tabular or flat shape.
- The emulsion (gelatin) is the sensitive **light-capturing layer**.

C. Silver halide

- The **silver halide crystal** has a **lattice structure**.
- Positively charged silver ions (**Ag⁺**) are at the center of the lattice.
- Negatively charged bromide or iodide (**Br⁻ and I⁻**) ions are located at the periphery of the lattice.
- Within the lattice is the area of **impurity (sensitivity center)**.
- As the film absorbs the light photons, an electron is released.
- **Photoelectrons** travel to the **sensitivity center**, where a negative charge attracts positive silver ions.
- **Free electrons and positive silver ions will join to form metallic silver.**
- Remaining bromide and iodide atoms travel to the gelatin portion of the emulsion to be removed during processing.
- **Four or more silver atoms** must form at the sensitivity center for it to be **"sensitized."**

D. Latent film image

- **Light photons** incident on the film are photoelectrically **absorbed and release electrons**.
- The result of light absorption in the film emulsion is a **latent image**.
- The latent image is composed of those silver atoms that have migrated to the sensitivity center.
- This latent image is **not visible** by the human eye.
- To view the latent image, it must be processed, resulting in a visible image.
- The **latent image centers** will become **black metallic** silver during **processing**, and therefore visible.
- Processing allows all silver atoms in the crystal to transform from Ag⁺ to Ag or metallic silver.
- **Creation of small grains of silver makes the image visible and viewable.**
- **Table 6.1** lists films used in radiology.

Table 6.1
Different film types used in radiology

Application	Emulsion	Safe light	Screen material
Mammographic	Single	Red	Rare earth
Green sensitive	Double	Red	Rare earth
Blue-violet sensitive	Double	Red or amber	Calcium tungstate
Laser	Single	Green	None

6.2 FILM PROCESSING

A. Development chemistry

- **Reducing agents** work on those crystals with silver atoms at the sensitivity center.
- Crystals without exposure remain intact and undeveloped.
- **Developer chemicals** are **reducing agents,** as they reduce **Ag^+ to Ag.**
- Hydroquinone and phenidone are reducing agents used in modern processors.
- When combined, they have an additive or synergistic effect for additional development.
- Buffering agents are added to reducers.
- **Preservatives** are added to the developer solution **to prevent oxidation of solution** over time.
- Developer solution also contains a **mild hardener,** glutaraldehyde, which prevents excessive swelling of the emulsion.
- Most processors have a developer **temperature of about 35 °C (95 °F).**

B. Fixing

- Upon completion of the developing process, the film is fed into the fixer tank.
- **Fixer is an acidic solution that halts the development chemicals.**
- Acidic properties of fixer are provided by acetic acid.
- In addition to stopping development, the thiosulfate in the **fixer clears undeveloped silver from the emulsion.**
- Thiosulfate is also known as **clearing agent** or **hypo.**
- **Hyporetention** occurs when thiosulfate is not removed from the emulsion, resulting in a **brownish colored stain on films** and often a sticky emulsion.
- Strong hardeners are contained in the fixer, as well as preservatives to prevent breakdown of the solution.

- **Fixer** hardens the emulsion providing a permanent image for archive.
- **Table 6.2** lists the principal chemicals used during development and fixing.

Table 6.2
Key chemicals used in film processing

Processor component	Chemical	Function	Comment
Developer	Phenidone	Reducing agent	Fast acting, produces low OD
	Hydroquinone	Reducing agent	Slow acting, produces high OD
	Glutaraldehyde	Mild hardener	Prevents excessive emulsion swelling
Fixer	Ammonium thiosulfate	Clearing agent	Removes undeveloped silver halide crystals
	Potassium alum	Strong hardener	Shrinks emulsion for proper drying/storage
	Acetic acid	Activator	Provides acidic environment to halt development

OD: Optical density

C. Washing and drying

- **Washing** removes all developer and fixer chemicals from the emulsion.
- The wash water should be ~3 °C (5 °F) below the developer solution temperature.
- Generally, 12 liters/min (3 gal/min) is used by the wash tank.
- **Filters** are present for incoming water lines and for the internal circulation system to **remove impurities and flakes of emulsion in solution.**
- If washing is incomplete, **hyporetention** may occur and cause artifacts.
- The **dryer system** consists of a fan, air tubes, and intake and exhaust vents.
- Dryer air tubes are directed at both sides of the film.
- Room air is heated and used in the dryer system, so it should be free of impurities and have a low humidity.
- **Damp/tacky films** are more likely due to a **lack of glutaraldehyde.**
- When processing films, a certain amount of each solution is depleted and must be replaced.

D. Processor mechanics

- **Entrance rollers** grab the film from the feed tray and send the film over a **microswitch** that initiates the replenishment system.

- The **replenishment system** will infuse each tank with the appropriate amount of solution for the film size that was processed.

- **Increasing replenishment will increase development and contrast.**

- The majority of rollers in the processor are **transport rollers 1 inch in diameter**.

- A **master roller is 3 inches in diameter** and is used to redirect a film along with planetary rollers and **metal guideshoes**.

- The transport system contains independent movable racks for each section, providing easy cleaning and repair.

- **Crossover racks** are used to guide a film from one tank to another and a **turnaround assembly** is used at the bottom of tanks to redirect films.

E. Safelights

- Radiographic film must be protected from light sources while in storage and in the dark room, except for handling time.

- Exposure to a light source prior to processing will increase **fog levels**.

- **Safelights** are a filtered light that **allows for handling of film** in a darkroom with minimal impact on image quality.

- Safelight **illumination levels** are affected by the **wattage** of the bulb, **distance** from the counter, and **type of filter** used.

- General darkrooms use a **7.5-** or **15-watt light bulb** mounted no closer than **1 meter** (3 feet) from the countertop.

- **Blue sensitive** film may be used with a **red or amber safelight**, as neither will cause fogging of the film if used at the appropriate wattage and distance.

- **Green sensitive** film may only be used with a **red safelight;** an amber safelight would cause excessive fog.

6.3 SCREENS/CASSETTES

A. Phosphors

- **Luminescent materials release light after stimulation** from an outside source, such as radiation.

- **Phosphors** release light and are known as "luminescent materials."

- As the x-ray photon is absorbed in the phosphor material, an outer shell electron is placed in a higher energy state.

- This electron will return to its place in the atom, and when doing that releases the **additional energy** as a **light photon.**

- Color of the light is determined by the type of phosphor.

- More light produced per x-ray photon is described as a high **conversion efficiency.**

- **Fluorescent** materials only emit light when stimulated, whereas **phosphorescent** materials will glow after excitation.

- **Radiographic screens are fluorescent materials.**

- **Phosphors** are selected for their **high atomic number,** aiding in the absorption of exit radiation from the patient.

- **Figure 6.1** demonstrates the relationship between absorption ability of a phosphor and photon energy.

B. Screens

- Originally, screens were **calcium tungstate** and emitted **blue light.**

- Newer phosphors are **rare earth materials** such as **gadolinium, lanthanum, and yttrium.**

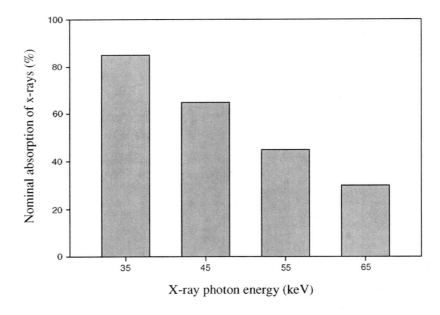

Figure 6.1
Nominal absorption of x-rays in a screen (%) as a function of x-ray photon energy.

- Rare earth screens are faster, absorbing more photons and producing more light per x-ray photon.
- The resulting light photons may be in the green color range.
- **Calcium tungstate screens have a conversion efficiency of ~5%, and rare earth can be as high as ~20%.**
- Light is produced **isotropically**, or in all directions.
- A **reflective layer** is placed at the posterior portion of the screen and reflects any light that reaches it back towards the film.
- **Reflective layers increase screen speed and also reduce image detail.**
- A base is used to provide a stable foundation for the phosphor layer.
- **Polyester** is commonly used as a **base material.**
- The **protective coating** prevents scratches and staining of the screen and is closest to the film.

C. Cassette

- **Two screens hold a double-emulsion film, which results in maximum x-ray absorption.**
- A **single screen** and film emulsion are used in **mammography** to maintain optimal detail.
- Cassettes are left to sit for ~20 minutes to allow any air pockets to escape.
- The cassette or housing for the film-screen combination has different materials for the tube side and the back side of the cassette.
- The **tube side** is composed of a **low atomic number** material (plastic or carbon fiber) to limit interaction between the cassette and the exit radiation.
- The **back portion** of the cassette is composed of a **high atomic number** material for maximum absorption.
- The high-attenuating back prevents **backscatter** from affecting image quality.
- A **spongelike** material is placed between the cover and the phosphor layer to allow maximum **film-screen contact.**
- The screen must be matched to the appropriate film type (**spectral matching**).
- Calcium tungstate screens emit in the blue-violet range and require blue-violet sensitive film.
- Rare earth screens may be green emitters and require green sensitive film.
- **Green sensitive** film is known as **orthochromatic film.**

D. Screen speed

- **Intensification Factor (IF)** is the ratio of the exposure required **with a screen** to the exposure required to produce the same optical density **without a screen**.
- **The IF can be used to calculate the reduction in technique for using a screen.**
- Screen is capable of absorbing higher kVp photons as compared to film.
- **Screen speed** is an indicator of the screen's ability to produce **light photons** from **x-ray photons**.
- The higher the **speed**, the greater the **light produced**.
- Screen speed is increased with larger phosphors, increased concentrations, and thicker phosphor (see **Figure 6.2**).
- Traditional calcium tungstate screens have a speed of 100.
- Other screens speeds are determined from this standard.
- **Regular** use screens are ~200–400 speed,
- **Extremity** screens are ~50–80.
- **Figure 6.3** shows increasing **screen speed** through increased screen thickness, and the corresponding decrease in **spatial resolution**.

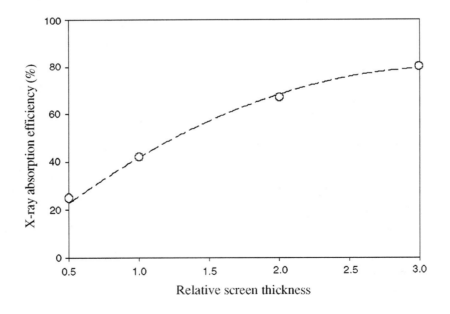

Figure 6.2
Typical x-ray absorption efficiency with increasing screen thickness.

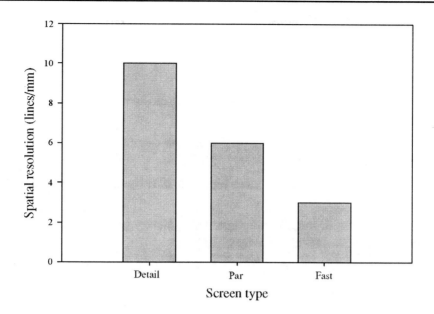

Figure 6.3
Nominal resolution performance (line pairs/mm) for different types of screens.

6.4 DIGITAL DETECTORS

A. Computed radiography

- **Computed radiography (CR)** makes use of photostimulable phosphors (PSPs).
- **Photostimulable phosphors** use a material, usually, **barium fluorohalide with europium (BaFBr:Eu or BaFI:Eu)**, which has photostimuable luminescence.
- **Photostimulable phosphors** exposed to radiation absorb the radiation.
- A portion of the energy absorbed is released immediately.
- The remainder of the energy is used to hold electrons in a higher-energy state than normal.
- **Electrons** held in an excited state are said to be in a **metastable state (latent image)**.
- When the plate is exposed to a light source, the remainder of the energy will be released.
- This released energy is known as **photostimulable luminescence (PSL)**.
- The **metastable state** will begin to degrade as time passes, losing **~25% in 8 hours**.
- The thickness of the **phosphor layer affects spatial resolution**.
- Thicker phosphors increase the spread of light in the phosphor, which **has inferior resolution**.

B. CR readers

- **Computed radiography (CR)** uses a radiation-sensitive plate protected by a cassette, very similar to film-screen imaging.
- **CR imaging plates** do not require processing in the traditional sense, but require **reading and erasure by a CR reader.**
- CR readers remove the imaging plate from the cassette housing and move it along a path within the reader.
- The **CR plate** is exposed to a **laser beam** to start the **photostimulable luminescence (PSL)** process.
- The CR reader laser may be a helium neon (HeNe) gas or a solid-state source, **collimated to ~50–100 nanometers (nm).**
- As the laser exposes the phosphor, light is released, which is captured and used to create an image.
- A **photomultiplier tube/photodiode** also has blue light emitted from the **CR plate.**
- Filters are used to ensure emission light (blue) is captured for image construction and to absorb any stimulation light (laser light).
- After reading the imaging plate, some **metastable** electrons may remain.
- The imaging plate requires an **erasure cycle.**
- An **intense white light** source is used to remove any residual information and to provide a "clean plate" for reloading into the cassette.

C. Indirect flat-panel detectors

- **Indirect flat-panel detectors** use a **scintillator** to convert x-rays into light, followed by a light detector that converts light into charge.
- **Cesium iodide (CsI)** and **gadolinium oxysulfide (Gd_2O_2)** are common scintillators that act as the capture element, absorbing x-ray photons and releasing light photons.
- **Amorphous silicon (a-Si)** absorbs the light photons and transforms to signal information that is captured by **thin film transistors (TFTs).**
- The **TFTs are arrayed in a matrixlike** pattern, allowing for reading in sequential rows of information.
- Each pixel is represented by the **scintillator**, with a portion of the surface used for the TFT and a capacitor.
- The more space occupied by the TFT, the less active space for image capture.
- The **active area is known as fill factor (~80%)** and the area used for electronics is referred to as **dead space (~20%).**

- It is important to remember that as **pixel size** decreases, and the size of the electronics stays the same, decreasing fill factor and increasing dead space result.

D. Direct flat–panel detectors

- **Direct flat-panel detectors** use a **photoconductor** to absorb x-rays and convert this directly to charge.
- **Amorphous selenium (a-Se)** is the most common photoconductor currently used in medical imaging.
- A layer of a-Se over a matrix of TFTs is used to absorb radiation.
- These **photoconductors detect x-rays directly**, and **no scintillators are required**.
- Photoconductors have a **voltage** applied, allowing for detection of **charges (electrons)** when irradiated.
- The a-Se converts radiation directly to electric signal that is captured by the TFT.
- The amount of signal is directly proportional to the **x-ray intensity** at the detector.
- Direct systems have very good **spatial resolution** because there is no spreading of charge, as when light spreads out in a scintillator.
- Direct flat-panel detectors have spatial resolution that is superior to indirect flat-panel detectors and to CR (photostimulable phosphors).

E. Quantum efficiency

- Any x-ray detector can be characterized by a detector **quantum efficiency (QE)**.
- QE is related to the **ability** of the detector to capture x-rays for digital imaging.
- **Material composition** is an important determinant of detector QE.
- **Table 6.3** lists elements used in x-ray detectors and their key x-ray absorption characteristics.
- Detector QE also depends on **x-ray photon energy and detector thickness**.
- **Table 6.4** shows how photon energy and detector thickness affect x-ray detection efficiency for a selenium detector.
- **Indirect flat-panel detectors** based on CsI and Gd_2O_2S generally have **high QE**.
- Direct flat-panel detectors that use Se have excellent QE at low energies (i.e., mammography).
- At high energies, Se detectors have poor QEs.
- **Photostimulable phosphors** generally have **low QEs**.
- Reduced QE of photostimulable phosphors occurs because these must be thin to minimize light scatter in the readout process.

Table 6.3
Properties of key atoms used in x-ray detectors
(photoconductors, photostimulable phosphors, and scintillators)

Element	Atomic number (Z)	K-shell binding energy (keV)	Density (g/cm^3)	Detectors types where atoms are encountered
Selenium (Se)	34	13	4.8	Photodetector
Iodide (I)	53	33	4.9	Scintillator
Cesium (Cs)	55	36	1.9	Scintillator
Barium (Ba)	56	37	3.5	Photostimulable phosphor
Lanthanum (La)	57	39	6.1	Scintillator

Table 6.4
Relative efficiency of selenium photoconductors for absorbing x-rays

Photon energy (keV)	X-ray absorption efficiency (%) for Se thickness of:	
	0.25 mm	0.5 mm
20	100	100
40	58	82
60	25	43
80	12	23
100	7	14

- **Figure 6.4** shows typical QE values for digital x-ray detectors.
- **Detective quantum efficiency (DQE)** can also be used to characterize x-ray detector performance.
- DQE is related to QE, and describes the combined signal and noise properties of imaging detectors.
- The best x-ray detectors should have comparable values of QE and DQE.

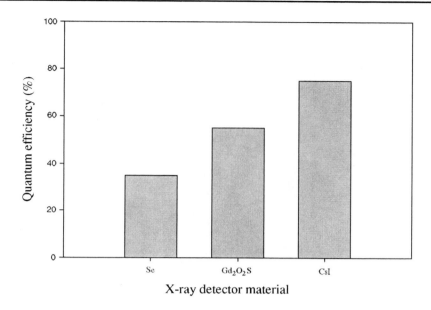

Figure 6.4
Nominal quantum efficiencies for three x-ray detectors
used in chest imaging (120 kVp).

QUESTIONS

Chapter 6: Detecting X-Rays

6.1   Film base is most likely made of:
A. polyester.
B. silver halide.
C. conductor.
D. semi-conductor.

6.2   What color dye is normally added to film for ease of viewing?
A. Green
B. Red
C. Blue
D. Yellow

6.3   Which of the following is least likely to be found in a film emulsion?
A. Bromine
B. Iodine
C. Chlorine
D. Chromium

6.4   Silver bromide crystals are embedded in a layer of:
A. gelatin.
B. polyester.
C. graphite.
D. potassium nitrate.

6.5   After reduction in a film developer, one is left with grains of:
A. silver.
B. bromine.
C. iodine.
D. chlorine.

6.6   A film developer is least likely to contain:
A. mild hardeners.
B. water softeners.
C. reducing agents.
D. buffering agents.

6.7   Fixers are most likely to contain:
    A. silver.
    B. reducing agents.
    C. clearing agents.
    D. purifiers.

6.8   Reducing the replenishment rate in automatic film processors is most likely to reduce:
    A. film contrast.
    B. processing time.
    C. developer temperature.
    D. image artifacts.

6.9   Which rollers are least likely to be found in an automatic film processor?
    A. Transport
    B. Master
    C. Subassembly
    D. Bearing

6.10   A light bulb in a darkroom is most likely to have a power rating of _____ W.
    A. 150
    B. 15
    C. 1.5
    D. 0.15

6.11   When exposed to x-rays, a luminescent material is most likely to emit:
    A. light.
    B. ultraviolet.
    C. charge.
    D. heat.

6.12   Phosphorescence materials are those that glow:
    A. during excitation.
    B. after excitation.
    C. for x-ray exposure.
    D. when heated.

6.13   The most important factor that affects the ability of a phosphor to absorb x-rays is the:
    A. atomic number.
    B. mass number.
    C. physical density.
    D. areal thickness.

6.14 Which of the following elements is least likely to be found in a rare earth screen?
   A. Tungsten
   B. Gadolinium
   C. Lanthanum
   D. Yttrium

6.15 A rare earth screen most likely has a conversion efficiency of _____ %.
   A. 1
   B. 3
   C. 10
   D. 30

6.16 Reflective layers in x-ray phosphors are likely to increase the phosphor:
   A. screen speed.
   B. x-ray absorption.
   C. conversion efficiency.
   D. image sharpness.

6.17 The time that a cassette should be left to sit to permit the escape of air pockets is most likely _____ minutes.
   A. 1
   B. 5
   C. 20
   D. 60

6.18 The tube side of a cassette would most likely be made of a material with an atomic number of _____ .
   A. 8
   B. 16
   C. 24
   D. 32

6.19 The light emitted by a Gd_2O_2S screen, and used to expose a film, is most likely:
   A. violet.
   B. blue.
   C. green.
   D. red.

6.20 The Intensification Factor (IF) of a 200-speed film-screen combination is most likely _____ .
  A. 2
  B. 5
  C. 15
  D. 40

6.21 A screen-film combination used for chest radiography would likely be classified as having a speed of _____ .
  A. 2
  B. 20
  C. 200
  D. 2000

6.22 Which of the following is a photostimulable phosphor?
  A. BaFBr
  B. $CdWO_4$
  C. GdO_2S_2
  D. $BaSO_4$

6.23 Energy stored in an exposed photostimulable phosphor is released by the use of:
  A. light.
  B. heat.
  C. voltage.
  D. pressure.

6.24 The signal that a photostimulable phosphor will lose in 8 hours is most likely _____ %.
  A. 1
  B. 5
  C. 25
  D. 90

6.25 The laser color used to read out photostimulable phosphors is most likely:
  A. ultraviolet.
  B. blue.
  C. green.
  D. red.

6.26 Detectors that use a scintillator are most likely known as:
  A. direct.
  B. indirect.
  C. direct or indirect.
  D. none of the above.

6.27 The most likely detector material in a digital chest x-ray unit is:
   A. CsI.
   B. NaI.
   C. Se.
   D. $CdWO_4$.

6.28 A TFT captures light and converts this to:
   A. electrons.
   B. heat.
   C. microwaves.
   D. x-rays.

6.29 The region used for electronics in a digital x-ray detector is known as the:
   A. fill factor.
   B. dead space.
   C. pixel area.
   D. TFT.

6.30 The ability of an x-ray detector to capture x-rays is known as the:
   A. quantum efficiency.
   B. conversion efficiency.
   C. quantum mottle.
   D. speed.

ANSWERS[1]

Chapter 6: Detecting X-Rays

6.1 A   Modern film base is polyester. Cellulose nitrate was once used, however it is flammable and unsafe.

p. 182 Bushong
p. 272 Carlton/Adler

6.2 C   A blue tint is added to ease eyestrain during reading of radiographs.

p. 182 Bushong
p. 272 Carlton/Adler

6.3 D   Silver halide crystals all contain silver mixed with bromide, iodide, or chloride. Chromium is not used.

p. 182 Bushong
p. 273 Carlton/Adler

6.4 A   Gelatin is used to hold the silver halide crystals due to its ability to allow penetration of chemicals for processing, transmission of light for viewing and inert properties.

p. 182 Bushong
p. 273 Carlton/Adler

6.5 A   Reducing agents act on Ag+, reducing it to Ag neutral or metallic silver.

p. 196 Bushong
p. 286 Carlton/Adler

6.6 B   Developer solutions will contain the reducing agents, buffering agents, and mild hardeners but do not contain water softeners.

p. 196 Bushong
p. 287 Carlton/Adler

6.7 C   Fixer contains clearing agents to clear undeveloped silver halide crystals from the emulsion.

p. 199 Bushong
p. 288 Carlton/Adler

6.8 A   Reduced replenishment rates will lower solution concentration, resulting in less development and a loss of contrast.

p. 202 Bushong
p. 292 Carlton/Adler

6.9 D   The transport system is composed of transport, master, and planetary rollers; turnaround and crossover assemblies; and the rack system to hold them all. Bearing rollers are not used.

p. 200 Bushong
p. 291 Carlton/Adler

6.10 B   15 W bulbs are used in diagnostic darkrooms.

p. 188 Bushong
p. 296 Carlton/Adler

6.11 A   Luminescent materials emit light in response to stimulation. In radiography screens, the stimulation is x-ray exposure.

p. 210 Bushong
p. 320 Carlton/Adler

---

[1] As a study aid, page numbers for additional study are given for the following references:
Bushong SC: *Radiologic Science for Technologists,* 9th ed. St. Louis, MO: Mosby, 2008.
Carlton RR, Adler AM: *Principles of Radiographic Imaging: An Art and a Science,* 4th ed. Albany, NY: Delmar Publishing Inc., 2005.

6.12	B	Phosphorescent materials glow after excitation and fluorescent materials glow during excitation.	*p. 210 Bushong* *p. 320 Carlton/Adler*
6.13	A	Absorption of an x-ray photon is directly proportional to the third power of the atomic number of the material with which it interacts.	*p. 167 Bushong* *p. 189 Carlton/Adler*
6.14	A	Tungsten is not a rare earth element.	*p. 208 Bushong* *p. 321 Carlton/Adler*
6.15	C	Calcium tungsten screens have a conversion efficiency of ~5%, whereas those of rare earths are ~10%.	*p. 212 Bushong* *p. 320 Carlton/Adler*
6.16	A	Screens with a reflective layer allow light directed toward the back of the cassette to be redirected toward the film, thereby increasing speed.	*p. 209 Bushong* *p. 319 Carlton/Adler*
6.17	C	At least 20 minutes should be allowed prior to returning a cassette to use.	*pp. 219 & 343 Bushong* *p. 488 Carlton/Adler*
6.18	A	The tube side of a cassette is made of a low atomic number material, i.e., carbon fiber with a Z of 6. The best choice is a Z of 8.	*p. 215 Bushong* *p. 325 Carlton/Adler*
6.19	C	Gadolinium oxysulfide rare earth screens emit a green light.	*p. 216 Bushong* *p. 321 Carlton/Adler*
6.20	D	The intensification factor of a 200-speed system is ~40; screen IFs range from 20–400.	*p. 211 Bushong* *p. 323 Carlton/Adler*
6.21	C	Screens used in general radiography are 200 speed.	*p. 210 Bushong* *p. 333 Carlton/Adler*
6.22	A	Barium fluorohalide phosphors are photostimulable.	*p. 413 Bushong* *p. 357 Carlton/Adler*
6.23	A	Photostimulable luminescence is defined as a material that emits some light when excited, while retaining some of that energy to be released at a later time.	*p. 413 Bushong* *p. 357 Carlton/Adler*
6.24	C	Photostimulable phosphors lose some of their latent image over time, and after ~8 hours about 25% of the image signal is lost.	*p. 415 Bushong* *p. 358 Carlton/Adler*
6.25	D	A red light source is used to stimulate the imaging plate for reading.	*p. 415 Bushong* *p. 358 Carlton/Adler*

6.26	B	Detectors that use a scintillator are "indirect" because x-rays are first converted to light and then light to signal (charge).	*p. 430 Bushong* *p. 356 Carlton/Adler*
6.27	A	Cesium iodide is a common scintillator used for digital imaging in indirect DR systems.	*pp. 427 & 592 Bushong* *p. 356 Carlton/Adler*
6.28	A	A TFT used with a-Si (a semiconductor) will absorb light photons and convert them to electrons.	*p. 430 Bushong* *p. 372 Carlton/Adler*
6.29	B	The area of a pixel that is not sensitive to radiation is known as the dead space.	*p. 431 Bushong* *p. 450 Carlton/Adler*
6.30	A	Quantum efficiency (QE) is the percentage of x-rays absorbed by a screen.	*p. 212 Bushong* *p. 319 Carlton/Adler*

Chapter 7

ANALOG AND DIGITAL IMAGES

7.1 Analog Images
7.2 Computers
7.3 Digital Images
7.4 Image Display

7.1 ANALOG IMAGES

A. Characteristic curve

- The relationship between radiation intensity and the resulting film density is known as the **characteristic curve.**

- **Characteristic curves** are also known as **H&D curves,** named for Hurter and Driffield who created the curve.

- Low-intensity regions are referred to as the **toe** and high-exposure areas as the **shoulder.**

- Film displays some level of density, even in the absence of exposure, which is called **fog.**

- Film components and dyes also add a slight level of density known as the **base.**

- **Base plus fog levels are ~0.2 OD.**

- **Maximum film OD is ~3.0.**

- Film development affects the shape of the characteristic curve.

B. Film contrast and latitude

- The **slope (gradient)** of the characteristic curve **determines film contrast.**

- The mean slope is measured between 0.25 and 2.0 OD.

- The mean slope is also known as **average film gradient.**

- **Film gradients above 1 amplify subject contrast.**

- Diagnostic radiography film has a gradient of ~2, mammography ~3.

- **Film latitude** describes the **range of exposure** levels that would provide acceptable image contrast.

- **Dynamic range** may also be used to describe film latitude.

- **Film latitude and film contrast are inversely related.**
- The greater the slope of the characteristic curve, the narrower the film latitude.
- Film having a **narrow latitude** has a **limited range of exposure values**, resulting in good image contrast.
- Wide-latitude film creates a low-contrast image due to the low gradient or slope.
- **Wide-latitude film** is used for high subject contrast studies, such as **chest imaging.**
- **Narrow-latitude film** is used for low subject contrast studies, such as **mammography.**

C. Laser film

- **Laser printers** are used with digital imaging modalities (CT, MR, etc.).
- A **red laser** is used to expose a red sensitive film developed for this application.
- Laser intensity is adjusted or modulated, based on the incoming electronic information from an imaging modality.
- Laser beam works in a **raster pattern** across the film, with **active trace (exposure)** and **inactive trace (nonexposure).**
- Laser printers are capable of printing a multitude of patterns, such as 1:1 or 12:1 image arrangements.
- Laser film is sensitized to red light, so it must be handled in complete darkness or in a darkroom equipped with a **green safelight.**
- A laser printer may be connected to a wet processor for seamless printing and processing, with no darkroom required.

D. Dry processing

- **Dry processing** does not require wet chemicals for image development.
- Dry processing is more environmentally friendly and also less expensive.
- Image quality of dry processing is comparable to that of wet processing.
- Advantages of dry processing include the elimination of darkroom maintenance and repair, i.e., chemical disposal and plumbing blockages.
- Dry processing also has a greater efficiency in image throughput.
- **Photothermography (PTG)** uses digital electronic information from a modality to modulate a **laser beam** over the film, similar to a laser camera.
- **Latent image** is then "processed" or exposed to **125° for ~15 seconds.**
- **Thermography (TG)** is a one-step process where a **heat source** is used to impart the image on the film (i.e., there is no latent image).
- Disadvantage of **TG is increased image blur.**

7.2 COMPUTERS

A. Computer basics

- **Computers** have hardware, software, and data stored within them for **problem solving**.
- **Hardware** represents the physical components of a computer system (e.g., monitor or mouse).
- **Software** consists of instructions for a computer.
- **Software speaks to the hardware** and directs the hardware's function.
- System software allows for communication between the user and the computer.
- **Operating systems** allow for use or communication with hardware (e.g., Windows®).
- **Programs** are instructions for specific functions.
- **Applications software** is most familiar to users (e.g., Word and Excel).
- The **central processing unit**, or **CPU**, is the calculation center.
- **Array processors** are to **increase speed.**
- Speed of processing is measured in **hertz** (e.g., 2 GHz).
- The main circuit board, the **motherboard**, in a computer contains RAM/ROM (memory), processors, and connections for additional components.

B. Memory

- **Random access memory**, or **RAM**, can be accessed quickly from a variety of places.
- RAM data are **"temporary,"** and are lost when the computer is switched off.
- **Read only memory**, or **ROM**, is the main memory of a computer.
- ROM data are **"permanent,"** and may be called "firmware."
- ROM is used to start the computer.
- Communication between the **hard drive** and **ancillary devices** is facilitated using **ROM**.
- **ROM BIOS (basic input and output system)** is stored in the main ROM.
- The motherboard will have areas for additional memory or devices.
- **Secondary memory** is similar to a file system, with data stored for retrieval at a later time.
- **Memory is measured in bytes;** one million bytes is a **megabyte (MB)**.

C. Storage

- **Storage** is the term used to describe **long-term memory**.
- Storage devices include tapes, diskettes, additional hard disks, CDs, DVDs, and flash drives.

Figure 7.1
Various storage media used in medical imaging: a CD contains up to
650 MB of data, MO–Disks may store 1 GB of data, with a thumb drive
holding up to 10 GB.

- A **CD** will likely hold **650 MB** of information.
- CD-R are recordable once and readable many times.
- CD-RW may be recorded and read many times, and are erasable.
- A **DVD** is very similar to a CD, but with a greater storage capacity, **20 GB**.
- **Flash drives** or jump drives utilize a **USB** port on a computer and are capable of storing several GB of data.
- **Figure 7.1** shows examples of storage media that may be used by x-ray technologists.
- **Hard disks** are contained in a protective housing and capable of **2 terabyte (TB)** storage.
- **Mainframe computers** consist of multiple hard disks allowing for **many TB** of storage that is easily accessible.
- A **RAID (redundant array of independent disks)** acts as a primary and backup disk drive, contained in one tower.
- **Jukeboxes** consist of up to **100 disks** and have been used to replace file rooms in imaging; it is a **virtual file room**.

D. Output

- **Output devices** allow users to receive information from the computer.
- Printers, monitors, and speakers are examples of output devices.
- A terminal is an input/output device that is networked to a computer.
- **Terminals** may be capable of computation (**intelligent**) or not capable of computation (**dummy**).
- Information must be shared between computers, so they must be connected.
- **Connections include wire, cable, or a wireless network.**
- Some communication is **analog** and requires the use of a **modem** to convert a digital signal to analog for transport.
- A modem is also required to receive digital information and convert to analog signal.
- **Data transmission** is measured in **bits per second (bps)** or kilobits per second (kbps).
- Data may be transmitted through traditional **phone lines, ISDN lines, DSL lines, or cable modems.**
- Cable is usually fast, whereas traditional phone lines are slow.

E. Picture Archiving and Communication System (PACS)

- A **PACS** replaces a traditional film file room.
- All digital images within a department are stored in the digital archive.
- **Digital Imaging and Communications in Medicine (DICOM)** "language" allows seamless communication between different imaging systems.
- Information from the **Radiology Information System (RIS)** must be fed to the modality-specific imaging equipment for acquisition purposes.
- The **RIS** will load **demographic information** into a work list at each modality so the technologist knows what exams are pending.
- If the patient has had prior imaging at the facility, the **prior images will be retrieved and loaded** in temporary memory **for comparison** (this is **pre-fetching**).
- Physicians in different parts of the facility may access images for review with others at the same time.
- A PACS must handle **a large volume of data.**
- PACS allows for retrieval of images within seconds and requires very little physical space.
- Backup or **redundant storage** is generally **at an off-site facility** and **updated daily.**
- **PACS is an expensive endeavor in terms of hardware and infrastructure but offers operational cost savings.**

7.3 DIGITAL IMAGES

A. Bits and bytes

- The smallest unit of information in a computer is a **bit**, which represents either a 0 or a 1.
- **A byte represents 8 bits.**
- A kilobyte represents 1024 bytes.
- A megabyte (MB) is ~1 million bytes.
- A gigabyte (GB) is ~1 billion bytes.
- A terabyte (TB) is ~1 thousand billion bytes.
- An **alphanumeric character** must be encoded, or transformed into computer language, usually into **8 bits, or a byte,** of information.

B. Gray scale and matrix size

- Digital images are composed of small boxes, or **pixels**, that are created by columns and rows within a **matrix**.
- **Pixels** are the individual **picture elements** in any two-dimensional image.
- 1 byte (8 bits) coding for a pixel can display 256 shades of gray.
- **Adding a bit doubles the number of shades of gray.**
- **Table 7.1** shows the relationship between the number of bits per pixel, and the corresponding number of gray scale levels in images.

Table 7.1

Relationship between number of bits per pixel and the number
of gray scales that can be displayed.

Number of bits per pixel	Number of gray scale levels	Comment
1	2	Pixel will be either black or white
8	256	Used to store/display nuclear medicine (NM) and ultrasound (US) images
10	1024	Typical value for chest x-ray image
n	2^n	1 word (i.e., 2 byte or 16 bit) displays 216 gray scale levels (i.e., 65,536)

- 9 bits can represent 512 shades of gray and 10 bits can represent 1024 shades of gray.
- The number of pixels along each dimension is the matrix size.
- 1024 pixels in both the horizontal and vertical dimensions results in an image that is 1k × 1k.
- The number of pixels is obtained from the product of the number of pixels assigned to the horizontal and vertical dimensions.
- **Image information** is the product of the **number of pixels** and the **number of bytes per pixel**.
- **Table 7.2** shows matrix size and pixel size in radiological imaging.
- An image with a 1k × 1k matrix and 1-byte coding of each pixel requires 1 MB of memory.
- The same image matrix size, but using 2-byte coding of each pixel, would require 2 MB.

Table 7.2
Typical matrix sizes, and pixel dimensions, in digital radiography

Imaging Modality	Matrix Size (Nominal)	Approximate Pixel Size (μm)
Computed Tomography	500 × 500	600
Digital photospot (e.g., barium meal)	1000 × 1000	250
Radiograph (e.g., chest x-ray)	2000 × 2500	170
Digital mammogram	3000 × 4000	80

C. Digital images

- A single view **chest x-ray** digitized to a 2k × 2.5k matrix using 2-byte coding of each pixel (2048 × 2560 × 2) thus requires **10 MB** of computer space (RAM, or memory).
- **Digital photospot** (e.g., Upper GI) and DSA images are generally 1k × 1k with 2-byte coding per pixel and requires **2 MB**.
- **Digital mammography** systems have **matrix sizes between 3k × 4k and 2-byte coding** of each pixel, and a **single mammography image** requires **24 MB** of memory.
- **CT images** are 512 × 512 with 2-byte coding per pixel, and require **0.5 MB** per image.

- The storage for the exam is the product of the number of images and 0.5 MB per image.
- Storage for a complete chest CT examination requires 50 MB.
- **Table 7.3** compares storage needs for exams from various modalities.
- **Compression** is used to combat both file size and time.
- **Lossless images** compress the data to **~50%** of the original size, and images are rebuilt **without loss of fidelity**.
- **Lossy compression** decreases file size by **~90%, but fidelity is lost** and the image cannot be reconstructed to the same resolution as before.
- **Lossy compression** may be used for **teleradiology** but is not normally used for archiving images.

Table 7.3
Storage requirements for digital images in medical imaging

Imaging Modality	Storage per Image (MB)	Storage Per Exam (MB)
Head CT (40 images)	0.5	20
Barium enema (5 images)	2	10
Chest x-ray (2 images)	10	20
Mammography (4 images)	25	100

D. Preprocessing digital images

- **Preprocessing** is done in the background and generally **automatic** to produce high-quality images.
- Preprocessing computations may include **pixel interpolation, lag correction, and noise correction.**
- **Pixel interpolation** will compensate for pixels that are not functioning, such that the missing information is estimated, resulting in a complete image.
- **Lag** correction is used when a high-exposure image precedes a low-exposure image, and some of the high exposure image is not erased and remains present (ghosting).
- **Noise correction** is required due to fluctuation in the electronics that control each pixel.
- Without noise correction, linear artifacts could be present.
- **Calibration images** are needed for artifact-free processing. Examples are offset images, gain images, and flat fielding.

- **Flatfielding** requires an exposure to the detector for evaluation and correction of the anode heel effect.

E. Postprocessing digital images

- **Postprocessing** is a **manual** function performed by the technologist or radiologist for better visualization of anatomy and pathology.
- **Annotation** is the addition of a text box to an image.
- **Window width and level** allow for the adjustment of the image contrast and brightness.
- **Magnification** of specific regions within the image is possible for a more-detailed examination of anatomy.
- Mammography benefits from magnification where additional images may be avoided.
- **Image flip**, or orientation, allows for an image to be rotated or flipped to the usual viewing position.
- **Image inversion** will reverse the gray shading within an image so anatomy that was black is now white.
- **Region-of-interest** may be used to view quantitative data within a set area.
- **Edge enhancement** accentuates areas of high contrast, such as boney edges for fracture visualization.
- **Figure 7.2** shows examples of image processing in chest radiography.

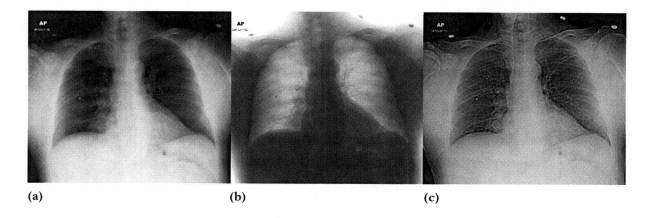

(a)   (b)   (c)

Figure 7.2

Examples of commonly used post-processing capabilities: (a) diagnostic image, (b) image inversion, and (c) edge enhancement.

7.4 IMAGE DISPLAY

A. Photometry

- **Luminous flux** is the intensity of light emitted, or brightness, from a source.
- Luminous flux is measured in **lumens (lm)**.
- One lumen of luminous flux incident on a single square foot is a **foot-candle (fc)**.
- **1 lux (lx)** equals 1 lumen per meter squared.
- 1 foot-candle = 10.8 lux.
- **Luminance** may also be used to describe the brightness of a source, i.e., soft copy monitors.
- **Luminance** is measured in units of candela per meter squared, or **nit**.

B. Viewboxes

- **Hard-copy images** are those printed or taken on film that can be read using a viewbox.
- **Viewboxes** consist of a light source, generally fluorescent bulbs with a Plexiglas™ covering.
- Light is transmitted through the Plexiglas and the radiograph is held by the viewbox.
- Viewboxes have a **luminance level of 1500 nit** for diagnostic radiography.
- The American College of Radiology (ACR) mammography accreditation program specifies a minimum intensity of 3000 nit for mammography films.
- Proper display of images on a viewbox requires **low ambient light levels**, less than **50 lux**.
- Viewboxes should emit a uniform intensity of light.
- Thickness and translucency of plastic surfaces should be identical for all viewboxes.

C. Digital monitors

- **Monitors** are generally **liquid crystal displays (LCDs).**
- **Nowadays cathode ray tubes (CRTs)** are not commonly used in radiology.
- LCDs have **less noise** than a CRT and a **wider gray scale.**
- LCD monitors must be viewed straight on, as increased viewing angle decreases image quality.
- Liquid crystal is a state of matter between liquid and solid, since it has some structure and some fluidity.

- These materials have an **electrical charge** and therefore can be aligned with the use of **magnetic fields.**

- The liquid crystals are placed between two layers of glass, with an intense backlight (white light) shining through the glass plates.

- **Filters** dictate the **color (red, green,** or **blue)** and intensity of each pixel.

- A significant amount of light is absorbed by the filters, and only a percentage of the face of the pixel is available for light transmission.

- Each **pixel** is "active" or able to be **controlled independently.**

- **Table 7.4** lists the types of monitors used in radiology departments.

Table 7.4
Display monitors in medical imaging, which are gray scale (not color)
and can be selected to display in portrait or landscape mode

Monitor Type★	Matrix Size	Applications
1 MP	1280 × 1024	Clinical review station (non-diagnostic quality)
2 MP	1600 × 1200	Computed tomography and magnetic resonance images
3 MP	2048 × 1536	Fluoroscopy, digital photospot, and radiography
5 MP	2000 × 2500	Mammography

★MP: MegaPixel

D. Monitor characteristics

- **Digital images are soft copy,** or delivered and read through electronic means and **monitors.**

- Images are stored as gray scale values assigned to specific pixels within a matrix.

- The **gray scale** of a pixel undergoes several conversions, first to a **presentation value (p-value)** then to a **digital driving level (DLL).**

- Pixel luminance values are derived from the application of a **look-up table (LUT)** to the DLL.

- Monochrome LCDs transmit ~10% of the light source, whereas color monitors transmit ~ 50%.

- The luminance of a monitor varies between L_{min} and L_{max}.

- The Digital Imaging and Communication Committee developed the **DICOM standard**.

- DICOM has developed the **Gray Scale Display Function (GSDF)**.

- **DICOM and GSDF** provide a standard for transfer of image data and maintenance of gray scale appearance.

E. Monitor QC

- The **Society of Motion Picture and Television Engineers (SMPTE)** has developed a display pattern for use with soft-copy viewing devices.

- The AAPM also has a pattern for use with soft-copy viewing devices.

- **Figure 7.3** shows both the SMPTE and AAPM test patterns.

- The SMPTE pattern assesses luminance levels, and it is important to view the **5% and 95% luminance patches** on the test pattern (see arrows in Figure 7.3a).

- Photometers must be calibrated for accuracy, and measure **monitor luminance and uniformity** in cd/m^2.

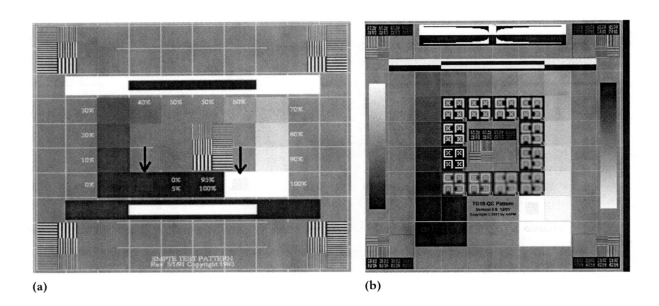

(a)   (b)

Figure 7.3

Test patterns used to evaluate the performance of a digital display: (a) SMPTE, (b) AAPM
Task Group 18-QC. (Image (a) © 1983, courtesy of the Society of Motion Picture
and Television Engineers; image (b) reproduced from Samei et al. (2005)
with permission from the American Association of Physicists in Medicine.)

Figure 7.4
Technologist measuring monitor brightness.

- **Geometric distortion** produces a display image that is altered from the original image data.
- Evaluation of line patterns and measurement of the test pattern provide data for the calculation of distortion.
- Routine testing may be done by the technologist and reviewed by a medical physicist.
- **Figure 7.4** show a technologist performing QC testing on a monitor.
- New/repaired equipment must undergo **acceptance testing by the medical physicist**, as well as an **annual inspection**.

QUESTIONS

Chapter 7: Analog and Digital Images

7.1   Characteristic curves convert radiation intensities into:
    A. film density.
    B. pixel values.
    C. monitor brightness.
    D. log exposures.

7.2   Laser film is most likely sensitive to:
    A. ultraviolet.
    B. green light.
    C. red light.
    D. microwaves.

7.3   Dry processing is least likely to eliminate:
    A. chemicals.
    B. darkrooms.
    C. plumbing.
    D. hard copies.

7.4   Which of the following is least likely to be an application?
    A. Windows
    B. Outlook
    C. Word
    D. Excel

7.5   Memory is best measured using:
    A. hertz.
    B. bytes.
    C. bits/s.
    D. hertz/s.

7.6   When a computer is switched off, data are most likely to be lost if stored in:
    A. RAID.
    B. ROM.
    C. RAM.
    D. DVD-RW.

7.7 A CD most likely holds _____ MB.
 A. 0.65
 B. 6.5
 C. 65
 D. 650

7.8 Storage of radiology images is most likely to use:
 A. DVD.
 B. RAID.
 C. RIS.
 D. HIS.

7.9 Which would likely be fastest in transmitting a digital chest x-ray?
 A. Phone line
 B. ISDN line
 C. DSL line
 D. Cable modem

7.10 Data transmission speeds are normally measured in:
 A. bits per second.
 B. hertz.
 C. bytes per second.
 D. none of the above.

7.11 The major benefit of a Picture Archiving and Communication System (PACS) is most likely:
 A. image processing.
 B. capital cost savings.
 C. operational efficiency.
 D. redundant storage not required.

7.12 Transfer of images between different manufacturers has been most aided by the use of:
 A. SMTPE.
 B. DICOM.
 C. Internet.
 D. JPEG.

7.13 How many bits in a byte?
 A. 2
 B. 4
 C. 8
 D. 16

7.14 How many bytes in a TB?
   A. 10^3
   B. 10^6
   C. 10^9
   D. 10^{12}

7.15 How many shades of gray can a bit display?
   A. 2
   B. 8
   C. 64
   D. 256

7.16 The matrix size of a chest x-ray is most likely:
   A. 1k × 1k
   B. 2k × 2.5k
   C. 4k × 6k
   D. 10k × 10k

7.17 The matrix size of a digital photospot image in a barium enema is most likely:
   A. 256 × 256
   B. 512 × 512
   C. 1024 × 1024
   D. 2048 × 2048

7.18 Data storage requirement of a chest x-ray is most likely _____ MB.
   A. 0.1
   B. 1
   C. 10
   D. 100

7.19 Data storage for a digital mammogram is most likely _____ MB.
   A. 0.25
   B. 2.5
   C. 25
   D. 250

7.20 When an image undergoes lossy compression of 90%, the retrieved image will likely reproduce the original:
   A. resolution.
   B. mottle.
   C. contrast.
   D. none of the above (is degraded).

7.21 Which of the following is *least* likely to relate to preprocessing raw x-ray image data?
A. Offset
B. Inversion
C. Flat field
D. Gain

7.22 Illuminance is most likely measured in:
A. lux.
B. nit.
C. candles.
D. candela.

7.23 A photometer is most likely to be calibrated in _____ .
A. cd/m^2
B. $cd\text{-}m^2$
C. cd^2/m^2
D. cd^2/m

7.24 The brightness of a mammography viewbox is most likely _____ nits.
A. 30
B. 300
C. 3000
D. 30,000

7.25 At which angle, measured from straight on, will a digital monitor be brightest?
A. 0
B. 15
C. 30
D. 45

7.26 The number of pixels on a 3 MP digital monitor displaying a chest x-ray is most likely:
A. 3000
B. 30,000
C. 300,000
D. 3,000,000

7.27 Which monitor size (MegaPixel) would most likely be used to review digital mammograms?
A. 1
B. 2
C. 3
D. 5

7.28 The percentage of light transmitted through a monochrome LCD monitor is most likely
_____ %.
A. 2
B. 10
C. 50
D. 90

7.29 A digital monitor is most likely to be tested using a pattern known as:
A. ASCII.
B. SMPTE.
C. DICOM.
D. HIS/RIS.

7.30 Evaluation of a SMPTE pattern would most likely use the following luminance patches:
A. 5% and 95%.
B. 10% and 90%.
C. 33% and 66%.
D. 50%.

ANSWERS[1]

Chapter 7: Analog and Digital Images

7.1   A   Characteristic curves describe the relationship between exposure and the resulting film density.

p. 275 Bushong
p. 307 Carlton/Adler

7.2   C   Laser film is sensitized to a red light source.

p. 189 Bushong
p. 381 Carlton/Adler

7.3   D   The use of dry processing eliminates darkrooms, processor chemical, and the plumbing issues associated with wet processing, but hard copies will still be present.

p. 206 Bushong
p. 381 Carlton/Adler

7.4   A   Windows is an operating system whereas Outlook, Word, and Excel are applications.

p. 407 Bushong
p. 343 Carlton/Adler

7.5   B   Memory is active storage and may be measured in bytes.

p. 402 Bushong
p. 344 Carlton/Adler

7.6   C   RAM memory is active memory and temporary memory. Information in RAM will be lost with loss of power.

p. 402 Bushong
p. 345 Carlton/Adler

7.7   D   A Compact Disk (CD) is capable of holding 650 MB of data.

p. 403 Bushong
n/a Carlton/Adler

7.8   B   A redundant array of independent disks, RAID, allows for backup of data for storage and retrieval. RAID storage may be used for a PACS.

p. 404 Bushong
p. 384 Carlton/Adler

7.9   D   Cable can function at a speed 1000 times that of phone lines, with ISDN and DSL lines somewhere in between those speeds.

p. 405 Bushong
n/a Carlton/Adler

7.10   A   Data transmission speeds are measured in bits per second, or kilobits per second (kbps).

p. 405 Bushong
p. 379 Carlton/Adler

7.11   C   PACS allows for increased efficiency of reading, reporting, and viewing of images.

p. 473 Bushong
p. 378 Carlton/Adler

---

[1] As a study aid, page numbers for additional study are given for the following references:
Bushong SC: *Radiologic Science for Technologists,* 9th ed. St. Louis, MO: Mosby, 2008.
Carlton RR, Adler AM: *Principles of Radiographic Imaging: An Art and a Science,* 4th ed. Albany, NY: Delmar Publishing Inc., 2005.

7.12	B	Transmission of digital images among equipment manufacturers with consistent gray scale representation is achieved using DICOM language.	*p. 479 Bushong* *p. 384 Carlton/Adler*
7.13	C	8 bits represent a byte of information in computer storage.	*p. 403 Bushong* *p. 344 Carlton/Adler*
7.14	D	The prefix tera represents 10^{12}.	*p. 34 Bushong* *p. 15 Carlton/Adler*
7.15	A	A bit can only represent one of two digits, a 0 or a 1, and it therefore can represent one of two shades of gray.	*p. 403 Bushong* *p. 378 Carlton/Adler*
7.16	B	A chest x-ray has a matrix size of 2k × 2.5k.	*p. 476 Bushong* *p. 345 Carlton/Adler*
7.17	C	A 1024 × 1024 matrix is used for digital photospot images.	*p. 439 Bushong* *p. 345 Carlton/Adler*
7.18	C	A typical digital chest image is 10 MB, resulting from 2k × 2.5k matrix and 2 bytes per pixel.	*p. 476 Bushong* *p. 345 Carlton/Adler*
7.19	C	A typical digital mammography image is 25 MB, resulting from a 4k × 3k matrix and 2 bytes per pixel.	*p. 476 Bushong* *p. 345 Carlton/Adler*
7.20	D	Lossy compression will not provide fine detail or contrast discrimination at the same level as the original.	*p. 490 Bushong* *n/a Carlton/Adler*
7.21	B	Pixel interpolation, offset, and gain images (flatfielding) are all part of preprocessing, whereas inversion is not.	*p. 471 Bushong* *n/a Carlton/Adler*
7.22	A	Illuminance is measured in lux (lx).	*p. 467 Bushong* *n/a Carlton/Adler*
7.23	A	Photometers are calibrated in cd/m^2.	*p. 480 Bushong* *p. 489 Carlton/Adler*
7.24	C	Mammography viewboxes require a greater luminance than conventional viewboxes, with a minimum of 3000 nits.	*p. 335 Bushong* *p. 488 Carlton/Adler*
7.25	A	LCD monitors have an angular dependency for viewing where quality decreases as viewing angle increases from 0°. A viewing angle of 0° is the brightest.	*p. 470 Bushong* *p. 384 Carlton/Adler*
7.26	D	A 3MP monitor has a nominal matrix of 3,000,000 pixels total.	*p. 470 Bushong* *p. 15 Carlton/Adler*

7.27	D	A 5MP monitor used to read mammography images has a nominal matrix of 5,000,000 pixels.	*p. 470 Bushong* *n/a Carlton/Adler*
7.28	B	Approximately 10% of the backlight is transmitted in a black and white monitor.	*p. 469 Bushong* *p. 384 Carlton/Adler*
7.29	B	The SMPTE test pattern is used for monitor assessment.	*p. 479 Bushong* *p. 383 Carlton/Adler*
7.30	A	When using the SMPTE pattern, the 5% and 95% patches are used to visualize gross luminance deviations.	*p. 479 Bushong* *p. 383 Carlton/Adler*

Chapter 8

PROJECTION RADIOGRAPHY

8.1 Radiographic Techniques
8.2 Radiography
8.3 Mammography
8.4 Spot Imaging/DA/DSA
8.5 Specialized Radiography

8.1 RADIOGRAPHIC TECHNIQUES

A. mA

- Beam **quantity** is primarily represented by the **mA.**

- As the mA increases, so does the number of x-rays produced.

- The number of x-ray photons in a beam is directly proportional to mA.

- As the x-ray quantity increases, so does the **patient dose.**

- Some radiographic systems will start an exposure at the highest mA station and drop the station over the course of the exposure, known as a **falling load generator.**

- The choice of mA is one of the main factors controlling receptor exposure.

- **The tube current, mA, has no effect on beam quality.**

B. kVp

- **kVp** is the controlling factor for **beam quality.**

- **Beam quality** is represented by the technical factor of **kVp** and the **filtration** of the beam.

- Increased kVp provides a more penetrating beam.

- Increased kVp also results in **increased scatter.**

- **kVp** is also a contributing factor to **beam quantity**, with increasing the kVp generally increasing the x-ray beam quantity.

- kVp requires a 4% change to result in a visible change in optical density.

- **15% increase in kVp will result in the same increase in optical density as a doubling of mAs.**

C. Exposure time

- **Exposure time** is recorded in **milliseconds (ms)**.
- **Single-phase generators** are limited and cannot decrease times below **8 ms**.
- **Three-phase generators** are capable of **1 ms** exposure times.
- **Falling load generators** provide for the shortest possible exposure time.
- Exposure times are kept to a minimum to prevent patient motion.

D. mAs

- Modern radiography systems allow for the selection of mAs. Separate mA and time stations are not available.
- **mAs = milliamperes (mA) × exposure time (s).**
- **mAs** is the controlling factor for **beam quantity**.
- Increasing the mAs results in an increase in receptor exposure.
- A 30% increase in mAs is required to visualize a change in film density.
- **Clinically, an increase of 100% or a decrease of 50% is applied to mAs when repeating an image for technical reasons.**

E. Distance

- Distance from the image receptor to the tube is generally **100 cm** (40 inches).
- Exception of **chest imaging** at **180 cm** (72 inches).
- As the distance from the image receptor to the tube increases, the x-ray beam intensity decreases.
- The fall-off in x-ray beam intensity is a result of x-ray beam divergence (**inverse square law**).
- The **direct square law** and the **indirect square law** allow the technologist to adjust for differences in SID (source-to-image receptor distance).
- **Direct square law** calculates change in **mAs** after a change in SID.
- Advantage of a long SID is less magnification.
- A long SID, however, also requires increased mAs and tube heating.

8.2 RADIOGRAPHY

A. Patients

- An average patient is considered **sthenic**.
- Decreased technical factors are used for the thin patient, **hyposthenic**.
- Increased technical factors are used for the larger patient, **hypersthenic**.

- Technical factors are significantly decreased for the extremely thin, small patient (**asthenic**).

- **Table 8.1** lists the "average" size patient that is used as a standard for technique selection.

- The thicker the patient, the greater the amount of radiation required to properly image the part.

- **Increases in mAs** are required when a **fixed kVp chart** is used.

- If mAs is increased to the maximum and additional exposure is required, an increase in kVp can be utilized.

- **Destructive pathology**, such as osteoporosis, will require a decrease in technical factors.

- **Additive pathology**, such as ascites, will require an increase in technique.

- Anatomical parts with a **high subject contrast**, lungs, can be imaged at **higher kVp** and lower mAs.

- For an abdomen with little **subject contrast**, a **lower kVp** technique must be used to accentuate subject contrast differences.

Table 8.1
Patient thickness values

	Average patient thickness	
Anatomical area	centimeter	inch
PA chest	28	11.0
AP abdomen	30	11.8
Lateral skull	16	6.3
Lateral cervical spine	13	5.1
AP knee	12	4.7

B. Receptor exposure

- An air kerma of **5 µGy (0.5 mR)** is normally required for a reasonable radiograph (average speed).

- **Optical density (OD)** is related to the **air kerma** incident on a film/screen.

- The greater the exposure, the greater the optical density; a numeric value is used to quantify OD.

- A clear or **unexposed film** has an **OD of ~0.20**, while a fully **exposed film** has an **OD of ~3.0**.

- An **overexposure** results in a **dark** image, and **underexposure** in a **light** one.

- Optical density is affected by the choice of **mAs, the kVp,** as well as **the SID.**

- **Table 8.2** lists technical factors for an average size patient.

- In **digital systems,** an air kerma of **5 µGy (0.5 mR)** is also required for a reasonable radiograph.

- For radiation intensity above 5 µGy (0.5 mR), reduce image mottle.

- For radiation intensity below 5 µGy (0.5 mR), increase image mottle.

- **Digital detectors have no speed indicator such as screen-film systems.**

- Operators vary the amount of radiation used to make digital images to control image mottle.

Table 8.2
Typical techniques in radiography

Factor	PA chest	AP abdomen	Lateral skull	Lateral cervical spine
kVp	110	80	80	75
mA	800	400	200	200
second	0.005	0.125	0.040	0.125
mAs	4	50	8	25
SID	180 cm (72 in.)	100 cm (40 in.)	100 cm (40 in.)	180 cm (72 in.)

C. Fixed kVp technique charts

- Fixed kVp technique charts are most common.

- **kVp** for any given type of examination is **based on penetration of the anatomical part.**

- The optimum kVp is selected for the anatomical part, varying the mAs with part thickness.

- Fixed kVp charts do not require patient measurement.

- Anatomical part thickness is assigned to one of three sizes (i.e., small, medium, large) when developing a fixed kVp chart.

- For the abdomen, small would likely be 14 to 20 cm, medium would be 21 to 25 cm, and large, 26 to 32 cm.

- **Small anatomical parts** would likely **reduce mAs by 30%.**

- **Large anatomical parts** would likely **increase mAs by 30%.**

- **Fixed kVp** technique charts use higher kVp, resulting in **lower patient dose** and **wider exposure latitude.**

- Fixed kVp technique charts do not require measuring of the patient and are **easier for technologists to use.**

D. Variable kVp technique charts

- **Variable kVp** technique charts use constant mAs and vary the kVp with part thickness.

- Variation of kVp with the thickness of the anatomical part is generally 2 kVp/cm.

- A rule used to create a variable kVp technique chart is to set the initial kVp at **2 × thickness of anatomy (cm) + 25.**

- For a high-voltage **single-phase generator, 30** is used, whereas **three-phase generators use 25** as the additive factor.

- **Figure 8.1** shows kVp variations for different generators.

- **Variable kVp technique charts** use lower kVp, resulting in **higher patient dose** and **less exposure latitude.**

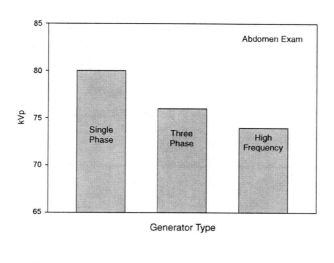

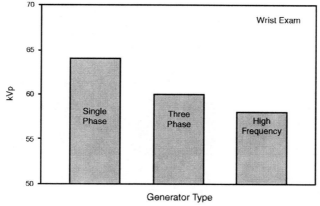

Figure 8.1
kVp used vs. Generator Type for abdomen and wrist exams.

E. Automatic Exposure Control (AEC)

- **Automatic Exposure Control** is a radiation detector used to measure the quantity of radiation reaching the image receptor.

- **AEC operates on the principle of a constant radiation intensity at the image receptor.**

- **AEC terminates exposure when a preselected intensity is reached.**

- **AEC units** are composed of **flat ionization chambers** located in front of the image receptor, which are **radiolucent**.

- AEC systems also have an **electronic timer as a backup** to the system, set to **150%** of the anticipated time.

- A **600-mAs safety limit** is a regulatory requirement for **AEC systems.**

- If the AEC fails to terminate the exposure, safety circuit terminates at 600 mAs, or 6 seconds.

- A guide for the selection of **kVp for specific anatomical parts is normally used.**

- **Optical density (OD)** selections (i.e., +1, 0, –1) modify the preselected intensity for changes in field size or anatomy.

- Three- to seven-position dial labeled "OD" (i.e., +1, 0, –1).

- **Figure 8.2** shows the change in mAs as OD settings are increased or decreased.

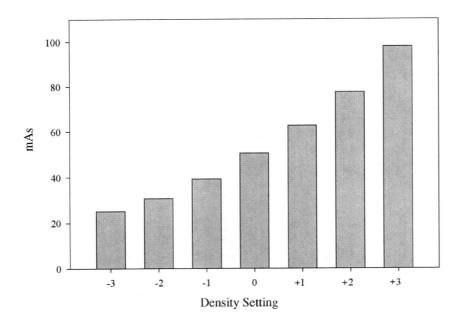

Figure 8.2

Changes in mAs relative to changing density settings
with a standard of 50 mAs for a density setting of zero.

- Each **OD step** increases or decreases **radiation exposure** at the image receptor by **~20%**.

F. Anatomically programmed radiography (APR)

- APR systems have all technical factors (kVp, mA, time/AEC cell selection) stored for a variety of examinations.
- Radiologic technologist selects the anatomical part to be imaged from a list or touch screen.
- Microprocessor selects kVp and mAs.
- APR uses AEC systems, increasing image consistency and decreasing repeat images.
- **Precise patient positioning is critical.**
- AEC systems must have the tissue of interest over the selected cells to ensure appropriate exposure.
- Early termination of the AEC occurs if the tissue of interest is not covering the AEC cells.
- For example, the peripheral soft tissue of the thigh overlies the AEC cells, not the femur.
- Early termination would also take place if primary beam exposes part of the AEC cell.

8.3 MAMMOGRAPHY

A. Overview

- **Mammography** is most often a **screening exam** done on asymptomatic patients.
- Screening exams consists of **two views per breast**, a **craniocaudal (CC)** and a **mediolateral oblique (MLO)**.
- Breast tissue is **fibrous, fatty,** and **glandular.**
- Younger breast tissue or that of a woman on hormone replacement tends to be more glandular in nature, or radiographically dense.
- Postmenopausal breast tissue is mostly fatty tissue and much easier to image.
- Age or hormonal status of a female has a great effect on breast composition.
- Because breast tissue is all **soft tissue,** it is very **difficult to image.**
- **Subject contrast is low** and must be accentuated.
- A **low kVp** is used to accentuate the subject contrast, typically in the **range of 25–28 kVp.**

B. X-ray sources

- **High-frequency generators** are used in mammography systems.
- Most mammography units have a **molybdenum (Mo) focal spot**.
- Mo provides a softer x-ray with characteristic **energies of 17 and 19 keV**.
- **Rhodium (Rh)** targets are provided by one vendor, which offer higher photon energies.
- Rhodium provides characteristic x-rays energies of 20 and 22 keV.
- In recent years, tungsten **(W)** tubes have also become available.
- Tungsten targets require silver filters with a K-edge of 25 keV.
- **Focal spots** in mammography are much smaller than diagnostic imaging, and generally are **0.3 and 0.1 mm.**
- The large focal spot will tolerate up to 100 mA, whereas the small is limited to 25 mA.
- The **central ray is at chest wall**, with a tube tilt to prevent projecting breast tissue off the image receptor.
- **Anode heel** effect is used to its advantage with the **cathode end** of the tube at **chest wall**.
- **Smaller anode angles** are used in mammography where irradiated areas are limited to 24 × 32 cm (10 × 12 in.)

C. Filtration and HVL

- X-ray tube **window** is made with **beryllium**, a very low attenuating material.
- **Mo, Rh,** and **Ag filters** maybe available.
- **Mo filter** is used on less dense breasts.
- **Rh filter** is used on **dense breast** as it creates characteristic radiation at **23 keV**.
- Silver filters are used with **W** targets, and offer higher average energies.
- Higher energies generally offer reduced radiation doses.
- **Total beam filtration less than 0.5 mm Al equivalent.**
- Filtration removes both the **low-energy photons that increase dose**, as well as the **high-energy photons that decrease contrast**.
- **Half-value layers (HVLs)** in mammography are typically **0.3 mm Al**, which are 10 times lower than conventional radiography.
- **Table 8.3** lists target filter combinations and their use in mammography.
- Mo/Mo has the lowest HVL, followed by Mo/Rh, and Rh/Rh, with W/Ag the highest.

Table 8.3
Target/filter combinations used in mammography + breast thickness

Target/Filter combination	kVp	Compressed breast density	Detector
Mo/Mo	~25	Normal	Screen/film
Mo/Mo	~27	Normal	Digital
Mo/Rh	>27	High	Digital
Rh/Rh★	>27	High	Digital

★When available

D. Screen–film mammography

- **Film-screen combinations** consist of one **film** emulsion and one **screen**.
- **Film** is on the **tube side** of the cassette with a screen at the back.
- Mammography film is generally **orthochromatic** and paired with a **green emitting screen**.
- Rare earth screens are commonly used, such as **gadolinium oxysulfide** (Gd_2O_2S).
- Posterior portion of the film is coated with an **absorbing dye** to prevent reflection of light onto the film.
- This is termed **halation** and decreases resolution due to increased light divergence.
- **Antihalation layers** lessen the speed of the system but maintain image detail.
- **Film** is manufactured for a **high contrast** image or steep H&D curve.
- Mammography **optical densities** between **1.6 and 2.0** are desired.
- Mammographic film contrast is better at these higher optical densities.

E. Digital mammography

- **Computed mammography** uses **photostimulable phosphor** plates for image acquisition.
- CR readers are used in a **high-resolution** mode to read mammography imaging plates.
- Computed mammography can be used with traditional mammography units, resulting in a cost savings compared with a full-field digital mammography system.
- Computed mammography has a **pixel size of 50 μm**.
- **Digital mammography uses both the direct and indirect methods of image capture.**

- Indirect digital mammography utilizes a CsI scintillator with a-Si.
- Direct digital mammography uses selenium (Se) (photoconductor) to detect x-rays.
- Digital mammography systems have **a pixel size of about 80 μm.**
- Digital mammography has been shown to be especially **advantageous for patients with dense, glandular breast tissue.**

F. Mammography imaging

- **SID** in mammography is **~65 cm.**
- **Compression** is used to decrease the OID (object to-image receptor distance) of lesions, adding to image detail and **reduced magnification.**
- Compression results in a thinner breast that creates **less scatter** and reduces the required mAs.
- A compressed breast is also **more uniform in thickness**, and patient **motion is decreased.**
- Breast compression is between **25–45 lb.**
- Grids are used due to the soft tissue nature of the anatomy and scatter produced.
- A **low ratio grid** is selected to assist with image quality, without increasing dose too much.
- **Honeycomb-like grids (HTC) can be used with a ratio of ~4:1.**
- Grids used in mammography have a **Bucky factor of 2.**
- Grids are used for all mammography imaging, except magnification images.
- **AEC in mammography is movable from chest wall to nipple.**
- Adjustable **AEC placement** allows the photocell to be placed under the area of **greatest tissue density/thickness.**
- AEC selects the proper **kVp/filter/mAs combination** based on breast composition.

8.4 SPOT IMAGING/DA/DSA

A. Spot/Photospot

- **Fluoroscopy imaging utilizes a low mA, resulting in non–diagnostic quality images.**
- When static images are obtained during a fluoroscopic examination, **radiography techniques are used, and the radiation intensity increases a hundredfold.**
- **Spot film** requires a **cassette** to be loaded into the fluoroscopy tower and held in a lead protective area.

- **At the time of exposure, the cassette is moved between the patient and the image intensifier (II).**
- Several images may be taken on one spot film, as lead protective diaphragms may be used.
- A **slight delay** does occur between depression of the exposure button and actual exposure because of the mechanical movement of cassette and diaphragm.
- A **photospot camera** utilizes the **output phosphor of the II** image for filming.
- Photospots are smaller images, **either 70 or 105 mm**.
- Sequential imaging may be done, up to **12 images per second**.
- Spot film is viewed on traditional viewboxes.

B. Digital photospot

- **Digital photospot images are acquired through digitization of the output from a TV camera (or CCD camera).**
- An **analog-to-digital converter (ADC)** receives the TV camera output signal.
- ADC systems are described by their sampling ability.
- An **8-bit ADC system (2^8)** results in sampled values between **0 and 255**.
- For a 10-bit system, sampled values fall between 0 and 1023.
- The digitized information is sent to a computer for storage and a television monitor for display.
- **Digital photospot imaging** requires a **higher spatial resolution** and image quality compared with fluoroscopy.
- Improved performance in digital photospot imaging is achieved by using high-quality TV scan modes.
- High-quality TV modes require a **1024 × 1024 matrix** and use a **progressive scan mode**.
- **Progressive scanning** allows all lines of a system to be **traced at one time (33 ms)**.
- TV cameras must also provide a high signal-to-noise ratio **(SNR) (1000:1)** for digital photospot imaging.
- Pixel size may be calculated if the II size and matrix are known.
- **Pixel size = FOV/matrix.**
- **Table 8.4** compares spot, photospot, and digital photospot imaging modes.

Table 8.4
Imaging modes in GI (barium) studies

Image type	Images/second	Resolution	Entrance skin air kerma (exposure)
Spot film	1	6 lp/mm	2 mGy (200 mR)
Photospot film	12	4 lp/mm	1 mGy (100 mR)
Digital photospot	7.5	2 lp/mm	0.5 mGy (50 mR)

C. Interventional Radiology (IR)

- **Interventional Radiography** requires suites with both an examination room and a control room with a workstation/control panel for equipment operation.

- The radiographic table is a **floating table**, able to extend away from its base for ease of use with the **C-arm imaging system**.

- **Multiple controls** allow for a sterile field that can be used by the physician (in exam room) or a non-sterile field used by the technologist (in control room).

- The patient couch may also be programmed to move along the patient's longitudinal axis (z-axis) to accommodate imaging of a contrast bolus from heart to toes.

- Currently, **digital imaging is used in IR suites**.

- IR suites provide a wide range of examinations requiring powerful, yet versatile equipment.

- Often a **C-arm tube/detector system** is available along with a **traditional overhead tube** for diagnostic imaging, such as chest radiography.

D. IR imaging systems

- The x-ray tubes are **dual focus** for both detail imaging, **small 0.3 mm**, and **large** for power loading, **1.0 mm**.

- The anode is also larger for **additional heat capacity**, up to **1 MHU**, and cooling.

- The **generators** must produce at least **100 kW** of power for rapid, high-load imaging used in digital subtraction imaging.

- Generally, a **3-phase 12-pulse generator** or high frequency is employed.

- Tube current (mA) is **hundreds of mA** during DSA imaging.

- The **x-ray tube is pulsed**, or rapidly turned on and off, creating **multiple static images**.

- **Interrogation time** is the time it takes the x-ray unit to turn on and make an exposure.

- **Extinction time** is the time it takes to turn the tube off or halt exposure.

- **Interrogation and extinction times under 1 ms** require a high-frequency generator.

- Anywhere from **1 to 10 images** may be obtained **per second**.

E. Digital Subtraction Angiography (DSA)

- Subtraction techniques are used to view contrast-filled vessels without interference of other tissues.

- The imaging chain uses **pulse imaging at higher mA**, with a **power injector** for contrast administration.

- An image, **the mask**, is taken **prior to contrast administration**.

- Contrast material is injected at a high rate via the power injector, and subsequent imaging of the contrast bolus is recorded.

- Subtraction removes the **mask image (bone and soft tissue)** from the **contrast bolus image (bone, soft tissue, and contrast)**.

- **Subtracted images** contain only the **contrast-filled vessel** with all other tissue removed, thus improving visibility of vasculature.

- Patient or equipment movement between the mask image and the DSA image will produce artifacts.

- **Figure 8.3** shows examples of images acquired during clinical DSA.

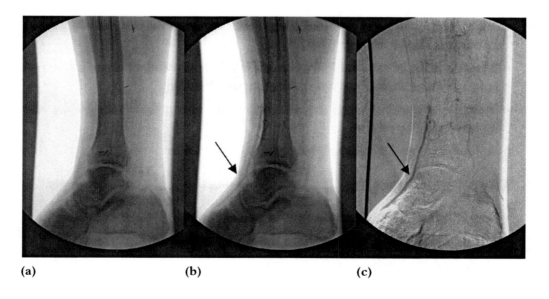

(a)   (b)   (c)

Figure 8.3
DSA images: (a) non–contrast image, (b) image with contrast,
and (c) digital subtraction image (arrows point to contrast–filled vessel).

- Several frames may be averaged together for better image quality, which is known as **image integration**.

8.5 SPECIALIZED RADIOGRAPHY

A. Tomography

- A conventional radiograph has structures superimposed on one another.
- **Tomography limits the superimposition of structures.**
- In tomography, the x-ray tube and the image receptor move opposite to each other, **blurring structures above and below the object plane.**
- The **object plane** is imaged **in focus**, with improved contrast.
- The fulcrum is the center of the object plane, or pivot point, in the x-ray tube image receptor movement pattern.
- The fulcrum level, slice position, is variable through changes in x-ray tube or table height.
- **Figure 8.4** shows a tomographic test tool imaged at two different slice positions; the number most in focus determines the slice's level.
- The degree of tube movement, **tomographic angle**, determines the object plane thickness, or slice thickness.
- Slice thickness is inversely proportional to the tomographic angle; i.e., larger tomographic angles result in thinner slices.
- Many patterns of x-ray tube and image receptor movement are available; the most common is **linear tomography.**
- The evaluation of calcified kidney stones is the most common use of tomography today, utilizing three consecutive tomographic slices.
- Tomography requires longer exposure times than conventional radiography, allowing for tube/receptor motion.
- A disadvantage of tomography is increased patient dose.

B. Magnification imaging

- **Magnification radiography** is used in neuroradiology and mammography.
- Magnification radiography improves the ability to view small objects.
- Magnification is induced through increases in OID, with a constant SID.

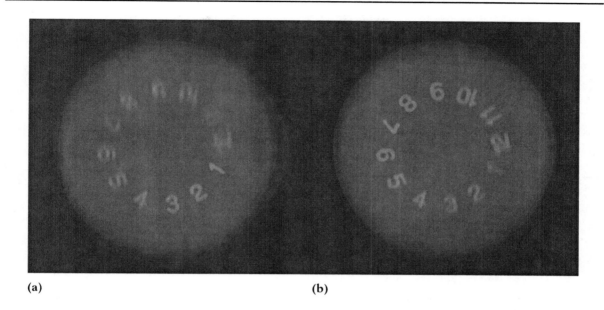

(a)   (b)

Figure 8.4
Linear tomographic images at different slice thickness: (a) 2 mm, (b) 8 mm.

- Magnification is calculated by the **magnification factor (MF) as SID/SOD**.
- SID is the source-to-image receptor distance and SOD is the source-to-object distance.
- **Table 8.5** summarizes magnification details in neuroradiology and mammography.
- An increase in focal spot blur occurs in magnification imaging, and small focal spots are used to reduce the effect.
- In mammography, magnification is used to assess microcalcifications.
- Small focal spot sizes (FSS) are mA limited, requiring an increase in time to maintain optimal exposure.
- **Exposure times may triple** in magnification imaging.
- Magnification imaging does not use grids due to the large OID, air gap. Scatter radiation does not impact the image receptor.
- Using the air gap allows for a **30% decrease in mAs** because no primary radiation is lost to the grid.

Table 8.5
Magnification techniques

Modality	Magnification factor	SID	OID
Neuroradiology	1.67	94 cm (37 in.)	56.3 cm (22.2 in.)
	1.25	94 cm (37 in.)	18.0 cm (7.1 in.)
Mammography	1.8	65 cm (25.6 in.)	28.8 cm (11.3 in.)
	1.5	65 cm (25.6 in.)	21.7 cm (8.5 in.)

C. Cardiac

- **Cinefluorography** is a special type of film used in interventional procedures, such as **cardiac catheterization.**
- Cine film is much like motion picture film, in that, it is on a reel, has **active (image) frames**, followed by an **inactive (blank) frame.**
- The active/inactive format requires the x-ray tube to be **synchronized or gated**, so that radiation is **on during the active frame and off during the inactive frame.**
- The pulsing of the x-ray tube decreases patient dose.
- Rolls of cine film are available in 100- and 500-foot lengths and is **35mm.**
- Cinefluorography provides excellent spatial resolution.
- Cardiac imaging does utilize digital imaging technology.
- Digital cardiac imaging utilizes a **CsI image intensifier** with **ADC of the TV camera output.**
- **Flat-panel detectors** have recently been introduced to cardiac imaging.

D. Tomosynthesis

- A new imaging system, **digital mammography tomosynthesis**, employs a digital detector with a moving x-ray tube, creating tomographic images of the breast.
- Tomosynthesis produces individual tomographic images of the breast and 3D reconstructions.
- The tube moves in a **15° arc**, with one picture taken every degree of movement.
- Exposure times are approximately **5 seconds.**
- Adequate breast **compression is required** for tomosynthesis to prevent motion artifacts.
- **Figure 8.5** shows examples of mammographic images and those obtained using tomosynthesis.

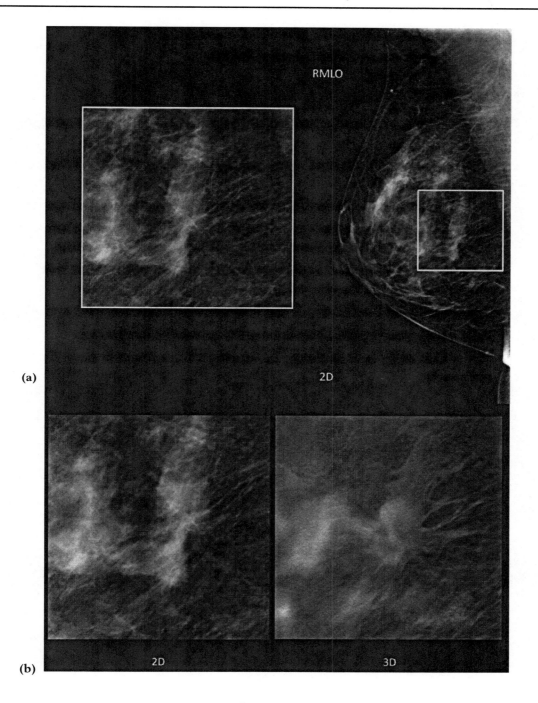

Figure 8.5
(a) Breast shows an area of asymmetry, within the box. (b) The area shown
in the 2D image (left) is unclear, but the same area in the 3D image (right)
clearly shows a spiculated lesion that is highly suspicious of malignancy.
(Images courtesy of Andrew Smith, Ph.D., Hologic, Inc.)

- **Radiation dose** is comparable with digital mammography exams.
- Tomosynthesis received **FDA approval in 2011**.

E. Dual Energy

- Dual Energy is an advanced imaging mode that can be used in **chest radiographic imaging**.
- A chest radiograph is obtained twice, **one at a low energy (kVp) and the second at a high energy (kVp)**.
- These two images are obtained in a very short time (e.g., 0.2 seconds apart).
- **Three views can be produced** consisting of a **standard** radiograph, a **soft tissue** image, and an image of the **bones** and any additional calcified structures.
- Dual Energy thus separates bone tissue from soft tissue, which allows radiologists to view these entities in separate images.
- The advantage of Dual Energy is that it **eliminates obstruction from overlying bones**.
- Dual Energy also provides more information on calcification content.
- The clinical utility of Dual Energy is currently being assessed in the medical imaging community.

QUESTIONS

Chapter 8: Projection Radiography

8.1   Doubling the x-ray tube current most likely increases number of x-ray photons by _____%.
   A. 50
   B. 100
   C. 150
   D. 200

8.2   The factor that has the greatest impact on x-ray beam quality is the _____.
   A. kVp
   B. mA
   C. s
   D. SID

8.3   The minimal percentage change in kVp that would result in a (clearly) visible change in film density is most likely _____%.
   A. 1
   B. 2
   C. 4
   D. 8

8.4   The mAs would most likely be measured in:
   A. coulombs.
   B. amperes.
   C. ohms.
   D. watts.

8.5   The percentage change in mAs that would result in a (clearly) visible change in film density is most likely _____%.
   A. 3
   B. 10
   C. 30
   D. 100

8.6   If the distance from an x-ray tube doubles, the relative x-ray intensity is _____%.
   A. 25
   B. 50
   C. 200
   D. 400

8.7   The most likely source-to-image receptor distance (SID) in chest radiography is _____ cm.
A. 50
B. 70
C. 100
D. 180

8.8   An emaciated (frail) patient would likely be called:
A. sthenic.
B. asthenic.
C. hyposthenic.
D. hypersthenic.

8.9   Imaging a patient with osteoporosis would likely require technical factors to:
A. decrease.
B. remain constant.
C. increase (slightly).
D. increase (a lot).

8.10 X-ray tube voltage most likely varies with anatomical thickness by _____ kV/cm.
A. 0.5
B. 1
C. 2
D. 4

8.11 Which of the following is least likely to be a type of technique chart?
A. Automatic Exposure
B. Variable kV
C. Fixed kV
D. Logarithmic kV

8.12 Imaging high-contrast regions such as the chest most likely requires the use of increased _____%.
A. kVp
B. mA
C. s
D. mAs

8.13 AEC systems used in diagnostic radiography typically have _____ cells.
A. 1
B. 3
C. 5
D. 10

8.14 Increasing the AEC density control to +1 from 0 would likely increase the mAs by _____%.
  A. 5
  B. 10
  C. 20
  D. 30

8.15 Which of the following is most likely used in an AEC system?
  A. Ionization chamber
  B. Thermoluminescent dosimeter
  C. Photostimulable phosphor
  D. Photoconductor

8.16 APR most likely stands for:
  A. Anatomically Programmed Radiography.
  B. Automatic Programming Radiology.
  C. Auto-exposure Programs of Radiation.
  D. Automatic Patient Radiation.

8.17 Which type of tissue is least likely to be seen in a mammogram?
  A. Fibrous
  B. Fatty
  C. Glandular
  D. Bone

8.18 What is the most likely x-ray tube voltage (kVp) in a mammogram?
  A. 15
  B. 25
  C. 35
  D. 45

8.19 The most likely x-ray tube target for a dedicated mammography system is:
  A. beryllium.
  B. molybdenum.
  C. rhodium.
  D. silver.

8.20 The standard focal spot size in a mammography system is most likely _____ mm.
  A. 0.3
  B. 0.6
  C. 1
  D. 2

8.21 Which of the following detector materials is least likely to be found in a digital mammography system?
   A. BaFBr phosphor
   B. CsI scintillator
   C. Se (Amorphous)
   D. AgBr crystals

8.22 The most likely focal spot size in magnification mammography is most likely _____ mm.
   A. 0.1
   B. 0.3
   C. 0.6
   D. 1

8.23 The grid ratio used in mammography is most likely:
   A. 2:1.
   B. 4:1.
   C. 8:1.
   D. 16:1.

8.24 The x-ray tube anode heat capacity in an Interventional Radiological suite is most likely _____ kHU.
   A. 1
   B. 10
   C. 100
   D. 1000

8.25 The most common type of artifact in digital subtraction angiography is most likely:
   A. motion.
   B. beam hardening.
   C. π-lines.
   D. backscatter.

8.26 The principal disadvantage of tomography is the effect on:
   A. Contrast.
   B. Resolution.
   C. Scatter.
   D. Dose.

8.27 The type of grid that is most likely used in linear tomography is:
  A. parallel.
  B. focused to 100 cm.
  C. focused 180 cm.
  D. no grid.

8.28 Which of the following is least likely to use magnification?
  A. Mammography
  B. Interventional radiology
  C. Chest radiography
  D. Neuroradiology

8.29 Magnification radiography is most likely to increase the:
  A. SOD.
  B. SID.
  C. SID + SOD.
  D. OID.

8.30 Energy subtraction imaging is most likely to require two images generated using different:
  A. x-ray tube voltages.
  B. tube currents.
  C. exposure times.
  D. filtrations.

ANSWERS[1]

Chapter 8: Projection Radiography

8.1   B   mAs (mA × seconds) is directly proportional to x-ray beam quantity.

p. 247 Bushong
p. 173 Carlton/Adler

8.2   A   kVp is the prime factor controlling beam penetrability and quality.

p. 245 Bushong
p. 175 Carlton/Adler

8.3   C   A 4% change in kVp is required for a visual change in image optical density.

p. 253 Bushong
p. 428 Carlton/Adler

8.4   A   mAs is measured in coulombs.

p. 245 Bushong
p. 173 Carlton/Adler

8.5   C   A 30% change in mAs is required for a visual change in image optical density.

p. 253 Bushong
p. 401 Carlton/Adler

8.6   A   The decrease in intensity is inversely proportional to the square of the distance of the object from the source. Doubling the distance thus reduces the intensity to 25%.

p. 66 Bushong
p. 177 Carlton/Adler

8.7   D   The standard SID for chest imaging is 180 cm and 100 cm for routine examinations.

p. 285 Bushong
p. 180 Carlton/Adler

8.8   B   Asthenic patients are small, frail, possibly emaciated, and often elderly.

p. 251 Bushong
n/a Carlton/Adler

8.9   A   Osteoporosis is a destructive bone disease, requiring a decrease in technical factors.

p. 252 Bushong
p. 252 Carlton/Adler

8.10   C   Variable kVp charts increase the kVp by 2 for each centimeter of tissue.

p. 261 Bushong
p. 520 Carlton/Adler

8.11   D   There are four types of technique charts: variable kVp, fixed kVp, high kVp, and AEC.

p. 260 Bushong
p. 499 Carlton/Adler

8.12   A   Use of a high kVp technique chart is appropriate for chest imaging to visualize the differing densities present in this anatomical area.

p. 263 Bushong
p. 423 Carlton/Adler

---

[1] As a study aid, page numbers for additional study are given for the following references:

Bushong SC: *Radiologic Science for Technologists,* 9th ed. St. Louis, MO: Mosby, 2008.

Carlton RR, Adler AM: *Principles of Radiographic Imaging: An Art and a Science,* 4th ed. Albany, NY: Delmar Publishing Inc., 2005.

8.13	B	Diagnostic AEC systems have three cells, two peripheral and one central.	*p. 264 Bushong* *p. 539 Carlton/Adler*
8.14	C	AEC density steps will change the mAs by 20% (surely).	*p. 264 Bushong* *p. 540 Carlton/Adler*
8.15	A	The most common type of AEC utilized is the flat-plate ionization chamber.	*p. 108 Bushong* *p. 101 Carlton/Adler*
8.16	A	Anatomically Programmed Radiography (APR) consists of a list of anatomical areas, with radiographic techniques preloaded for each view. The technologist selects the anatomical area and view, and the correct factors are applied.	*p. 265 Bushong* *p. 542 Carlton/Adler*
8.17	D	Mammography includes glandular, fibrous, and fatty tissues, but no bone imaging is involved.	*p. 320 Bushong* *p. 605 Carlton/Adler*
8.18	B	25 kVp is commonly used on an average size compressed breast.	*p. 323 Bushong* *p. 605 Carlton/Adler*
8.19	B	Mo targets are the norm, and only one vendor has offered a Rh target.	*p. 322 Bushong* *p. 611 Carlton/Adler*
8.20	A	Mammography tubes have effective focal spot sizes of 0.3 mm (standard) and 0.1 mm (magnification) available.	*p. 323 Bushong* *p. 608 Carlton/Adler*
8.21	D	Digital mammography may use BaFBr receptors. CsI with a-Si or Se detectors, but AgBr crystals are used in film (i.e., analog).	*p. 432 Bushong* *p. 623 Carlton/Adler*
8.22	A	Mammography tubes have effective focal spot sizes of 0.3 mm for routine imaging and 0.1 mm available for magnification imaging.	*p. 323 Bushong* *p. 608 Carlton/Adler*
8.23	B	Mammography utilizes a 4:1 grid.	*p. 327 Bushong* *p. 617 Carlton/Adler*
8.24	D	Interventional Radiology tubes have high heat capacities of 1000 kHU (1 MHU) for use in serial imaging scenarios.	*p. 364 Bushong* *p. 631 Carlton/Adler*
8.25	A	Misregistration artifact occurs if the anatomy imaged on the mask does not align with the anatomy in following images.	*p. 445 Bushong* *p. 634 Carlton/Adler*
8.26	D	Tomography results in long exposure times and high doses. Multiple images are often required, resulting in doses between 10–20 mGy (1–2 rad).	*p. 268 Bushong* *p. 587 Carlton/Adler*

8.27   A   Parallel grids are used in tomography with the grid's   *p. 268 Bushong*
             lines in the direction of tube movement.   *p. 591 Carlton/Adler*

8.28   C   Chest radiography would not use magnification.   *pp. 327 & 364 Bushong*
             Mammography regularly utilizes it, as does   *pp. 615 & 632 Carlton/Adler*
             IR/neuroradiology.

8.29   D   Mammography and Interventional Radiology utilize   *pp. 327 & 364 Bushong*
             magnification imaging, using an increased OID.   *pp. 457 & 615 Carlton/Adler*

8.30   A   Energy subtraction imaging uses one x-ray tube that   *p. 445 Bushong*
             modulates between x-ray tube voltages to produce   *n/a Carlton/Adler*
             alternating images at high and low x-ray photon energies.

Chapter 9

FLUOROSCOPY

9.1 **Image Intensifiers**
9.2 **Television**
9.3 **Imaging**
9.4 **Miscellaneous**

9.1 IMAGE INTENSIFIERS

A. Input image

- An **image intensifier (II)** is used to provide a bright dynamic image that is convenient to view.

- The II absorbs radiation exiting the patient and produces a visible output pattern corresponding to the anatomy that was imaged.

- The II is **a vacuum tube**, with either a glass or metal housing.

- The **input phosphor** is the first layer of the II and is made of **cesium iodide (CsI)**.

- CsI phosphors are manufactured as small pin-like structures, not flat tabular phosphors as seen in screens, allowing for better spatial resolution.

- The light exiting the **input phosphor** is absorbed by the **photocathode layer**.

- A **photocathode** absorbs light photons and releases electrons.

- Metal compounds are normally used to manufacture photocathodes.

- The quantity of **electrons released** from the photocathode is **directly proportional** to the intensity of **light emitted from the input phosphor**.

B. Output image

- Once electrons are released from the **photocathode**, they are attracted to the **II anode**.

- The **voltage across an image intensifier** is about **25 kV (25,000 V)**.

- The **anode** is a metal disk with an opening in the center where electrons are attracted and enter.

- Anodes in IIs are located close to the output phosphor.

- **Electrostatic focusing lenses** are placed along the path of electrons from cathode to anode.

- **Focusing lenses are highly negative.**

- **Output phosphors** absorb energetic electrons (25 keV) and release light photons.
- The output phosphor is usually composed of **zinc cadmium sulfide**.
- **A great deal of light is produced at the output phosphor for each electron that is absorbed.**
- **Table 9.1** details relative light output as a function of IIs diameter, where the output is directly proportional to the exposed input II area.

Table 9.1
Relative outputs for different II sizes

Image Intensifier diameter in cm	Relative light output for constant II intensity	Typical application
15	1	Cardiac
23	2.4	C–arm
36	5.8	Body – medium
43	8.2	Body – large

C. Brightness gain

- **Flux gain** is the **increase in light photons** from the input phosphor to the output phosphor.
- Flux gain is the number of light photons at output phosphor divided by number of x-ray photons at input phosphor.
- **A typical flux gain is 50.**
- **Minification gain** is the **decrease in image size** and the resulting **increase in intensity.**
- Minification gain is the input area divided by the output area.
- The area of the input and output are proportional to their respective diameters squared.
- An input phosphor of 25 cm with an output phosphor of 2.5 cm results in a minification gain of 100, $(25/2.5)^2$.
- **A typical minification gain is 100.**
- Combining flux and minification gain provides the total brightness gain.
- **Total Brightness gain is the product of the Flux gain and the Minification gain.**
- **Total Brightness gain** due to minification gain and flux gain is thus about **5000**.

D. Conversion factor

- Performance of an II can also be described using the **conversion factor**, which compares the light put out relative to the radiation entering the II.
- **Radiation incident on the II is expressed as the Air Kerma rate, and is measured in mGy/s.**
- **Light out of the II is expressed as the luminance, and is measured in candelas per meter squared (cd/m^2).**
- Current IIs have **conversion factors of 10–30 cd/m^2/µGy/s.**
- Decreasing field sizes requires an increase in exposure at the input phosphor to maintain light levels at the output phosphor.

E. Artifacts

- II **lag** is minimal.
- There is distortion at the outer edges of the image and a decrease in density, which is known as **vignetting.**
- A curved input and flat output phosphor create both **pincushion** and **barrel distortion.**
- **S wave distortion** results from external magnetic fields interfering with electrons crossing the II.
- **Veiling glare** is internal scatter from x-rays, light, or electrons, all of which decrease image contrast.
- Contrast ratios are measured by imaging a metal disk one-tenth the II diameter.
- A measure of the light intensity at the output phosphor is taken at the center and the periphery.
- **The contrast ratio is the light intensity at the periphery to that at the center.**
- Modern IIs have **contrast ratios of 20:1**.

9.2 TELEVISION

A. Television camera

- A **TV camera tube** contains an electron gun, electromagnetic coils, and a target assembly.
- The **electron gun** within the TV tube provides an electron stream through **thermionic emission.**
- A **control grid** maintains the electron beam while the **electromagnetic coils** are used to steer the beam in its **raster pattern.**

- The electron beam is directed at the **anode**, or the target assembly, which has three distinct layers.
- **Window** is the outside layer of the tube made of **thin glass**, allowing light from the II's output phosphor to penetrate its thickness.
- A thin layer of metal or graphite is placed on the inside of the window, known as a **signal plate**, which can **conduct electrons/signal**.
- The **target layer** is adjacent to the signal layer and **receives the electron beam** from within the tube.
- The **target is a photoconductive material** in that, when exposed to light, electrons are able to flow or it is conductive.
- In the absence of light, no electrons (signal) are able to be conducted.
- When light from the output phosphor exposes the target, image information flows out of the target in the form of a signal.
- The more intense the light incident on the TV camera, the greater the resulting signal, which is known as a **video signal**.

B. TV scan modes

- The image on a **CRT** is created using the same **raster pattern** used in the TV camera tube.
- **Interlacing raster patterns** will trace all even lines first, starting in the upper left corner working towards the upper right corner.
- The electron gun is turned off, so that it can again be directed at the next even line in the upper left corner, thus working its way through the whole image area.
- Then the odd lines will be scanned, so that as the light from the even lines starts to fade, the odd lines are traced, **creating an image frame.**
- An interlaced **frame** consists of **two fields**, or **both the even and odd lines together.**
- A standard TV system has are **60 fields per second** or **30 frames per second.**
- Interlacing scanning is used to prevent viewers from perceiving flicker.
- **Progressive scan modes scan each line sequentially.**
- Interlaced scan modes are identified as (i) and progressive scan modes as (p).

C. TV lines

- Most **CRT monitors** have **525 lines** of information to be traced or exposed by the electron gun.
- **High-resolution** systems may have **1024 lines**, offering better resolution.
- The number of **TV lines** determines the **vertical resolution.**

- Horizontal resolution is determined by how many times the electron gun can change intensity across the image or **bandpass**.
- Bandpass is measured in hertz, with **fluoroscopy** systems generally at **4.5 MHz**.
- The bandpass for a **1024-line TV system is 20 MHz**. **Table 9.2** lists the characteristics of standard and High Definition TV systems.
- The CRT has limited resolution and is seen as the **weakest link in the TV system**.

Table 9.2
Matrix sizes for digital TV systems

Definition	Aspect ratio	Number of TV lines	Pixels in each line
Standard	4:3	480	640
	16:9	480	704
High	16:9	720	1280
		1080	1920

D. Charge–Coupled Device (CCD)

- A **charge-coupled device (CCD) may replace the TV camera tube** in an image intensifier–based fluoroscopy system.
- CCDs absorb light from the output phosphor and release a digital video signal.
- A **CCD** contains a **silicon layer** that receives the output phosphor light, resulting in an electrical charge.
- This **charge is measured**, or **sampled**, pixel by pixel, sent to a computer for processing, and creates an image.
- **CCDs** are more light sensitive, are **stable**, and do not require a warm-up period.
- **CCDs** have a **linear response to radiation**, have **no image lag**, and require little maintenance.
- **CCDs generally do not improve fluoroscopic image quality**, but can be more reliable and cheaper.

E. Television monitor

- The television monitor allows for viewing of the image.
- TV also permits viewing the fluoroscopy images at multiple viewing locations.
- **Traditional TV monitors are cathode ray tubes (CRTs).**

- A CRT consists of a **glass envelope, electron gun, focusing coils, and a fluorescent phosphor**.
- **Signal** is received from the **TV camera tube** and modulated proportionally.
- The **electron gun** is modulated based on the incoming video signal and its direction controlled through the use of **external focusing coils**.
- The electrons are directed towards the **anode**, or fluorescent lining of the tube.
- This interaction produces visible light representing the anatomy imaged.
- Newer fluoroscopy systems may be equipped with Liquid Crystal Display (LCD) monitors.
- LCD monitors are covered in detail in chapter 7 of this review book.

9.3 IMAGING

A. Overview

- **Fluoroscopy** is similar to a motion picture where **dynamic imaging** can be performed.
- The dynamic image may be video recorded.
- Most fluoroscopy systems are designed with the x-ray tube below the table and the receptor above the patient.
- Fluoroscopy suites often include diagnostic equipment (overhead tube and Bucky) as seen in **Figure 9.1**.
- The addition of **TV monitoring** allowed for both the radiologist and others to **view the fluoroscopic image in real time**.
- **TV viewing** has the advantage of **adjustable contrast and brightness**.
- Static images may be taken during dynamic imaging.
- Static images are known as **spot films**, obtained using a radiographic cassette **in front of the II**.
- **Photospot images** are analog **images of the II output**.
- **Digital photospot** images are obtained by **digitizing the output** of the TV (or CCD).
- Digital photospot images are the norm in modern fluoroscopy imaging.
- **Cinefluoroscopy** images are obtained **by photographing the II output**, with rolls of 35mm film.

B. Lens system

- The image intensifier may be coupled to the TV camera tube with a **lens system**.
- The output phosphor and the window of the TV camera tube are of the same dimensions.

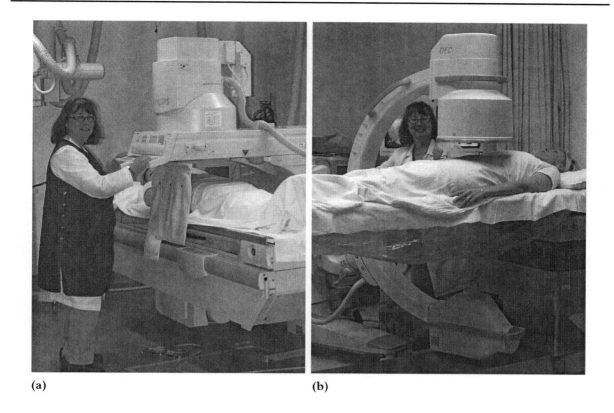

(a)   (b)

Figure 9.1
Example of a traditional image-intensified fluoroscopy suite in use (a)
and a mobile image-intensified C-arm system in use (b).

- **Lens system** consists of lenses to **maintain parallel light beams** and a mirror system that allows for **ancillary viewing/recording devices**.

- **Figure 9.2** shows where the lens is located in the fluoroscopy imaging chain.

- The lens aperture is wide open in fluoroscopy, but closed down in radiographic imaging.

- Light from the output phosphor enters the lens system and interacts with the TV camera tube for viewing.

- If a **static image** is desired, the **mirror system** intercepts the beam between the output phosphor and the TV camera tube.

- **The beam is split, with part of the beam reaching the TV camera tube and the other part directed to an ancillary device.**

- The **mirror is only utilized when static images are taken**.

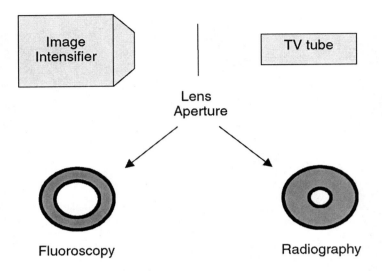

Figure 9.2
Open aperture used in fluoroscopy and a closed aperture
used in radiography. The open aperture allows more light through,
which is essential due to fluoroscopy's very low mA.

C. Techniques

- Fluoroscopy utilizes a **5 mA or less** technique.
- The x-ray tube voltage **(kVp) is selected appropriate for the part being imaged.**
- Imaging of **barium-filled structures** requires **100–120 kVp** for adequate penetration, i.e., single-contrast barium enema.
- **70–80 kVp** will be used for imaging of **iodine-based contrast media**, i.e., intravenous pyelogram (IVP).
- **Table 9.3** lists typical techniques used in fluoroscopy.
- **Total fluoroscopy time** is measured in **minutes**, not seconds.
- Dose is considerable due to the long exposure times.
- A timer within the system tracks overall exposure time and sounds a **warning bell when 5 minutes of exposure have passed.**
- Such timers operate as an indicator of exposure time in fluoroscopy for the radiologist.
- There are no legal limits on the total amount of fluoroscopy imaging time.
- **Grids are utilized during fluoroscopy** and are located between the patient and the II.
- Grids in fluoroscopy **reduce scatter radiation to the II**, and **require an increase in mA** that increases patient dose.

Table 9.3
Typical kV and mA values in fluoroscopy

Examination	kVp	mA	Comment
Arthrogram/Myelogram	75	0.5	Wrist 75 kVp and hip/spine 85 kVp
Cystogram	75	1.0	Lower kVp due to iodine's lower K-edge
Barium & air contrast	90	2.0	Higher kVp due to barium's higher K-edge
Barium - single contrast	110	3.0	Increased kVp for proper penetration

D. Automatic Brightness Control (ABC)

- In fluoroscopy, an **automatic brightness control (ABC)** regulates the amount of radiation to maintain a constant TV display.

- The amount of radiation is changed by **adjusting both tube current (mA) and tube voltage (kV)** to control image brightness.

- **The intensity of light at the output phosphor is measured and used by the ABC for adjustment.**

- When the **kVp is increased**, there is generally a **loss of image contrast**.

- Increasing kVp makes the beam more penetrating, and helps **to reduce patient doses**.

- When the mA is increased, image quality is maintained and contrast is not reduced.

- **Increasing mA** will also **increase patient doses** because the x-ray beam penetrating power is not increased.

- **Figure 9.3** shows examples of ABC radiation curves used in fluoroscopy.

- **ABC curves therefore can be used to control patient dose and image quality depending on diagnostic task at hand.**

E. Multifield image intensification

- IIs are generally **multifield tubes**, or capable of magnification.

- A **tri field II** may have input phosphors of **25/17/12 cm**.

- The **active area of the input phosphor is decreased**, resulting in increased magnification.

- In addition to the active area being altered, the **focal point within the II changes**.

- The increased **magnification requires the focal point farther from the output phosphor**.

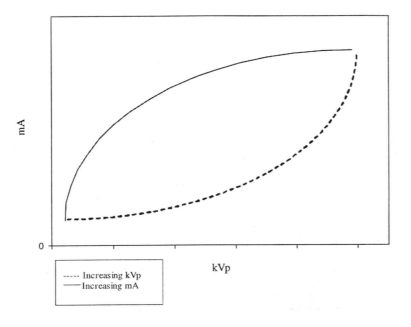

Figure 9.3
Image intensifier curve for use with Automatic Brightness
Control (ABC) where the bottom left region is for the smallest
patients and the upper right is for the largest patients. The solid
line demonstrates preferential increases in mA, and the
dotted line a preferential increase in kVp.

- Increasing the focal distance allows the smaller image to be displayed on the entire output phosphor, creating a larger image.
- Magnification imaging **improves spatial resolution.**
- **Magnification** will increase **entrance air kerma**, due to a decrease in minification gain.
- **Figure 9.4** shows how changing the II size affects exposed area, entrance air kerma, Kerma-Area Product, and spatial resolution.
- Use of small fields improves visibility of small detail, and increases the entrance air kerma (skin dose).
- The total amount of energy deposited in the patient (i.e., Kerma-Area Product), however, is independent of the size of II being used.

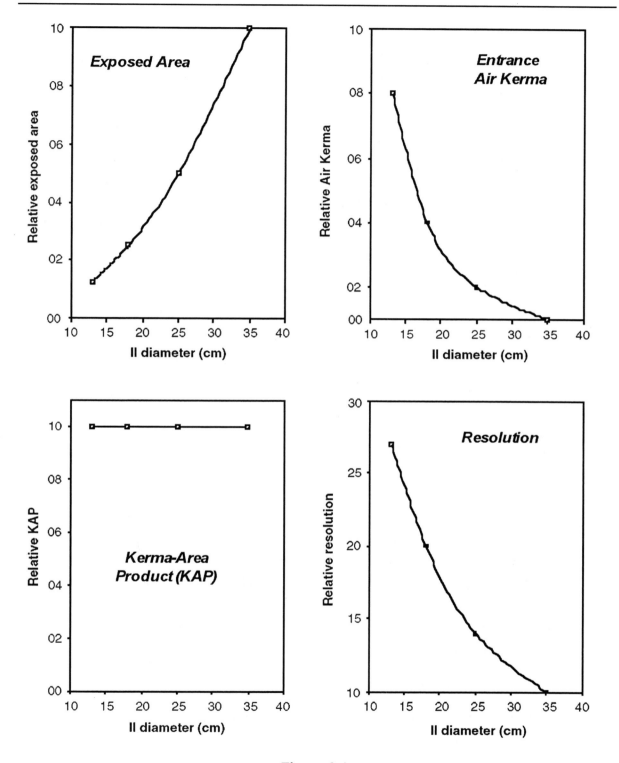

Figure 9.4
Relative II imaging performance characteristics (Area, Air Kerma,
KAP, and Resolution) as a function of II diameter.

9.4 MISCELLANEOUS

A. Mobile C-arms

- Mobile C-arm units are used for **intraoperative fluoroscopic procedures.**
- These mobile systems comprise a C-arm tube detector assembly, a dual monitor system, and a control panel.
- **High-frequency generator** provides **40–110 kVp and 0.1–6 mA.**
- Most C-arm systems use a **16-cm or 22-cm II** coupled with a CCD camera.
- Scatter suppression is achieved through an 8:1 or 10:1 ratio grid.
- Focal spot size range from 0.3 mm for detail imaging to 1.8 mm used for high heat capacity.
- **Collimation** is available on C-arm systems, often circular in shape.
- C-arm systems are very versatile in their use—capable of angulation, rotation, wig wag, and horizontal and vertical motions.
- **Figure 9.1** shows an example of a C-arm system.
- Flat-panel image receptors (FPIR) have also been mounted onto C-arms.
- **FPIR occupy less space** and therefore are much easier to position.
- FPIR have a **1.6k × 1.4k matrix.**

B. Digital fluoroscopy

- In **digital fluoroscopy** the TV camera (or CCD) **output is digitized.**
- An **analog-to-digital converter (ADC)** is used.
- Digital image data are passed through a computer to process the images.
- After processing, these images are then displayed on a monitor.
- There is **no time delay** because computers are "fast."
- When images are acquired by a computer, the "last image" can be displayed after the radiation is switched off.
- Display of the "last image" in this manner is known as **Last Image Hold (LIH).**
- **Last image hold is a regulatory requirement in the United States (June 2006).**

C. Pulsed fluoroscopy

- **Real-time fluoroscopy** acquires images at **30 frames per second.**
- **Pulsed fluoroscopy** acquires frames that are less than real time.
- Frames rates are therefore <30 per second in pulsed fluoroscopy.
- Typical pulsed fluoroscopy frame rates are **7.5 or 15 frames per second.**

- In pulsed fluoroscopy the **dose per frame is also increased**.
- Higher doses per frame are required to reduce the perceived level of noise.
- **When the pulsed fluoroscopy frame rate is reduced, patient dose is reduced less than the frame rate reduction.**
- **Table 9.4** shows typical dose savings that may be achieved in pulsed fluoroscopy.
- Halving the frame rate might reduce the patient dose rate by 30%, not the expected 50%.
- Pulsed fluoroscopy should be used when this does not adversely affect diagnostic performance.

Table 9.4
Nominal patient dose rates using of pulsed fluoroscopy,
and corresponding rate of image acquisition rate

Pulse rate	Relative dose (%)	Relative image data (%)
Continuous (i.e., 30/s)	100	100
15/s	75	50
7.5/s	50	25
3/s	20	10

D. Image processing

- In digital fluoroscopy, image processing can occur in real time.
- **Digital temporal filtering** adds successive frames together, **averaging the pixel values**.
- Temporal filtering is thus a form of frame averaging.
- **Random noise is reduced by the use of temporal filtering.**
- **Figure 9.5** shows how frame averaging can reduce image noise.
- Temporal filtering can also causes noticeable lag.
- There is a tradeoff between the amount of "lag" and the amount of "noise".
- In temporal filtering, more lag generally implies less noise, and vice versa.
- **Temporal filtering could also reduce patient doses because quantum mottle is lower.**

E. Flat-panel detectors

- **Flat-panel image receptors (FPIR)** are now replacing the II for fluoroscopy applications.

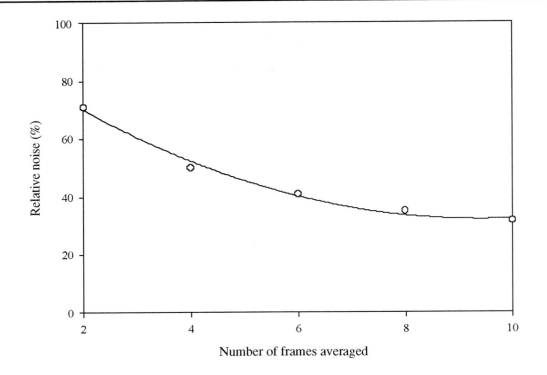

Figure 9.5
Noise reductions by frame averaging.

- An advantage of FPIR is the reduced size compared with II systems, allowing for ease of equipment movement and patient positioning.
- Most interventional suites now make use of FPIR systems.
- FPIR are capable of producing **dynamic** and **static images**, so cassettes are not needed.
- In Interventional Radiology, the detectors of FPIR generally use CsI scintillators.
- FPIR are not subject to the pincushion and barrel distortion as seen in II images.
- FPIR are **stable, do not degrade** over their lifetime, and **are not subject to magnetic fields.**
- **FPIR are similar to DR detectors.**
- Use of FPIR will expand, and replace conventional radiographic/fluoroscopic (R/F) systems when the system price becomes competitive.

QUESTIONS

Chapter 9: Fluoroscopy

9.1   The interior of an image intensifier most likely contains:
    A. air.
    B. nitrogen.
    C. xenon.
    D. vacuum.

9.2   The input phosphor of an II is most likely made of:
    A. NaI.
    B. CsI.
    C. Se.
    D. NaCl.

9.3   When a photocathode absorbs light, it most likely emits:
    A. electrons.
    B. protons.
    C. infrared.
    D. heat.

9.4   The charge on electrostatic focusing lenses is:
    A. neutral
    B. positive
    C. negative
    D. alternating (+ and −)

9.5   Output phosphors on IIs absorb energetic electrons and release:
    A. light.
    B. heat.
    C. current.
    D. X-rays.

9.6   The increase in light photons at the II output phosphor relative to the light photons at the input phosphor is known as the:
    A. brightness gain.
    B. conversion gain.
    C. magnification gain.
    D. flux gain.

9.7   For a given flux gain (FG) and minification gain (MG), the brightness gain is given as:
A. FG + MG.
B. FG × MG.
C. FG/MG.
D. MG/FG.

9.8   The brightness gain of an II is most likely _____ .
A. 5
B. 50
C. 500
D. 5000

9.9   S wave distortion is most likely caused by:
A. magnetic fields.
B. electric fields.
C. faulty focusing.
D. insufficient power.

9.10 Which of the following is most likely an II artifact?
A. π-line
B. Vignetting
C. Beam hardening
D. Focal blooming

9.11 The target material in a TV camera is most likely a:
A. semiconductor.
B. conductor.
C. photoconductor.
D. insulator.

9.12 The TV signal is directly proportional to the incident amount of:
A. light.
B. voltage.
C. charge.
D. current.

9.13 A TV camera makes use of a focused beam of:
A. light.
B. X-rays.
C. protons.
D. electrons.

9.14 The frame rate (per second) of a television camera/display in the United States is most likely _____ .
   A. 2
   B. 4
   C. 30
   D. 60

9.15 The number of TV lines displayed on a standard R/F monitor is approximately _____ .
   A. 250
   B. 500
   C. 1000
   D. 2000

9.16 The bandpass (MHz) of a 1000-line fluoroscopy TV system is approximately _____ .
   A. 5
   B. 10
   C. 20
   D. 40

9.17 A CCD would most likely replace the:
   A. TV camera.
   B. lens.
   C. ABC.
   D. none of the above (or another distractor).

9.18 A cathode ray tube is least likely to contain a:
   A. fluorescent phosphor.
   B. electron gun.
   C. focusing coils.
   D. charge-coupled device.

9.19 The electron gun of a TV monitor is modulated by a:
   A. bandwidth.
   B. video signal.
   C. multiplexer.
   D. focusing coil.

9.20 The gap between an II and a TV camera is *least* likely occupied by a(an):
   A. lens system.
   B. aperture.
   C. mirror.
   D. grid.

9.21 The most likely x-ray voltage for a cystogram examination is _____ kVp.
    A. 55
    B. 75
    C. 95
    D. 110

9.22 Fluoroscopy is most likely performed using an x-ray tube current of _____ mA.
    A. 3
    B. 10
    C. 30
    D. 100

9.23 In fluoroscopy, a warning bell sounds every _____ minutes.
    A. 1
    B. 3
    C. 5
    D. 10

9.24 A fluoroscopy Automatic Brightness Control system is *least* likely to adjust the x-ray tube:
    A. kV and mA.
    B. exposure time (s).
    C. kV.
    D. mA.

9.25 Halving the input diameter of the II would most likely increase the x-ray tube current by a factor of _____ .
    A. 1.5
    B. 2
    C. 3
    D. 4

9.26 Doubling the magnification in fluoroscopy with IIs will change the exposed phosphor area to _____ .
    A. 1/2
    B. 1/4
    C. 1/3
    D. 1/8

9.27 Digital fluoroscopy image display rates (per second) are most likely _____ .
 A. 0.3
 B. 3
 C. 30
 D. 300

9.28 In digital fluoroscopy the TV camera (or CCD) output is digitized using a(n):
 A. ADC.
 B. DAC.
 C. CAD.
 D. none of the above.

9.29 A flat-panel detector is least likely to be made of:
 A. CsI.
 B. Se.
 C. Gd_2O_2S.
 D. ZnCdS.

9.30 Patient dose is most likely reduced by the use of:
 A. temporal filtering.
 B. spatial filtering.
 C. edge enhancement.
 D. window/leveling.

ANSWERS[1]

Chapter 9: Fluoroscopy

9.1   D   The image intensifier is a vacuum tube made of glass or metal.

p. 349 Bushong
p. 568 Carlton/Adler

9.2   B   The input phosphor of an image intensifier is made of needlelike crystals of CsI for increased spatial resolution.

p. 350 Bushong
p. 568 Carlton/Adler

9.3   A   The photocathode is a photoemissive material, releasing electrons when stimulated by light photons.

p. 350 Bushong
p. 568 Carlton/Adler

9.4   C   The electrostatic focusing lenses control the spread of the electrons as they cross the II, so the lenses are made negative to repel the electrons.

p. 351 Bushong
p. 569 Carlton/Adler

9.5   A   The output phosphor absorbs electrons that have passed through the anode and converts their energy into visible light.

p. 351 Bushong
p. 570 Carlton/Adler

9.6   D $$\text{Flux gain} = \frac{\text{\# of light photons output phosphor}}{\text{\# of x-ray photons input phosphor}}$$

p. 351 Bushong
p. 571 Carlton/Adler

9.7   B   Total brightness gain is equal to the product of flux gain and minification gain.

p. 351 Bushong
p. 571 Carlton/Adler

9.8   D   Total brightness gain is ~5000 for image-intensified systems.

p. 351 Bushong
p. 572 Carlton/Adler

9.9   A   S wave distortion results from magnetic fields altering the electron pattern as it crosses the image intensifier.

p. 352 Bushong
p. 570 Carlton/Adler

9.10   B   Vignetting is the loss of image brightness at the periphery.

p. 352 Bushong
p. 573 Carlton/Adler

9.11   C   The target is a photoconductive material, in which, when illuminated, it conducts electrons and when dark it behaves as an insulator.

p. 345 Bushong
p. 575 Carlton/Adler

---

[1] As a study aid, page numbers for additional study are given for the following references:
Bushong SC: *Radiologic Science for Technologists,* 9th ed. St. Louis, MO: Mosby, 2008.
Carlton RR, Adler AM: *Principles of Radiographic Imaging: An Art and a Science,* 4th ed. Albany, NY: Delmar Publishing Inc., 2005.

| 9.12 | A | The TV signal sent to the CRT is directly proportional to the light at the output phosphor and which is incident on the TV camera tube. | *p. 354 Bushong* *p. 570 Carlton/Adler* |

| 9.13 | D | An electron gun is used to produce electrons for acceleration to the signal plate target assembly. | *p. 354 Bushong* *p. 574 Carlton/Adler* |

| 9.14 | C | There are 30 TV frames/second (two TV fields in a TV frame). | *p. 356 Bushong* *p. 575 Carlton/Adler* |

| 9.15 | B | Interlaced raster patterns consist of 262.5 lines per TV field for a total of 525 lines per frame. | *p. 356 Bushong* *p. 575 Carlton/Adler* |

| 9.16 | C | High-quality 1000-line CRT monitors have a bandpass of ~20 MHz. | *p. 357 Bushong* *n/a Carlton/Adler* |

| 9.17 | A | A CCD may be used in place of a TV camera tube. | *p. 439 Bushong* *p. 570 Carlton/Adler* |

| 9.18 | D | A CRT contains a phosphor screen for viewing, an electron gun, and focusing coils, but does not contain a CCD. | *p. 356 Bushong* *p. 576 Carlton/Adler* |

| 9.19 | B | The incoming video signal from the TV camera tube controls the modulation of the electron gun within the CRT monitor. | *p. 352 Bushong* *p. 570 Carlton/Adler* |

| 9.20 | D | Most fluoroscopy units use a lens system with a beam splitting mirror and an aperture to couple the II and the TV camera tube, but a grid is not used at this location. | *p. 355 Bushong* *p. 578 Carlton/Adler* |

| 9.21 | B | A kVp of 75 is appropriate for use with iodinated contrast agents, such as cystograms. | *p. 166 Bushong* *n/a Carlton/Adler* |

| 9.22 | A | Fluoroscopy tubes operate at less than 5 mA. | *p. 347 Bushong* *p. 566 Carlton/Adler* |

| 9.23 | C | A timer will sound when 5 minutes of fluoroscopic imaging has been reached. | *p. 584 Bushong* *n/a Carlton/Adler* |

| 9.24 | B | ABC will adjust the kVp, mA, or both, but is independent of the total fluoroscopy exposure time. | *p. 347 Bushong* *p. 572 Carlton/Adler* |

| 9.25 | D | Halving the input diameter reduces the exposed area to a quarter, and will quadruple the mA (intensity) used. | *p. 352 Bushong* *p. 570 Carlton/Adler* |

| 9.26 | B | Doubling the magnification halves the diameter, and reduces the exposed area to one quarter. | *p. 352 Bushong* *p. 570 Carlton/Adler* |

9.27 C Digital fluoroscopy operates at 30 frames per second, the same as analog fluoroscopy. *p. 418 Bushong* *n/a Carlton/Adler*

9.28 A An ADC samples a continuous variable signal and converts it to a discrete value. These discrete bits of information are then fed to a computer for processing and storage. *p. 443 Bushong* *p. 570 Carlton/Adler*

9.29 D ZnCdS is used to make the output of an image intensifier. FPIR may be made of a-Se if direct, or if indirect they may utilize Gd_2O_2S or CsI. *p. 440 Bushong* *p. 570 Carlton/Adler*

9.30 A Temporal filtering, or frame averaging allows for the combining of frames to reduce noise. *n/a Bushong* *n/a Carlton/Adler*

Chapter 10

COMPUTED TOMOGRAPHY

10.1 CT Basics
10.2 CT Images
10.3 Imaging Chain
10.4 Technology
10.5 Clinical Aspects

10.1 CT BASICS

A. History

- Traditional radiographic imaging is limited by superimposition of structures.
- Radiography has limited ability to demonstrate subtle contrast differences in tissue.
- Radiography is capable of displaying a density difference of 10%, whereas CT is capable of showing differences of less than 0.5%.
- **Figure 10.1(a)** shows a skull radiograph where all soft tissues are essentially invisible.
- This limitation has been overcome by CT, which **eliminates overlapping** of anatomical structures.
- CT stands for **Computed Tomography**.
- CT images are transverse images, showing slices or sections through the body.
- **Figure 10.1(b)** shows a head CT image, where soft tissues are clearly visible.
- Slices or sections are also known as transaxial, and CT was initially called Computed Axial Tomography (CAT) scanning.
- **Godfrey Hounsfield** first developed a clinical CT scanner in the early 1970s.
- **Alan Cormack** and **Godfrey Hounsfield** shared the 1979 Nobel Prize in Medicine.

B. Rays

- For each position of the x-ray tube, a fan beam is passed through the patient.
- **Fan beam angles are up to 50°.**
- Measurements of the transmitted x-rays are made by a (curved) **linear array of detectors**.
- Each detector measures the x-ray intensity that transmitted through the patient.

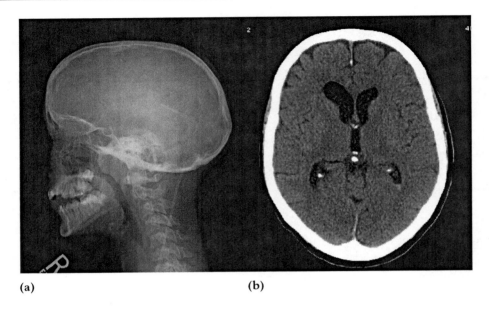

Figure 10.1
Skull radiograph (a) displays limited soft tissue with superimposition
of structures. CT Head image (b) shows differentiation of
gray/white brain matter without superimposition.

- The **transmitted intensity** is directly related to the **attenuation sum** by tissues in the patient.
- This transmitted intensity is known as a **ray sum**.

C. Projections

- Approximately 800 detectors generate **800 numbers (ray sums)** at each angular location of the x-ray tube.
- This collection of 800 ray sums is called a **projection**.
- Projections are acquired as the x-ray tube rotates around the patient.
- CT scanners **acquire approximately 1000 projections** in a single x-ray tube rotation.
- **Table 10.1** details the relationship between the type of detector array, the number of detectors, and what is measured.
- A graphical plot of projections as a function of x-ray tube angle is called a **sinogram**.
- CT images are derived mathematically from projection data sets (i.e., sinograms).

D. Filtered back projection

- Generating an image from the acquired data involves determining the **linear attenuation coefficients** of each individual pixel.

Table 10.1
Detector terminology

Detector description	Number of individual detectors	What is measured
Single detector	1	Ray sum
1D detector array	800	Projection
2D detector array (64 slice)	64 × 800	64 projections
2D detector array (320 slice)	320 × 800	320 projections

- A **mathematical algorithm** takes the projection data (i.e., raw data) to reconstruct the CT image (image data).
- The mathematical algorithm makes use of **"back projection"** and mathematical filters.
- Back projection starts with the measured attenuation, which is the ray-sum value.
- Using back projection, each pixel along the x-ray path is allocated equal values.
- Back projection would **generate (unacceptably) blurred images** of the scanned object.
- Modern scanners use filtered back projection image reconstruction algorithms.
- **Filtered back projection** can generate accurate images of the scanned object.
- Projection data first **convolved with a mathematical filter**, where convolution is a special type of mathematical multiplication.
- After the convolution, also known as filtering, the filtered projections are then back projected.

E. Iterative reconstruction

- **Iterative methods** (trial and error) have been used to reconstruct CT images from projection data.
- One example of an iterative technique is **algebraic reconstruction techniques (ART)**.
- **Iterative reconstruction algorithms** may offer an effective means for **minimizing CT artifacts (e.g., streak).**
- Iterative techniques could also **reduce the amount of noise** in reconstructed images.
- **Dose reductions** may therefore be possible using iterative reconstruction.
- Iterative techniques require about **100 times the computing power** of conventional filtered back projection.

- Iterative reconstruction algorithms have replaced filtered back projection in single photon emission computed tomography (SPECT) and positron emission tomography (PET).
- It is likely that iterative reconstruction techniques will also eventually replace filtered back projection methods in CT imaging.

10.2 CT IMAGES

A. Matrix and FOV

- CT images consist of **rows and columns**, also known as an **image matrix**.
- A single CT image (slice or section) is made up of an array of **512×512 pixels**.
- Total number of pixels is therefore 512×512, which is approximately **250,000 pixels**.
- Each box in a matrix is known as a **pixel or picture element**, and represents a numerical value.
- The **depth of a voxel** represents the **z-axis** of a slice, or the **slice thickness**.
- **Voxel size may be calculated using the pixel size and slice thickness.**
- A **field of view (FOV)** is the diameter of the irradiated area.
- **Head scans** normally use an **FOV of ~25 cm**, whereas body scans use an **FOV of ~40 cm**.
- The field of view may be reduced by reducing the fan beam angle.
- **Regions outside of a reduced FOV will still be exposed to radiation.**
- A **pixel dimension** may be obtained by dividing the field of view (mm) by the matrix size.
- When the field of view is 250 mm for a head scan, the pixel dimension is 0.5 mm.
- When the field of view is 500 mm for a body scan of an oversized adult, the pixel dimension is 1 mm.

B. Hounsfield Units

- CT images show values of relative linear attenuation.
- A pixel with a **high number** means that this region **attenuates x-rays strongly**.
- A pixel with a **low number** means that this region **attenuates x-rays weakly**.
- The numerical value of a CT pixel is known as a **CT number** or **Hounsfield Unit (HU)**.
- The HU of material x is $HU_x = 1000 \times (\mu_x - \mu_{water})/\mu_{water}$ where μ_x is the attenuation coefficient of the material x and μ_{water} is the attenuation coefficient of water.
- The HU value of **water is always 0**.
- **Air has an HU of –1000** because air attenuation is negligible compared to water.
- HU values in clinical CT are approximate, but may be used to characterize tissue.

Table 10.2
Comparison of material density, effective atomic number and resulting HU

Material	Density (g/cm³)	Effective atomic number	Hounsfield Unit (approximate)
Air	0.0013	7.6	−1000
Fat	0.91	5.9	−100
Water	1.0	7.4	0
Soft tissue	1.0	7.5	50
Bone	1.9	13	1000
Iodine	4.9	53	3000

- **An HU of −100 indicates fat** whereas an **HU of +50 is typical of soft tissue.**
- **Table 10.2** shows some common materials, and their corresponding HU values.

C. Reconstruction filters

- Different filters may be used in **filtered back projection reconstruction.**
- Commercial CT scanners typically offer **6 or 7 filters** for clinical use.
- The choice of filter in the reconstruction algorithm offers **tradeoffs between spatial resolution** and **(random) noise.**
- **Some filters (e.g., bone) permit reconstruction of fine detail but with increased noise.**
- An inner ear CT examination is an example of where a bone filter would be used to get the best possible spatial resolution.
- **Other filters (e.g., soft tissue) decrease noise but also decrease spatial resolution.**
- An abdominal CT would likely use a soft-tissue filter that minimizes noise and would improve visibility of low-contrast metastatic lesions in the liver.
- Some examinations may require the construction of two image sets with different filters for each.
- Trauma head imaging requires the use of a soft-tissue filter for visualization of brain matter and reconstruction with a bone algorithm for examination of the boney calvarium.
- The choice of the **best filter** to use with the reconstruction algorithm always **depends on the clinical task.**

D. Image display

- CT images are viewed on monitors.
- Each pixel shows a brightness (gray scale value) that is proportional to the HU value.

- **A single pixel is typically represented by 12 bits.**
- 12 bits is capable of displaying **4096 (2^{12}) individual gray level values.**
- In CT the level is within a range of values known as **CT numbers** or **Hounsfield Units.**
- **HU range from –1000 to +3000 (Table 10.2).**
- Application of a **window width and level** allows for selection of specific regions of the gray scale for viewing purposes.
- **Level** influences the **image brightness**, and window **width** modifies image **contrast.**
- A window width of 100 HU and a window level (center) of 0 HU displays HU less than –50 as black, HU greater than 50 being white, and HU equal to 0 would be mid gray.
- **Table 10.3** shows typical window width and level settings for common CT examinations.
- **Window (width and level) settings only affect the displayed image.**
- Window and level settings do not change the reconstructed stored image data.
- **Figure 10.2** shows the effects of adjusting window width and level in a chest CT.

Table 10.3
Typical window/level settings used in clinical CT

Type of examination	Window	Level
Posterior fossa	140	40
Lung	1500	–600
Abdomen (soft tissue)	400	40
Abdomen (liver)	150	70

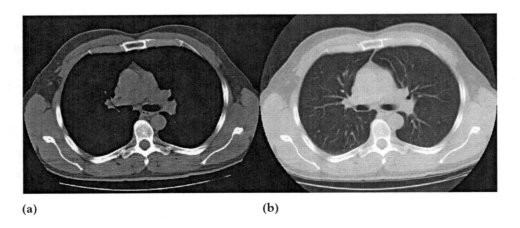

(a)   (b)

Figure 10.2
Chest CT image displayed using a soft tissue (a) and lung (b) window width/level settings. Soft-tissue window width/level typically is 400/40, with lung window width/level of 1500/–600.

E. 3D displays

- **Multiplanar reformating (MPR)** refers to the generation of coronal, sagittal, or oblique images from reconstructed axial images.

- **Maximum intensity projection (MIP)** uses only the highest value pixels to display in an image.

- MIP images are used to visualize blood vessels containing iodinated contrast agent.

- **Minimum intensity projection (MinIP)** uses only the lowest value pixels, often air-filled, to display an image.

- MinIP images are used to assess the airway or air-filled colon.

- **3D or volume rendering (VR)** of CT data can be used to show tissue and structures of clinical interest.

- **Shaded surface display (SSD)** shows surfaces when viewed using a virtual source of light that is used to provide an appearance of depth or shadowing.

- **Figure 10.3** shows examples of post processing in CT imaging.

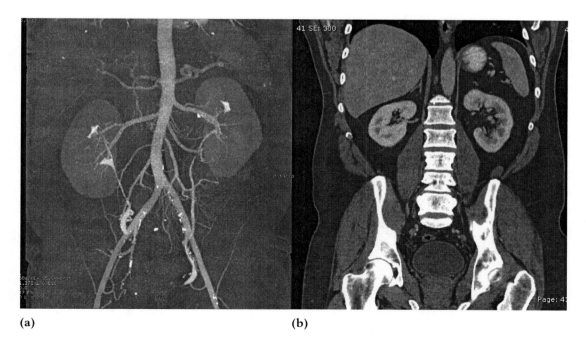

(a)   (b)

Figure 10.3
Post processing of CT image data showing a MIP (a) and MPR (b).

10.3 IMAGING CHAIN

A. X-ray generation

- The **CT gantry** contains the x-ray tube and the high-voltage generator.
- **High-frequency generators** are used in CT to supply power to the x-ray tube.
- Generators need to provide stable tube currents and voltages.
- Tube voltages are between **80 kV and 140 kV**.
- Tube currents are up to **1000 mA**.
- CT x-ray tubes have a large focal spot with a size of ~1 mm.
- X-ray tubes rotate at speeds of **0.3 to 0.5 seconds per 360° in body CT**.
- **Power loading** on CT x-ray tubes can be as high as **~100 kW**.
- **Figure 10.4** demonstrates power levels in CT scanners for the last 30 years.
- Anode must tolerate heat loads of **5 MJ (8 MHU)** with very rapid cooling rates.
- Fans or blowers may also be employed to help with heat dissapation.
- **CT x-ray tubes** are expensive, costing upwards of **$200,000**.
- **New oil-bathed CT tubes (Straton)** have been developed to **withstand even greater heat loads**.

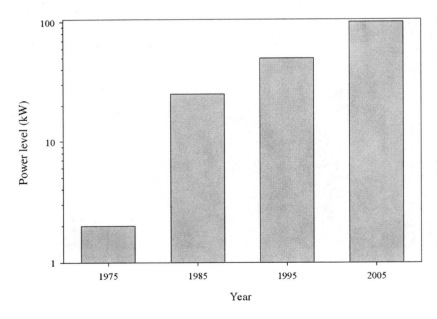

Figure 10.4
CT x-ray generator power levels since
the introduction of CT in the 1970s.

B. X-ray beam filtration

- The x-ray tube **anode-cathode axis is aligned perpendicular to the imaging plane**, which reduces the heel effect.
- Copper or aluminum filters are used to filter the x-ray beam.
- **The typical filtration on a CT x-ray tube is ~6 mm Al.**
- CT scanner x-ray beams have a **half-value layer (HVL) up to 10 mm Al.**
- High x-ray beam filtering will reduce beam-hardening artifacts.
- A **bow tie filter**, known as a **beam-shaping filter**, is placed between the x-ray tube and the patient.
- Bow tie filters attenuate little in the center, but attenuation increases with increasing distance from the central ray.
- Bow tie filters are made of a **low-Z material** such as **Teflon**™ to minimize beam-hardening differences.
- Bow tie filters **minimize the dynamic range** of exposures at the detector.
- **Different bow tie filters are used for head and body exams due to differences in anatomy.**

C. Collimation

- CT scanners are equipped with **prepatient** and **predetector collimators.**
- **Prepatient collimators** act as a traditional collimator, restricting the **FOV and z-axis thickness.**
- Prepatient collimation defines the beam width.
- Beam width on a **single-slice scanner** is about **10 mm.**
- Beam widths for **64-slice and 320-slice scanners** are about **40 mm and 160 mm**, respectively.
- Like scatter removal grids, **predetector collimators reduce scatter radiation.**
- **Thin lamellae** can be used to minimize scatter.
- Anti-scatter collimation is located between the detector elements oriented along the long patient axis and aligned with the x-ray focus.

D. Radiation detectors

- Detectors measures the intensity of radiation transmitted through the patient along each ray.
- Modern CT scanners use **scintillators** that are approximately **1 mm wide.**
- Because of magnification, a 1-mm wide detector corresponds to a **width at the isocenter (patient) of about 0.5 mm.**

- Scintillators produce light after x-ray photons are absorbed.
- Scintillation detectors are coupled to a light detector, such as **photodiodes**.
- CT detectors should have **rapid signal decay**, and **low afterglow characteristics**.
- CT detectors have a **quantum efficiency greater than 90%**, which refers to the percentage of incident x-ray photons that are absorbed.
- Scintillators **convert about 10%** of absorbed x-ray energy into light energy.
- CT detectors produce electric signals proportional to the incident radiation intensity.
- Each detector signal is **digitized** and **stored in a computer**.
- CT detectors include **cadmium tungstate ($CdWO_4$)** and **cesium iodide (CsI)**.

E. Computers

- Due to the large amount of data created in CT, a **high-capacity computer** is required.
- **Array processors** are used for image reconstruction.
- Array processors decrease reconstruction time, the time from scan completion to a viewable image.
- Image reconstruction involving millions of data points may be performed in less than a second.
- Storage options used in CT include **magnetic tape and optical disks**.
- **Digital videotapes** are used due to the high storage capacity and fast access to data.
- **Optical disks** hold very large amounts of data, have easy access, and are inexpensive.

10.4 TECHNOLOGY

A. Scanner generation

- In 1972, the **EMI scanner was the first CT scanner introduced** into clinical practice.
- EMI scanners used a **pencil beam** and sodium iodide (NaI) detectors that moved across the patient (i.e., translated) to obtain one projection data set.
- The x-ray tube and detector were **rotated 1°** and another projection was obtained (rotation), with 180° of rotation obtained.
- EMI scanner was a **translate/rotate acquisition geometry**, which is known as a **first-generation system**.
- The CT scanner "generation" defines the acquisition geometry.
- Second-generation scanners also use **translate-rotate technology** but have **multiple detectors and a fan-shaped beam**.

- Third-generation scanners use a **wide rotating fan beam** coupled with a **large array of detectors (rotate-rotate system)**.
- The geometric relationship between the tube and detectors does not change as it rotates 360° around the patient (**curvilinear detector array**).
- Fourth-generation scanners have a rotating tube and a fixed ring of detectors in the gantry (**rotate-fixed system**).

B. Slip-ring technology

- All current CT scanners use **slip-ring technology** where high voltages are applied using contact rings in the gantry.
- Slip rings consist of multiple **rings with corresponding brushes/blocks** that allow the transfer of energy and information to and from the detectors and tube.
- The need for cables attached to the detector and tube has been eliminated and continued rotation is now possible.
- **Slip rings made volume/helical/spiral imaging possible.**
- Slip rings are a permanent structure in scanners, and the brush/blocks need periodic replacement due to wear.
- **Current multi-detector CT (MDCT) systems use slip-ring technology and third-generation acquisition geometry.**

C. Axial scanning

- **Axial** or **sequential imaging** provides **individual images** through the body, similar to slices of bread in a loaf.
- The patient table is stationary as the tube detector assembly rotates about the patient.
- The projection data are reconstructed into an image.
- The table is moved and the process repeated.
- The **slice thickness** and **index** are determined at the start of the study and **cannot be changed**.
- Axial imaging has **long scan times** and increased incidence of patient motion.
- Long scan times prevent the effective use of IV contrast, so **IV contrast is not commonly used with axial scan modes**.
- Axial imaging can be used for (non-contrast) **head imaging**.

D. Helical scanning

- In helical CT acquisitions the **patient is moved along the horizontal axis as the x-ray tube rotates around the patient**.
- **The relationship between table and tube motion is called pitch.**

- Pitch is the **table movement distance during each x-ray tube rotation divided by the total x-ray beam width**.
- For a **40-mm beam width**, if the **patient moves 80 mm** during the time it takes for the x-ray tube to rotate through 360°, the **pitch is 2**.
- **Table 10.4** shows examples of pitch in CT.
- Increasing pitch generally reduces the scan time and patient dose.
- Helical imaging creates **only partial information** for a slice to be reconstructed.
- **Interpolation**, the estimation of a value between known points, is used for image reconstruction in helical data sets.
- Information from the spiral data just prior to and just after the desired slice is needed for interpolation to occur.
- **Reconstructed images can have a greater thickness than the collimation, but *cannot* be less than the collimation.**

Table 10.4

Pitch in helical CT for a 64-slice CT scanner with a nominal beam width of 40 mm

Table speed (mm/s)	X-ray tube rotation speed (seconds per 360°)	Pitch
40	0.5	0.5
	1	1
80	0.5	1
	1	2

E. Multi-detector CT (MDCT)

- MDCT scanners have **multiple detector arrays** and thereby allow **multiple slices** to be acquired per 360° x-ray tube rotation.
- Four-slice MDCT, introduced in 1998, produces four images (slices) per 360° x-ray tube rotation.
- **Figure 10.5** shows the historical evolution of the number of slices in MDCT system.
- Each 64-slice MDCT has **64 detector arrays**, where **each detector array has 800 detectors**.
- Detector widths (along the patient's z-axis) are about 0.6 mm.
- **One rotation of a 64-MDCT scanner generates 64 slices, each with a thickness of 0.6 mm.**

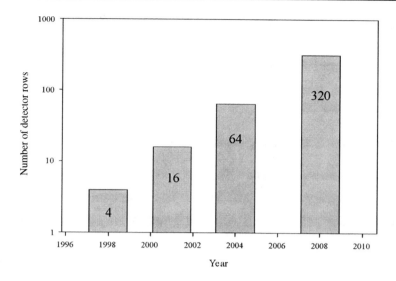

Figure 10.5
Number of CT detector rows in commercial CT scanners
as a function of year of introduction.

- MDCT scanners with thin z-axis slices now have **isotropic resolution**, permitting non-axial reconstructions with the same resolution as axial reconstructions.
- The number of x-ray tube rotations, for a pitch of 1, is given by the scan length (L) divided by the beam width.
- A 64-slice CT (~40 mm beam width) scanner performing an abdominal scan with a length of 32 cm requires only eight x-ray tube rotations.

10.5 CLINICAL ASPECTS

A. CT operation

- Patient couches are composed of a **carbon fiber** to minimize x-ray attenuation.
- Tables are given a **weight limit for patient safety** and to ensure **accurate movement**.
- The **patient couch is indexed**, such that each image is assigned a bed position that can be located on the scout images.
- CT operator console typically has two monitors.
- One monitor is used for entry and manipulation of patient demographic information and scan protocol selection.
- The other monitor is used for viewing images and post processing activities.

- The **technologist selects the appropriate scanning protocol.**
- **Scanning protocols** select the appropriate **kVp, mA, rotation time, and pitch/table feed** for the specific examination.
- Image display selections include: **reconstruction algorithm, slice thickness, image reconstruction index, and the display window width and level.**

B. Digital projection radiograph

- All CT examinations begin with acquisition of a projection radiograph.
- Projection radiographs are also known as **topographic** or **scout image.**
- The projection radiograph is obtained by **advancing the patient couch** through the gantry with the **tube in a fixed position.**
- Projection radiographs are **used to define the anatomy** to be imaged in the CT examination.
- **Posterior anterior and lateral scout images** may be obtained for anatomical landmarks and for use in **dose modulation.**
- **Dose modulation software** uses the attenuation information gained during scout imaging to **adjust exposure during the helical CT examination.**

C. Adult CT

- **Higher kVp values** (140 kVp) may be used in head CT scanning (posterior fossa) to help **minimize beam-hardening artifacts.**
- In head CT scanning, x-ray tube rotations times are longer (~1 s) where motion is minimal, and higher radiation doses are required to minimize quantum mottle.
- **Routine adult head CT scan use ~300 mAs.**
- **FOV of 250** mm with a **scan length of ~150 mm** is common in head CT.
- Image reconstruction is done using a **soft-tissue algorithm** and a **detail algorithm.**
- In body CT scanning, the **faster rotation times** are employed to minimize the scan time.
- Short scan times reduce motion artifacts, and help minimize the amount of iodinated contrast material administered to the patient.
- **Adult body scans use 120 kVp and ~200 mAs.**
- Higher kVp may also be used to improve penetration of larger patients, and **reduced x-ray tube voltages** (80 kVp) are used in angiography.
- Field of view is 400 mm and scan lengths are 300 to 400 mm.

D. Pediatric CT

- When scanning **children**, it is important that **reduced techniques** are employed.
- Reduced techniques are possible because x-ray penetration is much greater in children than in adults.
- **Technique reductions may be achieved by reducing the mAs, reducing the kVp, or reducing both.**
- **Sizeable technique reductions** are generally possible when performing **body CT examinations in very young children.**
- **Table 10.5** shows technique reductions recommended by Image Gently™.
- The achievable reduction depends both on the size of the child and the imaging task.
- **Technique reductions** in **pediatric head CT** examinations are **modest, because excellent image quality is essential.**

Table 10.5
Technique (mAs) reductions in pediatric CT (abdomen and head values),
as recommended by Image Gently (see web site★)

Patient age	Relative radiation intensity (%)	
	Head	Abdomen
Newborn	75	40
1-year-old	85	50
5-year-old	90	60
10-year-old	95	65
Adult	100	100

★www.imagegently.org.

E. Artifacts

- **Partial volume artifact** is the result of averaging the linear attenuation coefficient in a voxel that is heterogeneous in composition.
- **Patient motion** artifacts occur due to the use of a **longer exposure time** in CT **(0.5–2 s).**
- Both **voluntary** and **involuntary** motion takes place.
- The movement creates **inconsistencies in reconstruction** and thus artifacts.
- High-density structures (e.g., metal implants) produce **star artifacts.**

- **Beam-hardening artifacts** are caused by the polychromatic nature of the x-ray beam.

- As the lower energy photons are preferentially absorbed, the beam becomes more penetrating, **causing underestimation of the attenuation coefficient (HU)**.

- Modern multi-detector CT (MDCT) scanners have **software to correct beam-hardening artifacts**.

- **Ring artifacts** may arise in **third-generation systems** if a single detector is faulty or the CT scanner is not properly calibrated.

- **Out-of-field artifacts** result from tissue lying beyond the single field of view (SFOV) (e.g., when a patient for a chest CT cannot raise arms above head).

- **Figure 10.6** shows examples of common CT artifacts.

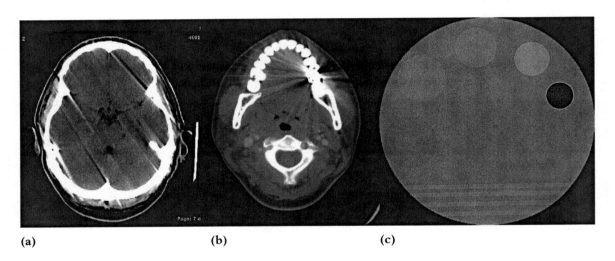

(a)   (b)   (c)

Figure 10.6
CT artifacts patient motion (a), metal (b), and detector artifact (c).

QUESTIONS

Chapter 10: Computed Tomography

10.1   The major limitation of projection radiography is most likely:
A. superimposition of structures.
B. poor spatial resolution.
C. inadequate image contrast.
D. high levels of image mottle.

10.2   The first clinical CT scanner was developed by:
A. Roentgen.
B. Becquerel.
C. Coolidge.
D. Hounsfield.

10.3   A single CT projection most likely contains how many measurement values (i.e., ray sums)?
A. 10
B. 100
C. 1000
D. 10,000

10.4   Back projection implies allocating attenuation along a row of pixels:
A. equally.
B. logarithmically.
C. exponentially.
D. randomly.

10.5   Current commercial CT scanners likely reconstruct images using:
A. back projection.
B. filtered back projection.
C. iterative reconstruction.
D. algebraic reconstruction.

10.6   The major limitation of iterative reconstruction for CT is:
A. high computing power.
B. low spatial resolution.
C. too many artifacts.
D. high image noise.

10.7   The most common matrix size in CT is:
         A. 128 × 128.
         B. 256 × 256.
         C. 512 × 512.
         D. 1024 × 1024.

10.8   A 0.5 mm × 0.5 mm pixel, with a slice thickness of 10 mm, has a volume of _____ mm^3.
         A. 0.1
         B. 0.25
         C. 1
         D. 2.5

10.9   What is the likely pixel size (mm) when the body CT field of view is 50 cm?
         A. 0.25
         B. 0.5
         C. 1
         D. 2

10.10   The Hounsfield Unit of water is most likely:
         A. −1000.
         B. 0.
         C. +1000.
         D. Depends on kV.

10.11   Use of a bone reconstruction would likely improve image:
         A. detail.
         B. noise.
         C. contrast.
         D. artifacts.

10.12   Use of a soft-tissue reconstruction would likely improve image:
         A. detail.
         B. noise.
         C. contrast.
         D. artifacts.

10.13   The number of bits used to code a CT pixel is most likely _____ .
         A. 4
         B. 8
         C. 12
         D. 16

10.14   If the window width is 1000, and the level is 0, which pixel value will appear black?
     A. −500
     B. 0
     C. 500
     D. 1000

10.15   Which is least likely to be a CT image display mode?
     A. MIP
     B. VR
     C. SSD
     D. FOV

10.16   The most likely x-ray tube voltage in a CT examination is _____ kV.
     A. 45
     B. 75
     C. 120
     D. 150

10.17   The most likely x-ray tube current in a CT examination is _____ mA.
     A. 0.5
     B. 5
     C. 50
     D. 500

10.18   The most likely x-ray tube rotation time in a body CT examination is _____ seconds.
     A. 0.1
     B. 0.5
     C. 1
     D. 5

10.19   CT focal spot size is most likely _____ mm.
     A. 0.3
     B. 0.6
     C. 1.2
     D. 2.5

10.20   Total filtration for a CT x-ray tube is most likely _____ mm Al.
     A. 1
     B. 3
     C. 6
     D. 12

10.21   Bow tie filters are most likely to reduce the detector:
A. dynamic range.
B. scatter absorption.
C. absorption efficiency.
D. dead time.

10.22   The half-value layer for a CT scanner is most likely _____ mm Al.
A. 1
B. 2
C. 4
D. 8

10.23   The x-ray beam width on a 64-slice CT scanner is most likely _____ mm.
A. 0.4
B. 4
C. 40
D. 400

10.24   A single x-ray detector width on a 320-slice CT scanner is most likely _____ mm.
A. 0.1
B. 0.5
C. 2
D. 10

10.25   The most likely x-ray detection efficiency of a CT detector is _____%.
A. 5
B. 25
C. 50
D. 90

10.26   Axial scanning is most likely to be performed when imaging the:
A. head.
B. chest.
C. abdomen.
D. pediatrics.

10.27   The "generation" descriptor of modern CT scanners is most likely:
A. second.
B. third.
C. fourth.
D. fifth.

10.28   The total number of individual detectors on a 64-slice CT scanner is most likely:
A. 64.
B. 64 × 64.
C. 64 × 64 × 64.
D. 64 × 800.

10.29   The optimum x-ray tube voltage for imaging the posterior fossa is most likely _____ kVp.
A. 80
B. 100
C. 120
D. 140

10.30   The optimum x-ray tube voltage for imaging iodinated contrast is most likely _____ kVp.
A. 80
B. 100
C. 120
D. 140

ANSWERS[1]

Chapter 10: Computed Tomography

10.1	A	Radiography has objects, whereas CT is not limited in this way.	*p. 368 Bushong* *n/a Carlton/Adler*
10.2	D	Godfrey Hounsfield was responsible for the development of the first commercial CT scanner.	*p. 368 Bushong* *p. 643 Carlton/Adler*
10.3	C	As many as 1,000,000 data points are collected by 1000 detectors, resulting in ~1000 measurements or data points per detector.	*n/a Bushong* *p. 646 Carlton/Adler*
10.4	A	Back projection distributes attenuation evenly, resulting in a blurring of image data.	*p. 376 Bushong* *p. 659 Carlton/Adler*
10.5	B	Filtered back projection is used for image reconstruction.	*p. 376 Bushong* *p. 660 Carlton/Adler*
10.6	A	Iterative reconstruction requires substantial computer power.	*n/a Bushong* *n/a Carlton/Adler*
10.7	C	CT units commonly utilize a 512 × 512 matrix.	*p. 375 Bushong* *p. 663 Carlton/Adler*
10.8	D	A calculation of the volume element or voxel is the product of the length, width, and depth of the voxel (i.e., 0.5 × 0.5 × 10), so that the volume is 2.5 mm^3.	*p. 375 Bushong* *p. 663 Carlton/Adler*
10.9	C	Pixel size is calculated by dividing the matrix size into the FOV, such that a 500-mm FOV divided by a 512 matrix would be ~1.0 mm.	*p. 376 Bushong* *p. 663 Carlton/Adler*
10.10	B	The Hounsfield Unit of water is always zero.	*p. 376 Bushong* *p. 657 Carlton/Adler*
10.11	A	A bone or detail filter provides good spatial resolution at the cost of an increase in noise.	*p. 379 Bushong* *p. 665 Carlton/Adler*

---

[1] As a study aid, page numbers for additional study are given for the following references:
   Bushong SC: *Radiologic Science for Technologists,* 9th ed. St. Louis, MO: Mosby, 2008.
   Carlton RR, Adler AM: *Principles of Radiographic Imaging: An Art and a Science,* 4th ed. Albany, NY: Delmar Publishing Inc., 2005.

10.12	B	A soft-tissue or smooth filter improves contrast.	*p. 379 Bushong* *p. 665 Carlton/Adler*
10.13	C	Most CT systems have a 12-bit system or are capable of resolving 4096 gray shades.	*p. 376 Bushong* *p. 348 Carlton/Adler*
10.14	A	With a level of 0 and a width of 1000, pixels above 500 appear white and those below −500 will appear black.	*p. 456 Bushong* *p. 349 Carlton/Adler*
10.15	D	FOV is the diameter of the scanned area, not a CT image display mode.	*p. 375 Bushong* *p. 663 Carlton/Adler*
10.16	C	Most CT adult exams use 120 kVp.	*p. 377 Bushong* *p. 651 Carlton/Adler*
10.17	D	An mA of 500 is typical of current CT.	*n/a Bushong* *p. 651 Carlton/Adler*
10.18	B	A rotation time of 0.5 seconds is often used in body imaging to minimize patient motion and to increase scan speed.	*n/a Bushong* *p. 651 Carlton/Adler*
10.19	C	CT scanners use a focal spot size of ~1.2 mm.	*p. 373 Bushong* *p. 651 Carlton/Adler*
10.20	C	Filtration in CT is greater due to the higher voltages routinely used (120 kVp), with 6 mm Al equivalent being common.	*n/a Bushong* *n/a Carlton/Adler*
10.21	A	Beam shaping or bow tie filters are used to compensate for the oval shape of the patient's anatomy, thus providing a reduced dynamic range at the detector.	*p. 370 Bushong* *p. 669 Carlton/Adler*
10.22	D	HVL in CT is greater due to the higher voltages routinely used (120 kVp) and the heavily filtered x-ray beam; with an HVL of ~10 mm Al being typical.	*n/a Bushong* *n/a Carlton/Adler*
10.23	C	A 64-channel detector would have a beamwidth of 40 mm.	*n/a Bushong* *p. 654 Carlton/Adler*
10.24	B	Detectors in MDCT systems are about 0.5 mm.	*n/a Bushong* *p. 654 Carlton/Adler*
10.25	D	Scintillator crystals with photodiodes have a better than 90% absorption rate.	*p. 374 Bushong* *p. 654 Carlton/Adler*
10.26	A	Axial imaging of the brain is standard practice.	*n/a Bushong* *n/a Carlton/Adler*

10.27   B   The third-generation acquisition geometry is currently used in MDCT.   *p. 371 Bushong*
n/a Carlton/Adler

10.28   D   A 64-detector scanner will have 64 rows of detectors with ~800 detectors per row.   *p. 374 Bushong*
p. 650 Carlton/Adler

10.29   D   When imaging the very dense posterior fossa, a kVp of 140 is most appropriate.   *p. 372 Bushong*
p. 651 Carlton/Adler

10.30   A   An 80 kVp beam has an average energy very close to 33 keV (K-edge of iodine), which increases photoelectric absorption and results in a high image contrast.   *p. 446 Bushong*
p. 324 Carlton/Adler

PART III. DOSE, QUALITY, AND SAFETY

Chapter 11

RADIATION DOSIMETRY

11.1 Radiation Units
11.2 Incident Radiation
11.3 Absorbed Doses
11.4 CT Dosimetry
11.5 Effective Doses

11.1 RADIATION UNITS

A. Air Kerma

- The **International Commission on Radiation Units and Measurements (ICRU)** developed standard units based on the SI system.

- SI units are utilized by all countries except the United States.

- **Air Kerma** is the SI unit that is currently used to quantify the x-ray beam intensity.

- Kerma stands for the *Kinetic Energy Released per unit Mass*.

- Intensity is directly related to the number of x-ray photons in a beam.

- Air Kerma is the kinetic energy transferred from x-ray photons to electrons.

- **Air Kerma** is measured in **joules per kilogram (J/kg):**

    1 J/kg is 1 Gray (Gy).

- The Air Kerma value from x-ray sources obeys the inverse square law.

B. Exposure

- **Exposure** is the total charge of electrons liberated per unit mass of air by the x-ray photons.

- Exposure is the non-SI unit used to **quantify the x-ray beam intensity.**

- **One roentgen (R) is equal to the 2.58×10^{-4} C/kg.**

- 1 R is equal to 1000 mR, and is still used in some radiology departments in the United States.

- The roentgen applies to photons (x-rays and gamma rays) but not particles such as electrons.

- An exposure of **1 R corresponds to an Air Kerma of 8.7 mGy.**

- Scientific publications have **replaced exposure (R) with Air Kerma (mGy).**

- 1 R is often approximated as ~10 mGy Air Kerma, and 10 mGy Air Kerma is approximated as ~1 R.

C. Absorbed dose

- **Absorbed dose (D)** measures the amount of **radiation energy (E)** absorbed per unit **mass (M)** of a tissue (i.e., **D = E/M**).

- Absorbed dose is specified in **gray (Gy)** in SI units.

- **One gray is equal to 1 J of energy deposited per kilogram.**

- In the non-SI system, the **rad** was the unit of absorbed dose.

- The rad was derived from the expression radiation absorbed dose.

- **1 Gy = 100 rad and 1 rad = 10 mGy.**

- It is helpful to specify the absorbing medium explicitly (i.e., absorbed dose to skin entrance, absorbed dose to liver, etc.).

D. Integral dose (energy imparted)

- The **integral dose** is simply the total energy (mJ) that a patient absorbs.

- **Integral dose and energy imparted have the same meaning.**

- A chest x-ray radiograph imparts about 2 mJ of energy to the patient.

- Head radiographs impart about 5 mJ and abdominal radiographs impart about 20 mJ.

- By contrast, a 500-W microwave oven produces 500,000 mJ every second.

- Energy imparted in a microwave oven is much greater than in a radiograph, and increases the food temperature.

- **X-rays deposit very little energy,** but this energy is ionizing, which breaks apart biologically important molecules such as DNA.

E. Equivalent dose

- **Equivalent dose** quantifies biological damage by *different types* of radiation.
- For the same absorbed dose, alpha particles cause much more biological damage than x-rays.
- The **equivalent dose (H)** is the **absorbed dose (D)** multiplied by a radiation **weighting factor (w_R)**.
- Mathematically, $H = D \times w_R$.
- **Equivalent dose is expressed in sieverts (Sv).**
- Use of w_R permits comparisons of effects of different types of radiation on a common scale.
- For **x-rays, gamma rays,** and electrons $w_R = 1$.
- An absorbed dose to the skin of 1 Gy (100 rad) from x-rays corresponds to a skin-equivalent dose of 1 Sv (100 rem).
- For **alpha particles** and **neutrons,** w_R may be as high as 20.
- **Equivalent dose** is primarily used for radiation protection purposes as an *approximate indicator* **of biological harm.**
- Dosimetry units are shown in **Table 11.1.** Examples of measurement devices used in dosimetry are shown in **Figure 11.1.**

Table 11.1
Summary of dosimetry units used in x-ray imaging

Quantity	Units	Comments
Air Kerma	mGy	Quantifies the intensity of x-ray beams
Exposure	C/kg or roentgen	Has been replaced by Air Kerma
Absorbed dose	mGy or rad	Quantifies how much any tissue absorbs from any incident x-ray beam
Integral dose	mJ	Total energy absorbed by a patient undergoing any x-ray examination
Equivalent dose	mSv or rem	Obtained by multiplying absorbed dose to an organ by radiation weighting factor and used to predict the likelihood of biological harm

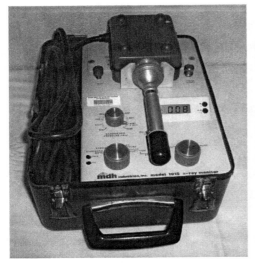
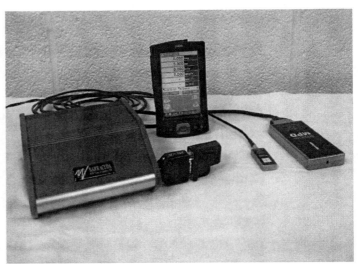

(a) **(b)**

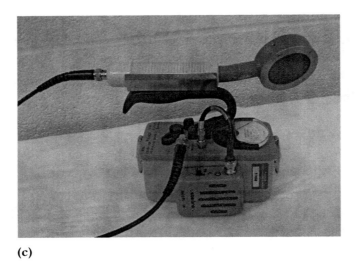

(c)

Figure 11.1
Examples of radiation measurement/detection devices.
(a) Ionization chamber; (b) Solid-state detector; (a) and (b) are used
for the measurement of the primary x-ray beam.
(c) Geiger-Mueller tube used to detect radioactive isotope
contamination in nuclear medicine.

11.2 INCIDENT RADIATION

A. Entrance Air Kerma (EAK)

- **Entrance Air Kerma (EAK)** is a measure of the amount of x-ray radiation intensity incident on the patient undergoing an x-ray examination.

- The EAK value is **measured** at the point **where the x-ray beam would enter the patient**, but is obtained in the absence of the patient.

- Values of EAK are thus **measured "free in air"** and do not include backscatter radiation from the patient.

- **The EAK is measured "free in air"** by placing an ionization chamber at the appropriate distance from the x-ray tube and using the patient technique factors (kVp and mAs).

- **Values of the EAK** are easy to measure but **do not quantify the amount of radiation** received by the patient.

- Patient doses (e.g., skin dose, embryo dose, organ dose) can be derived from EAK values via appropriate conversion factors (see below).

B. Radiography

- For a lateral **skull radiograph**, a typical **EAK value is 1.5 mGy**.

- An AP (or PA) skull would likely double the EAK value for a lateral skull.

- For a **PA chest radiograph**, the EAK is generally **0.1 to 0.2 mGy**.

- A lateral chest has EAK values about four times higher than a PA chest radiograph.

- For an **AP abdominal radiograph**, the EAK value is about **3 mGy**.

- EAK values for extremities are very low (< 0.1 mGy).

C. Fluoroscopy

- Because fluoroscopy involves continuous exposure, **Air Kerma rates in mGy/minute** are the units used.

- Entrance Air Kerma rates in fluoroscopy typically range from **10 to 100 mGy/min**.

- An **average-sized patient** entrance skin Air Kerma rate in fluoroscopy is **30 mGy/min**.

- Larger patients require more radiation in fluoroscopy, which is achieved either by increasing the x-ray tube voltage (kV) and/or increasing the tube current (mA).

- **Figure 11.2** shows a typical variation of EAK rates as a function of patient thickness.

- Magnification imaging in fluoroscopy will cause an increase in entrance Air Kerma rate as shown in **Figure 11.3**.

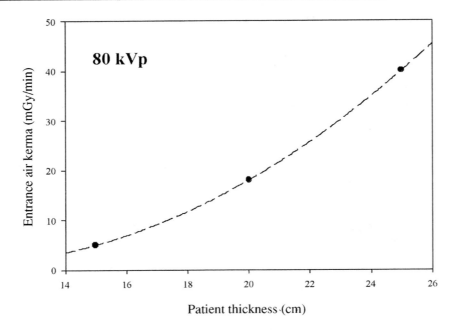

Figure 11.2
Entrance Air Kerma (EAK) rates in fluoroscopy
as a function of patient thickness.

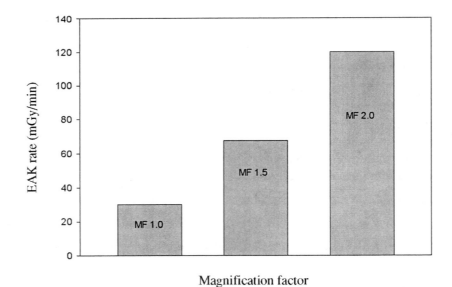

Figure 11.3
Effect of magnification in fluoroscopy on Entrance
Air Kerma (EAK) rate. Using a magnification mode of 1.5 and 2.0
increases the EAK by a factor of 2.4 and 4.4, respectively.

D. Regulations

- In the United States, the legal limit for **entrance skin kerma rate is 100 mGy/min (10 R/min)**.

- No regulatory limits apply when a fluoroscopy imaging chain acquires diagnostic images.

- Diagnostic images include cardiac cine, DSA, and photospot.

- **High-dose modes** in fluoroscopy may be activated to maintain image quality in **very large patients**.

- Special activation mechanisms as well as visible/audible indicators are present to indicate when high-dose mode is being used.

- The maximum Air Kerma rate in high-dose mode is **200 mGy/min (20 R/min)**.

E. Kerma Area Product (KAP)

- **The entrance Air Kerma is independent of the x-ray beam area.**

- At constant techniques, a 10 cm × 10 cm beam area and 20 cm × 20 cm beam area have similar EAK values.

- Compared to a 10 cm × 10 cm field, the 20 cm × 20 cm field results in **four times more energy** deposition in the patient.

- The best quantity that takes into account **the *total* amount** of radiation incident on the patient is the **Kerma Area Product (KAP)**.

- KAP is the product of the **entrance Air Kerma** and **cross-sectional area of the x-ray beam**.

- **KAP is independent of the measurement location** because increases in beam area are offset by the reduction of beam intensity (**inverse square law**).

- KAP can be used to compare doses from different imaging systems (or facilities) for similar types of examinations on similar-sized patients.

- KAP values **indicate relative radiation risks** for similar types of examinations performed on similar-sized patients.

- **Table 11.2** shows typical KAP values in radiography and fluoroscopy.

- Kerma Area Product is also known as the Dose Area Product (DAP), and the terms KAP and DAP are interchangeable.

Table 11.2
Typical KAP values in radiography, fluoroscopy, and IR

Image acquisition	Entrance Air Kerma (mGy)	Kerma Area Product (Gy-cm^2)
Skull radiograph	1.5	0.5
AP chest x-ray	0.2	0.2
Abdominal x-ray	3	3
Fluoroscopy (1 min)	20	10
Spot image (Ba study)	1	0.5
DSA image★ (abd)	6	2

★Taking into account that two frames are required to generate one DSA frame

11.3 ABSORBED DOSES

A. Air Kerma (free in air) and doses

- For the same Air Kerma (intensity), **absorbed dose** depends on the **material** or **tissue** that is placed into the x-ray beam.

- The radiation absorbed by a medium is determined by the characteristics of the absorber (density, atomic number, etc.), as well as the x-ray beam energy.

- An Air Kerma of **1 mGy (100 mR)** will result in an absorbed dose in **soft tissue of approximately 1.1 mGy (110 mrad)**.

- An Air Kerma of **1 mGy (100 mR)** will result in a **bone dose of 4 mGy (400 mrad)**.

- **Doses** in radiology also **need to account for backscatter.**

- An x-ray beam incident on a patient will also result in x-ray photons from within the patient being backscattered.

- Backscatter is the ratio of the radiation intensities with and without the patient being present.

- **Values of backscatter in diagnostic radiology are about 1.4.**

- Skin doses will be higher than entrance Air Kerma because tissue absorbs more radiation than air (×1.1), and because of backscatter (×1.4).

- **An entrance Air Kerma of 1 mGy results in skin doses of about 1.5 mGy.**

B. Skin doses

- **Skin doses** are generally specified at the location **where the x-ray beam enters the patient**.
- Skin doses are numerically about 50% higher than the entrance Air Kerma.
- Skin doses in radiography are generally very low.
- Pediatric skin doses will generally be lower than for adults.
- An **average-sized patient (23 cm)** undergoing fluoroscopy will have a skin dose rate of about **45 mGy per minute**.
- An average-sized patient undergoing 10 minutes of fluoroscopy may result in a skin dose of 450 mGy.
- Skin doses can be substantially increased for larger patients.
- Interventional Radiology (IR) is complex, has long fluoroscopy times, and can generate many images.
- Because of this, IR may result in deterministic effects.
- **Fewer than 1 in 10,000 patients** undergoing IR by qualified personnel **suffer from serious deterministic effects**.

C. Organ (embryo) doses

- **Entrance Air Kerma may be converted into absorbed doses** to any organ located within the patient.
- Organ doses are generally much lower than skin doses.
- If the x-ray beam does not directly irradiate the embryo, the embryo dose may be taken to be very low.
- **Embryo doses** may be estimated from entrance Air Kerma values.
- The **x-ray projection is important** when determining embryo doses.
- **Table 11.3** provides typical values of entrance Air Kerma and the corresponding values of embryo dose in abdominal radiography.

Table 11.3
Entrance Air Kerma (EAK) and embryo doses in abdominal/pelvic
radiography when the embryo is directly irradiated

Projection	EAK (mGy)	Embryo dose (mGy)
AP	3	1
PA	3	0.6
Lateral	6	0.3

- **Patient size** is an additional factor that needs to be taken into account when estimating embryo doses.
- Larger patients require more radiation for adequate penetration, but this will also result in more attenuation between the entrance and the location of the embryo.
- **Estimating embryo doses generally requires input from a Qualified Medical Physicist.**

D. Gonad doses

- **Gonad doses** refer to the radiation received by the testes in males and the ovaries in females.
- The genetic risk in any exposed individual is generally deemed to be low and of no direct clinical concern.
- Gonad doses have been used to quantify the **genetically significant dose (GSD),** which is an index of **potential genetic damage in exposed populations.**
- GSD accounts for gonad dose and the number of offspring likely to be produced.
- When a population receives a gonad dose equal to the GSD, the genetic harm equals that from current medical exposures.
- The **National Council on Radiation Protection and Measurements (NCRP) reported the U.S. GSD at about 0.3 mGy in 1980.**
- Gonad doses are now **of little concern in diagnostic radiology**, and GSD values are rarely subject to scientific investigation.
- **Nonetheless, use of gonad shields is still common practice and useful as a precautionary principle.**

E. Mammography

- In mammography, the **average glandular dose (AGD)** is obtained from a measurement of the **entrance Air Kerma using a breast phantom.**
- AGD values depend on x-ray beam techniques (kV and mAs), beam filtration, breast thickness, and composition.
- **AGD are obtained using a phantom simulating a 4.2-cm thick breast with 50% glandularity.**
- Increasing the x-ray tube voltage when the image receptor intensity is kept constant will reduce AGD because of increased x-ray beam penetration.
- **AGD values are about 1.5 mGy (150 mrad) per image.**
- Digital mammography has slightly lower AGD values than screen-film because of the use of higher beam qualities (i.e., increased kV and/or filtration).

- **Patient doses can differ markedly** from the AGD obtained using a breast dosimetry phantom because of differences in breast size and composition.

11.4 CT DOSIMETRY

A. Computed Tomography Dose Index (CTDI)

- Manufacturers specify CT doses by the **CT dose index (CTDI)**.
- CTDI is obtained from the dose distribution that occurs when the x-ray tube performs **one single 360° rotation with no table motion.**
- CTDI values are **measured using a pencil-shaped ionization chamber** in terms of Air Kerma, and are specified in **mGy**.
- An **acrylic cylinder** with a 16-cm diameter is normally taken to represent an adult patient head.
- The head CT dosimetry phantom can also represent a pediatric abdomen.
- An acrylic cylinder with a 32 cm diameter is normally taken to represent an adult body.
- Most patients are smaller than a 32 cm acrylic phantom, and dose measurements made in this phantom will underestimate patient doses.

B. Clinical CTDI

- CTDI measurements may be made at the periphery and at the center of the phantom are called $CTDI_p$ and $CTDI_c$, respectively.
- **A weighted CTDI (i.e., $CTDI_w$) is defined as $2/3$ $CTDI_p$ + $1/3$ $CTDI_c$.**
- Doses in helical scanning modes with a **pitch of 1.0 are similar** to those resulting from contiguous axial scanning.
- When pitch is less than 1.0, doses increase because of overlap. When pitch is greater than 1.0, doses decrease because scan energy is deposited in a larger volume.
- A pitch of 2 will halve dose, and a pitch of 0.5 will double the dose.
- **CTDI is inversely proportional to pitch.**
- To account for different pitch values in helical scanning, the volume $CTDI_{vol}$ has been introduced as $CTDI_w/Pitch$.
- $CTDI_{vol}$ is expressed in mGy.
- **Figure 11.4** shows $CTDI_{vol}$ for head and body phantoms, illustrating that **body doses are about half head CTDI due to increased attenuation.**

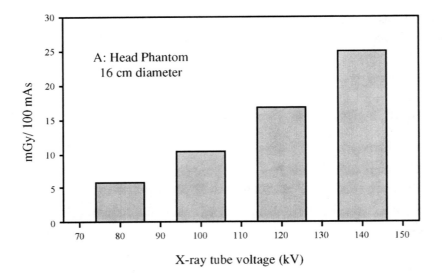

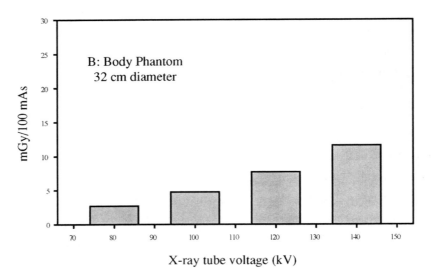

Figure 11.4
Average values of CTDI$_{vol}$ as a function
of x-ray tube voltage (per 100 mAs).

C. Dose-Length Product (DLP)

- **CTDI$_{vol}$ is independent of the total scan length.**
- The total amount of radiation received by the patient, however, is directly proportional to the scan length.

- The **Dose-Length Product (DLP)** is the **product of CTDI$_{vol}$ and scan length**.

- The DLP is proportional to the total dose (energy) imparted to the patient.

- **DLP** is a good measure of the total amount of **radiation incident on a patient**.

- A typical **head CT examination has a DLP of 1000 mGy-cm**, where CTDI is measured in 16-cm phantoms.

- A **chest, body, or pelvic CT examination would have a DLP of 600 mGy-cm**, where CTDI is measured in 32-cm phantoms.

- A chest abdomen pelvic CT scan would have a DLP of 1500 mGy-cm.

- CTDI and DLP measures are shown in **Table 11.4**, and it is very important that the phantom size (16 cm or 32 cm) is always specified.

Table 11.4
Common Computed Tomography Dose Index (CTDI) measures used in CT dosimetry

Quantity	Units	Comments
CTDI$_{air}$	mGy	CTDI measured at the CT scanner isocenter in the absence of any patient or dosimetric phantom
CTDI$_p$	mGy	CTDI measured at the periphery (i.e., 1 cm from edge) of an acrylic dosimetric phantom
CTDI$_c$	mGy	CTDI measured at the center of an acrylic dosimetric phantom
CTDI$_w$	mGy	Equal to 1/3 (CTDI$_c$) + 2/3 (CTDI$_p$), and measured in either 16–cm (head) or 32–cm (body)
CTDI$_{vol}$★	mGy	Equal to CTDI$_w$ divided by pitch
Dose-Length Product (DLP)★	mGy-cm	Product of CTDI$_{vol}$ and the scan length L (cm)

★Metrics easily available to the technologist

D. Adult CTDI

- **The American College of Radiology (ACR)** runs a CT Accreditation Program, including CT dosimetry data.

- Mean values of CTDI$_{vol}$ for an adult head are 58 mGy (16-cm phantom), and for an adult abdomen, 18 mGy (32-cm phantom).

- **CT doses are directly proportional to the mA and to the scan rotation time.**

- Increasing the x-ray tube voltage from **80 kV to 140 kV, increases doses fivefold**.

- Performing multi-phase studies can substantially increase patient doses.
- For constant techniques, performing four phase examinations (pre-contrast, arterial, venous, and equilibrium) would quadruple the patient dose.
- **Multi-detector CT (MDCT) has radiation doses similar to those of axial CT for similar image quality.**

E. Pediatric

- Pediatric doses depend on both patient characteristics and selected techniques.
- Doses in infants and young children are much higher than for adults when performed using the same techniques.
- **The Food and Drug Administration (FDA) issued an advisory in 2001 to reduce radiation doses to pediatric patients.**
- Increasing the patient size from 20 to 100 kg reduces x-ray beam penetration by a factor of 30.
- **Reduced techniques** are possible because x-ray penetration is much greater in children than in adults.
- **The American College of Radiology (ACR)** CT Accreditation Program includes specific CT dosimetry requirements for pediatric examinations.
- The ACR provides resources to assist in dose reduction techniques, such as the Image Gently™ web site, www.imagegently.org.
- Pediatric body examinations should be performed with a **reduction in dose by a factor of ~3** compared with adult examinations.

11.5 EFFECTIVE DOSES

A. Effective dose

- Skin doses are poor predictors of patient stochastic radiation risk.
- Problems with skin doses include the fact that they **fail to account for the exposed body region, x-ray beam area, and x-ray penetration.**
- The **effective dose (E)** is obtained by taking into account the equivalent dose to all exposed organs, as well as each organ's relative radiosensitivity.
- **E** is obtained by multiplying **equivalent dose (H)** to an organ by the **organ weighting factor (w)**, and **summed for all irradiated organs.**
- The organ weighting factor (w) is a measure of the relative organ radiosensitivity for the induction of stochastic effects.
- The **most radiosensitive organs** are the red bone marrow, colon, lung, breast, and stomach.

- The **effective dose** is expressed in terms of the **equivalent dose (mSv)**.

- The effective dose (E) is the uniform whole-body dose that results in the same stochastic detriment as any non-uniform pattern of dose.

- A major benefit of the **effective dose** is that it permits all radiological examinations that use ionizing radiations to be directly compared using a single common scale.

B. Computing effective doses

- KAP may be converted to effective dose by taking into account irradiation geometry and x-ray beam quality.

- **PA chest radiographs have E/KAP of ~0.2 mSv/Gy-cm².**

- Effective dose per unit skin dose for **AP chest radiographs is ~0.3 mSv/Gy-cm²**, and for **lateral chest radiographs is ~0.15 mSv/Gy-cm²**.

- For **AP abdominal** radiographs, the effective dose per unit skin dose is **~0.2 mSv/Gy-cm²**.

- E/KAP conversion factor for newborns is an order of magnitude higher than for adults.

- CT DLP doses can be converted into an effective dose using E/DLP conversion factors.

- **E/DLP values for 32-cm diameter phantoms are generally twice as high as E/DLP values for 16-cm diameter phantoms.**

C. Radiography

- The **effective dose** of a chest radiographic examination (**PA + lateral views**) is typically **0.05 mSv (5 mrem)**.

- The effective dose of a complete skull radiographic examination is ~0.1 mSv (10 mrem).

- The effective dose of a complete **abdominal radiographic examination is ~0.5 mSv (50 mrem)**.

- Radiation doses in projection radiography are low in comparison to GI studies, Interventional Radiology, and CT.

D. Fluoroscopy and IR

- Effective doses in GI studies depend on total fluoroscopy time as well as the number of photospot images.

- **Table 11.5** summarizes common fluoroscopy examinations, highlighting increased effective dose as fluoroscopy time and spot images increase.

Table 11.5

Common fluoroscopy exam time, images, and dose information

Type of examination	Typical fluoroscopy time (minutes)	Number of spot films	Effective dose (mSv)
Barium swallow	1 to 2	9 to 15	1 to 2
Upper GI	2 to 3	12 to 15	2 to 4
Barium enema	3 to 5	6 to 12	4 to 8

- Effective doses for a **cardiac catheterization** examination are ~7 mSv (700 mrem).
- Therapeutic catheterization of the heart vessels is likely to result in higher radiation doses.
- **Cerebral angiography** has effective doses that range from **1 to 10 mSv (100–1000 mrem)**.
- Abdominal interventional radiography includes hepatic, renal, mesenteric studies, as well as those of the aorta.
- Typical effective doses in **abdominal angiography** are **~20 mSv (2000 mrem)**.
- **Peripheral angiography** studies have effective doses of **~5 mSv (500 mrem)**.

E. **CT**

- Effective doses in **head CT** scans are **1 to 2 mSv (100–200 mrem)**.
- Effective doses in **chest CT** scans are **5 to 10 mSv (500–1000 mrem)**.
- For a single-phase exam, effective doses in pelvis + abdominal CT scans are 5 to 10 mSv.
- A three-phase exam (pre-contrast, arterial phase, venous phase) would likely triple the patient effective dose.
- Effective doses for CT of the **extremities** would be less than **1 mSv (100 mrem)**.
- **Figure 11.5** shows how CT effective doses vary with age when the amount of radiation used (i.e., DLP) is kept constant.

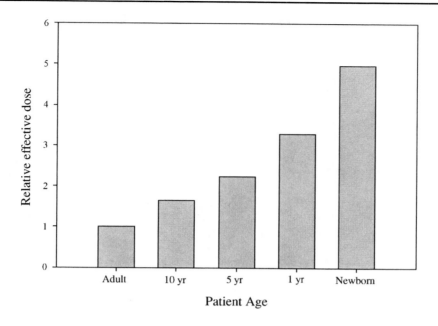

Figure 11.5
Relative effective dose for CT examination as a function
of patient age, showing a large increase when CTDI and DLP
are kept constant for a small patient size.

QUESTIONS

Chapter 11: Radiation Dosimetry

11.1   In the SI system of units, the intensity of an x-ray beam is best measured as:
   A. air kerma.
   B. exposure.
   C. air dose.
   D. equivalent dose.

11.2   An exposure of 1 roentgen may be taken to be an Air Kerma of about _____ mGy.
   A. 0.1
   B. 1
   C. 10
   D. 100

11.3   Absorbed dose is the energy absorbed per unit:
   A. density.
   B. mass.
   C. time.
   D. power.

11.4   The units of equivalent dose are:
   A. C/kg.
   B. dimensionless.
   C. Gy.
   D. Sv.

11.5   The radiation weighting factor for x-rays is _____ .
   A. 1
   B. 2
   C. 10
   D. 20

11.6   When the skin dose in an x-ray examination is 10 mGy, the skin equivalent dose is _____ mSv.
   A. 1
   B. 2
   C. 10
   D. 20

11.7   The Entrance Air Kerma (EAK) is least affected by the x-ray:
A. tube potential (kV).
B. tube current (mA).
C. exposure time (ms).
D. beam area (cm^2).

11.8   Entrance Air Kerma would most likely be measured using:
A. ionization chambers.
B. Geiger Mueller tubes.
C. NaI crystals.
D. photomultiplier tubes.

11.9   Then entrance Air Kerma for a normal-sized adult undergoing abdominal fluoroscopy (PA) is most likely _____ mGy/min.
A. 0.3
B. 3
C. 30
D. 300

11.10   The maximum Air Kerma rate (mGy/minute) in high-dose fluoroscopy is currently:
A. 50.
B. 100.
C. 200.
D. No limit.

11.11   The units of Kerma Area Product (KAP) are:
A. Gy/cm^2
B. Gy-cm^2
C. Gy-cm
D. Gy

11.12   An Air Kerma of 1 mGy would likely correspond to a soft-tissue dose of _____ mGy.
A. 0.5
B. 0.9
C. 1.1
D. 1.5

11.13   An Air Kerma of 1 mGy would likely correspond to a bone dose of _____ mGy.
A. 0.5
B. 1
C. 2
D. 4

11.14   The backscatter factor in diagnostic radiology is most likely _____ .
A. 0.7
B. 1.1
C. 1.4
D. 2.0

11.15   An entrance Air Kerma (free in air) of 1 mGy will most likely result in a skin dose of _____ mGy.
A. 0.75
B. 1.0
C. 1.25
D. 1.5

11.16   Skin dose for a chest radiograph is most likely _____ mGy.
A. 0.15
B. 1.5
C. 15
D. 150

11.17   For an AP projection, the ratio of the embryo dose to the entrance Air Kerma is most likely _____.
A. 1:1
B. 1:2
C. 1:3
D. 1:4

11.18   In 1980, the Genetically Significant Dose (GSD) in the United States was reported to be _____ mGy.
A. 0.003
B. 0.03
C. 0.3
D. 3

11.19   Mean Glandular Doses per image in mammography are most likely _____ mGy.
A. 0.5
B. 1.5
C. 5
D. 15

11.20 Using Automatic Exposure Control (AEC) increasing which x-ray tube parameter is most likely to reduce the mean glandular dose?
A. Current (mA)
B. Exposure time
C. Voltage (kV)
D. Focus size

11.21 Head CTDI doses are measured using an acrylic cylinder with a diameter of _____ cm.
A. 8
B. 16
C. 24
D. 32

11.22 The volume CTDI (CTDI$_{vol}$) is obtained by dividing the weighted CTDI (CTDI$_w$) by the CT:
A. pitch.
B. table speed.
C. gantry rotation time.
D. beam width.

11.23 Volume CTDI (CTDI$_{vol}$) and weighted CTDI (CTDI$_w$) are equal for a pitch ratio of:
A. 0.5.
B. 1.
C. 2.
D. All pitch values.

11.24 A typical adult head CTDI$_{vol}$ would likely be _____ mGy.
A. 2
B. 6
C. 20
D. 60

11.25 Units of Dose-Length Product (DLP) are:
A. mGy
B. mGy/cm
C. mGy-cm
D. (mGy-cm)^2

11.26   The ACR suggests a dose reduction by a factor of _____ from adult to pediatric body CT protocols.
A. 2
B. 3
C. 4
D. 5

11.27   The typical adult effective dose from a chest examination is most likely _____ mSv.
A. 0.05
B. 0.5
C. 5
D. 50

11.28   The typical adult effective dose from an upper GI examination is most likely _____ mSv.
A. 0.03
B. 0.3
C. 3
D. 30

11.29   The typical adult effective dose from a diagnostic cardiac catheterization is most likely _____ mSv.
A. 0.07
B. 0.7
C. 7
D. 70

11.30   The typical adult effective dose from a head CT examination is most likely _____ mSv.
A. 0.2
B. 2
C. 20
D. 200

ANSWERS[1]

Chapter 11: Radiation Dosimetry

11.1	A	Air Kerma is the SI unit used to measure exposure in air or intensity.	*p. 34 Bushong* *p. 140 Carlton/Adler*
11.2	C	One roentgen of exposure is equivalent to approximately 10 mGy Air Kerma.	*p. 34 Bushong* *p. 140 Carlton/Adler*
11.3	B	Absorbed dose is the amount of energy deposited per unit mass (J/kg).	*p. 34 Bushong* *p. 140 Carlton/Adler*
11.4	D	Equivalent dose is measured in sieverts (Sv).	*p. 618 Bushong* *p. 140 Carlton/Adler*
11.5	A	Radiations used in diagnostic radiology all have a radiation weighting factor of 1.	*p. 34 Bushong* *p. 141 Carlton/Adler*
11.6	C	The skin equivalent dose is equal to the skin dose because the x-ray radiation weighting factor is 1.	*p. 635 Bushong* *p. 141 Carlton/Adler*
11.7	D	Entrance Air Kerma values are measured free in air at the entrance skin distance. Any factor that affects beam quantity or quality would affect the EAK, but not the x-ray beam area.	*p. 34 Bushong* *p. 140 Carlton/Adler*
11.8	A	An ionization chamber would be placed free in air at the same location as the entrance skin.	*p. 589 Bushong* *p. 142 Carlton/Adler*
11.9	C	Entrance Air Kerma in fluoroscopy ~30 mGy/min for an average adult.	*n/a Bushong* *p. 579 Carlton/Adler*
11.10	C	*High-dose mode* fluoroscopy is limited to an Air Kerma of 200 mGy/min in the United States.	*p. 311 Bushong* *p. 202 Carlton/Adler*
11.11	B	Kerma Area Product is given in Gy-cm^2.	*n/a Bushong* *n/a Carlton/Adler*
11.12	C	Tissue doses are slightly higher than air doses, so an Air Kerma of 1 mGy results in a tissue dose of 1.1 mGy.	*p. 35 Bushong* *p. 186 Carlton/Adler*

---

[1] As a study aid, page numbers for additional study are given for the following references:
  Bushong SC: *Radiologic Science for Technologists,* 9th ed. St. Louis, MO: Mosby, 2008.
  Carlton RR, Adler AM: *Principles of Radiographic Imaging: An Art and a Science,* 4th ed. Albany, NY: Delmar Publishing Inc., 2005.

11.13	D	Bone doses are much higher than air doses, so an Air Kerma of 1 mGy results in a bone dose of 4 mGy.	*p. 168 Bushong* *p. 186 Carlton/Adler*
11.14	C	Diagnostic radiography has a backscatter factor of ~1.4.	*n/a Bushong* *n/a Carlton/Adler*
11.15	D	Skin doses will be higher than the entrance Air Kerma due to higher absorption in skin and backscatter.	*n/a Bushong* *p. 202 Carlton/Adler*
11.16	A	A skin dose of ~0.15 is typical in chest radiography and an entrance Air Kerma of 1 mGy will result in a skin dose of 1.5 mGy.	*n/a Bushong* *p. 202 Carlton/Adler*
11.17	C	Attenuation in the soft tissues results in the embryo dose that is numerically one-third of the entrance Air Kerma.	*p. 610 Bushong* *n/a Carlton/Adler*
11.18	C	In 1980 the Genetically Significant Dose was estimated at 0.3 mGy by the NCRP.	*p. 601 Bushong* *p. 139 Carlton/Adler*
11.19	B	A mean glandular dose of 1.5 mGy (150 mrad) is common in mammography.	*p. 602 Bushong* *p. 621 Carlton/Adler*
11.20	C	Increasing the kVp allows for a decrease in mAs and an overall dose savings.	*p. 322 Bushong* *p. 614 Carlton/Adler*
11.21	B	A 16-cm acrylic phantom is used for CTDI measurements in adult head protocols.	*n/a Bushong* *n/a Carlton/Adler*
11.22	A	The volume CTDI is obtained by dividing the weighted CTDI by the pitch.	*n/a Bushong* *n/a Carlton/Adler*
11.23	B	A pitch of 1 results in equal values of weighted and volume CTDI.	*n/a Bushong* *n/a Carlton/Adler*
11.24	D	A $CTDI_{vol}$ of ~60 Gy is typical for an adult head CT.	*p. 603 Bushong* *p. 667 Carlton/Adler*
11.25	C	The DLP is calculated by multiplying the $CTDI_{vol}$ by scan length, resulting in a value measured in mGy-cm.	*p. 635 Bushong* *n/a Carlton/Adler*
11.26	B	Pediatric body scans typically use 3 times less radiation than adult scans.	*n/a Bushong* *n/a Carlton/Adler*
11.27	A	A chest exam, PA and lateral, has an effective dose of ~0.05 mSv.	*n/a Bushong* *n/a Carlton/Adler*
11.28	C	An effective dose of ~3 mSv is typical.	*n/a Bushong* *n/a Carlton/Adler*

11.29   C   A cardiac catheterization (diagnostic) has an effective dose   *n/a Bushong*
                of ~7 mSv.   *n/a Carlton/Adler*

11.30   B   Head CT scans in adults have effective doses of ~2 mSv.   *n/a Bushong*
                                                                                     n/a Carlton/Adler

Chapter 12

IMAGE QUALITY

12.1 Resolution (Theory)
12.2 Resolution (Practice)
12.3 Contrast
12.4 Noise
12.5 Radiographic Artifacts

12.1 RESOLUTION (THEORY)

A. What is resolution?

- **Resolution** is an imaging system's ability to differentiate two adjacent objects as independent.

- Resolution may also be described as **spatial resolution, high-contrast resolution, sharpness, detail,** or **blur**.

- Imaging systems with good resolution will show adjacent structures as individual and separate.

- Imaging systems with poor resolution will show adjacent structures as one larger, blurry-edged structure.

- Resolution may be measured using **specialized tools** that are designed with a **high subject contrast.**

- **A loss of resolution occurs because of blur caused by focal spot size, image receptor size, and motion.**

B. Line pairs and MTF

- Resolution in radiography and mammography is expressed in **line pairs per millimeter (lp/mm).**

- A **line pair** consists of **a lead bar and an interspace of equal dimension (Figure 12.1).**

- Calculating object size is done by **dividing the distance (mm) by the number of objects.**

- For example, 1 lp/mm represents 2 objects, where one is a 0.5 mm lead bar and the other a 0.5 mm interspace.

- The smaller the object, the higher the line pairs per millimeter, and vice versa.

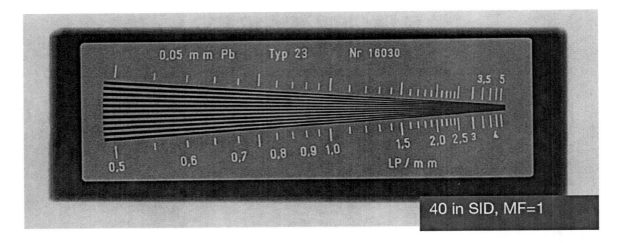

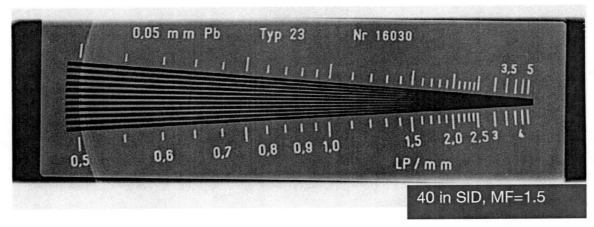

Figure 12.1
Line pair phantom radiograph without magnification (a) and with magnification (b).

- The **human eye is limited to 5 lp/mm** at a 25-cm viewing distance.
- With closer inspection the human eye can resolve 30 lp/mm.
- The **Modulation Transfer Function (MTF)** is also used to describe resolution.
- The MTF is a graphical representation of the **ratio of the output to input signal amplitude as a function of spatial frequency.**
- An **MTF of 1.0 is a perfect replication of the object imaged.**
- An MTF close to 1.0 is more likely with larger objects that correspond to low spatial frequencies.

- An MTF of 0.1 is more likely with very small objects that correspond to high spatial frequencies.

C. Motion blur

- **Motion creates blur in an image.**
- Motion can be that of the **patient, tube,** or **image receptor.**
- Patient motion is the most likely to affect image quality.
- Patient motion may be **voluntary,** i.e., lowering an arm during a lateral chest image.
- Patient motion is also **involuntary,** i.e., cardiac motion.
- The use of high mA and the **shortest exposure time** reduces the likelihood of motion.
- The use of high mA stations may be limited due to focal spot loading.
- **Clear instructions** and use of **immobilization devices** reduce patient motion.

D. Focal spot blur

- The focal spot has a finite **area resulting in blurred images.**
- The blurring at the edges of objects is described as **penumbra.**
- The **penumbra** results from x-ray production at slightly different locations within the focal spot.
- The inherent blur caused by an area focal spot is known as **focal spot blur** or **geometric unsharpness.**
- **Focal spot blur is directly related to focal spot size.**
- Very small, pointlike focal spots have negligible focal spot blur.
- Geometric factors that **increase magnification** also **increase focal spot blur (Figure 12.1).**
- **Magnification radiography generally increases large object-to-image receptor distances (OIDs), and smaller focal spots must be used to minimize focal spot blur.**
- Magnification mammography increases visibility of small structures, such as microcalcifications.
- Interventional radiography employs magnification imaging in angiography procedures.

E. Receptor blur

- The ability of a system to resolve objects is **limited by the size of the detector**.
- **Direct capture film** provides the **highest resolution** in radiography.
- Screens used in radiography **limit the resolution**.
- Light produced from the absorption of x-rays in the screen spread prior to reaching the film.
- **Increased screen speeds** are thicker and therefore **have a loss of resolution (more blur)**.
- **Digital systems are detail limited to the pixel size.**
- Digital systems cannot display objects less than pixel size.
- **Fluoroscopy resolution is dependent on the width of the TV line.**
- **CT detector elements limit the detail** that can be recorded.
- **Image receptor thickness or size must be smaller than the objects of radiological interest.**

12.2 RESOLUTION (PRACTICE)

A. Radiographic resolution

- **Direct capture film** has a resolution of **~100 lp/mm**.
- Direct capture film resolution is controlled by the size of the grains in film emulsion.
- **200-speed screen-film** systems have a resolution of **5 lp/mm**.
- **Mammography** screen-film systems have a resolution of **15 lp/mm**.
- ACR accreditation requires mammography resolution to be 11 lp/mm perpendicular to the anode-cathode axis and 13 lp/mm parallel to the axis.
- **Digital imaging resolution** requires knowledge of the **sampling frequency, matrix, and pixel size**.
- **Table 12.1** shows the effect of sampling frequency and pixel size on resolution.
- A chest image has a matrix of 2k × 2.5k and is 35 cm × 43 cm in size.
- A sampling frequency in the chest image is 2k over the 35 cm width, 5.7 per mm.
- **Limiting resolution is half the sampling frequency, 2.9 lp/mm.**
- Flat-panel image receptors have a constant sampling frequency, and their resolution is independent of FOV.

Table 12.1
Relationship between pixel size, sampling frequency,
and limiting spatial resolution in medical imaging

Pixel size mm (µm)	Sampling frequency (pixels per mm)	Limiting spatial resolution (line pairs per mm)
0.05 (50)	20	10
0.10 (100)	10	5
0.15 (150)	6.7	3.4
0.20 (200)	5	2.5

B. Image intensifiers (IIs) and TVs

- **Image-intensified fluoroscopy resolution is controlled by the input phosphor, generally cesium iodide (CsI).**
- CsI is manufactured as pinlike crystal, resulting in limited light divergence.
- **CsI image intensifier tubes** have a limiting resolution of **5 lp/mm.**
- In television systems, the **number of TV lines** controls the **vertical resolution.**
- A TV system **line pair** is composed of **one black line** and **one white line.**
- A TV system with N lines should be able to show N/2 line pairs.
- In practice, however, TV systems show 30% less than N/2, and this loss is known as the **Kell factor.**
- Increasing from a 500- to a 1000-line system has twice the limiting vertical spatial resolution.
- **Bandwidth** describes the TV system's ability to modulate the electronics across a TV line and controls **horizontal resolution.**
- A **525-line TV system** has a **5 MHz** bandwidth, and a **1000-line TV system** has a **20 MHz** bandwidth.
- Horizontal and vertical TV system resolutions are designed to be similar.

C. Fluoroscopy resolution

- **Small focal spots** used in fluoroscopy results in negligible focal spot blur.
- The TV system, however, greatly reduces fluoroscopy resolution.

- A typical fluoroscopy resolution is 1 lp/mm.
- **The use of magnification mode, electronic zoom, improves resolution.**
- **Magnification mode** electronically limits the FOV.
- A doubling of resolution results from halving the FOV electronically.
- When the magnification mode is fixed, resolution is not affected by any changes in x-ray beam collimation.

D. Digital photospot imaging

- **Digital photospot images** are normally obtained **using the image intensifier imaging chain.**
- The **weak link** in the II imaging chain is the **TV camera.**
- **Digital photospot** imaging therefore requires a **high-quality TV system.**
- Digital photospot imaging uses a high-resolution 1000-line TV system.
- The **sampling frequency** of digital photospot is **4 per mm.**
- **Digital photospot** imaging has a limiting resolution of **2 lp/mm.**
- **Digital subtraction angiography (DSA)** also has a **2 lp/mm** resolution.
- Flat-panel detectors are beginning to replace image intensifiers.
- **Resolution of a flat-panel detector is ~3 lp/mm.**
- **Table 12.2** shows representative limiting resolution values in radiology.

Table 12.2

Representative values of limiting spatial resolution in projection radiography

Imaging modality	Limiting resolution (line pairs per mm)	Relative resolution* (%)
Fluoroscopy	1	7
DSA/Digital photospot	2	13
Digital radiography	3	20
Screen–film radiography	5	33
Digital mammography	7	47
Screen–film mammography	15	100

*Screen–film mammography 100%

E. CT resolution

- Typical **body CT** uses an **FOV of 350 mm** and a **matrix of 512**.
- The sampling frequency is 1.4 pixels per mm and the resulting **limiting spatial resolution is 0.7 lp/mm**.
- Typical **head imaging** uses an **FOV of 250 mm** and a **matrix of 512**.
- The sampling frequency is 2 pixels per mm and resulting **limiting spatial resolution is 1 lp/mm**.
- In CT, resolutions can also be expressed in lp/cm where 1 lp/mm corresponds to 10 lp/cm.
- Focal spot and detector blur limit improvements in CT resolution.
- **In-plane resolution (x, y axis)** may be improved by reducing the reconstruction field of view (FOV).
- For example, **pixel size = FOV/matrix** (320 mm/512 = 0.625 mm pixel).
- Use of a **detail reconstruction filter** provides the **best spatial resolution**.
- **MDCT longitudinal resolution (z axis)** is dependent on **detector width**.
- MDCT with 64 (or more) detector arrays provides **isotropic resolution of ~0.7 lp/mm**.
- CT imaging has a much lower limiting spatial resolution than radiography (see **Table 12.2**).

12.3 CONTRAST

A. Subject contrast

- **Subject contrast** is the difference in intensity at the image receptor for different tissues.
- The **differential attenuation** of the x-ray beam between a lesion and its background allows the lesion to be visualized.
- Lesion size, density, and atomic number all affect subject contrast.
- Use of contrast materials (air, iodine, barium, etc.) increases subject contrast.
- **Contrast agents** with increased density and atomic number have **increasing differential absorption**.
- **Scatter radiation** reaching the image receptor reduces contrast.
- **Grids** are used to prevent scatter radiation from reaching the image receptor.
- **Grid use results in increased contrast.**
- Subject contrast must be present for image contrast to be visible.

B. Film contrast

- Film contrast depends not only on subject contrast but also on **film density** and **film contrast.**

- Film density must be in the appropriate range for image contrast evaluation.

- A film with a **mean optical density of ~1.5** results from proper exposure.

- **Underexposed** films have optical densities below 0.5 OD.

- **Overexposed** films have optical densities above 2.0 OD.

- Under- and overexposures will markedly reduce image contrast.

- **Film contrast** is measured by the **slope of the characteristic curve.**

- The mean slope between 0.25 OD and 2.0 OD represents the **film gradient.**

- **Film gradients greater than 1 amplify subject contrast.**

- **Radiographic film** gradients of **2** are common, whereas **mammography film** gradients are **3** or higher.

- **Table 12.3** provides examples of common film types used in Radiology.

Table 12.3
Film type, average gradient, and use in radiology

Film type	Gradient	Comments
Chest	2.0	Low film gradient required due to high subject contrast
Extremity	2.2	Lower film gradient required due to high subject contrast
Abdomen	2.5	Increased film gradient required due to moderate subject contrast
Mammography	3.5	Markedly increased film gradient required due to minimal subject contrast

C. Latitude and contrast

- **Film latitude** is used to describe the range of exposure that results in good image visibility (contrast).

- Film latitude is **inversely related** to film contrast.

- Films with higher gradients have a narrower range of exposure.

- A **wide latitude film** is described as having a **low image contrast**.
- Wide latitude films have a large range of exposures that produce satisfactory images.
- Wide latitude or low-contrast film is used for high subject contrast examinations.
- The chest is a **high subject contrast** area—air-filled lungs and mediastinum—that does not require an amplification of subject contrast.
- Mammography is a **low subject contrast** exam and requires an amplification of subject contrast.
- **High-contrast film is required to differentiate soft tissues within the breast.**

D. Digital contrast

- Image contrast in digital imaging is dependent on the monitor brightness of a lesion and its background.
- Digital image contrast can also be affected by **digital processing**.
- The digital image contrast display may be **adjusted by window controls**.
- Display contrast is controlled through the use of **window level and window width**.
- **Window width is inversely related to display image contrast.**
- Wide window width results in a low-contrast image and vice versa.
- Images may be obtained with low inherent contrast and displayed digitally with a higher contrast.
- Decreasing window width increases display image contrast.
- **Digital imaging also allows for multiple displays of contrast images to be viewed,** i.e., analysis of a chest image under low- and high-contrast displays.

E. Contrast and photon energy

- **Photon energy is a controlling factor for subject contrast.**
- **Low-energy x-ray beams** result in **high subject contrast**.
- Low-energy x-ray beams result in marked intensity differences between imaged tissues.
- **Increasing average photon energy decreases the intensity difference between tissues.**
- Increasing the kVp or adding filtration will increase the average photon energy.
- Maintaining adequate patient penetration must always be taken into account before any adjustment to the optimal choice of kVp.
- **Improved visualization of an iodine-contrast–filled structure can generally be achieved by reducing the kVp.**

- Decreasing CT kVp from 120 kVp to 80 kVp, for example, is common in vascular imaging.
- **Figure 12.2** shows the effect of changing kVp on image contrast in film radiography.
- A high-contrast image may also be described as having a narrow latitude, whereas a low-contrast image is said to have a wide latitude.

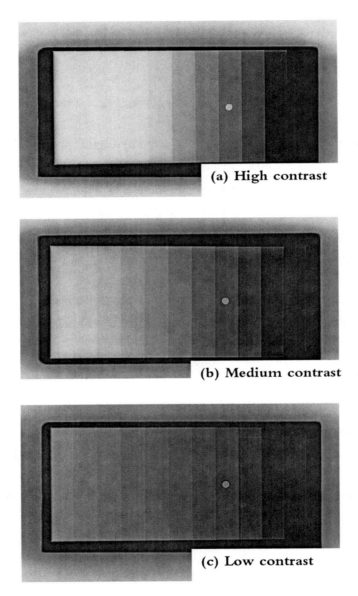

Figure 12.2
Radiograph of a step wedge showing three levels
of contrast. Image (a) utilized 55 kVp; (b) and
(c) used 65 and 75 kVp, respectively.

12.4 NOISE

A. What is noise?

- **Noise is the random variation in image intensity at a constant intensity (exposure).**
- Noise affects the ability to view lesions and other pathologies.
- Increasing the noise level reduces the ability to visualize the lesion.
- High noise levels prevent the detectability of low-contrast structures.
- In radiology, **noise (random) is often referred to as mottle.**
- **At a constant Air Kerma, random fluctuations in x-ray intensity** result in a grainy (i.e., mottled) image appearance.
- The number of photons incident on a detector determines the quantum mottle.
- Quantum mottle is inversely related to the number or intensity of photons at the detector.
- **Increasing the intensity,** Air Kerma, incident **at the detector will decrease mottle.**
- **Table 12.4** shows the relationship between x-ray exposure (number of x-rays) and noise.
- A satisfactory chest radiograph is produced when about 5 μGy (0.5 mR) is incident on the image receptor.

Table 12.4

Relationship between the numbers of x-ray photons used to make a radiograph, and the corresponding noise level

Average number of x-ray photons (per pixel)	Fluctuations in pixel value (standard deviation)
100	±10%
1000	±3%
10,000	±1%
100,000	±0.3%

B. Projection radiography

- **Screen-film image mottle is a combination of screen, film, and quantum mottle.**
- **Screen mottle** results from non-uniformity in the screen and is minimal.
- **Film mottle** results from the granular structure of film emulsion and is minimal.
- **Quantum mottle** is the major source of noise in a screen-film image.
- A typical exposure in chest radiography is **5 μGy**, which determines the amount of mottle in the resultant image.

- **Screen thickness does not affect mottle because** although thicker screens absorb more of the incident x-rays, fewer x-rays are incident on the receptor.
- The increase in absorbed photons due to increased thickness offsets the reduced exposure in regard to mottle.
- **CR requires more radiation** than screen-film to maintain the same level of noise.
- Thin phosphor layers are essential to minimize light scatter during read out, which reduces x-ray absorption.
- **CsI detectors require less exposure** than screen-film to maintain the same level of noise because they absorb more of the incident radiation.

C. Fluoroscopy/Spot imaging

- **Fluoroscopy uses low mA techniques,** which increases image mottle.
- Fluoroscopy (analog and digital) Air Kerma at the II is ~0.01 μGy per frame.
- Fluoroscopy **quantum mottle is significantly more** than in radiography.
- **Digital fluoroscopy** allows for multiple frames to be averaged.
- **Averaging images decreases mottle and increases image lag.**
- **A photospot image requires one-fifth the exposure of a radiograph at the receptor.**
- A photospot **Air Kerma at the image receptor is ~1 μGy.**
- Digital subtraction angiography (DSA) images have no anatomical information.
- The **lack of background** anatomy **increases the visibility of mottle;** it is more apparent.
- **DSA imaging** combines two images, **increasing the mottle level.**
- **DSA requires much greater Air Kerma at the image receptor to achieve a clinically acceptable level of quantum mottle.**
- **Air Kerma at the detector in DSA imaging is ~5 μGy (0.5 mR).**

D. CT

- **CT quantum mottle** is determined by the number of x-ray photons used.
- **Random fluctuations** in intensity result in a **~3 HU variation within the image.**
- An image of a water phantom results with 68% of pixels with HU between 0 and ±3.
- The number of photons used to create an image is directly proportional to the mAs.
- **Quadrupling the mAs would halve the mottle in a CT image.**
- **Figure 12.3** shows CT images exposed at increasing mAs values, resulting in decreasing noise levels.
- Increasing the slice thickness will also decrease mottle.
- **Doubling a slice thickness will double the number of photons available.**

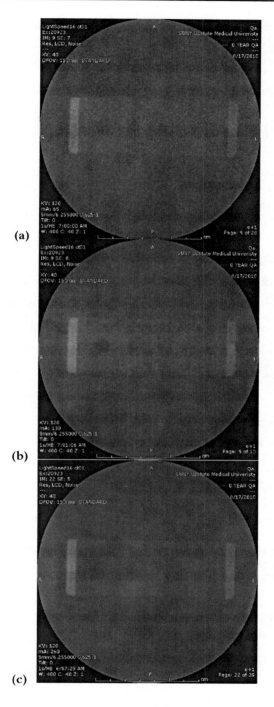

Figure 12.3

CT images of a low contrast phantom
at varying exposure and noise levels.
Images (a), (b), and (c) utilized 65 mAs, 130 mAs,
and 260 mAs, respectively. Resulting noise levels
(standard deviations) were measured to be 8.3, 5.3, and 2.9.

- In practice, four 1 mm acquired slices, viewed as one 4-mm slice, will have half the mottle.
- **Reconstruction filter** selection contributes to the noise in an image.
- Reconstruction filters used to **increase spatial resolution** (i.e., detail) **also increase noise.**
- Reconstruction filters used to **decrease noise** (i.e., standard) **also decrease spatial resolution.**

E. Contrast detail phantoms

- **Low-contrast detectability** describes the ability to differentiate a lesion from the background where the image's contrast difference is minimal.
- Low-contrast detectability is sometimes called **contrast resolution.**
- **The curve is a plot of the perceivable object size as a function of contrast.**
- Contrast detail phantoms **have drilled holes arranged in rows and columns.**
- The **rows have varying size**, ranging from "large" to "small."
- The **columns vary in depth**, to mimic different attenuation (i.e., contrast) levels.
- The result is a phantom of both varying size and contrast differences.
- High-contrast objects are easily seen, even when small.
- Low-contrast objects are easily seen when large.
- A **contrast detail curve** provides an overview of an imaging systems performance.

12.5 RADIOGRAPHIC ARTIFACTS

A. Film

- Boxes of film should be stored on end (like books on a shelf) to prevent pressure marks.
- Rough treatment of a film may result in an **increased density mark, scratches/kink marks.**
- **Static artifacts** are a concern in the darkroom with three types of static occur: **tree, crown, and smudge.**
- Static is prevented through proper humidity and temperature levels (~65 °F and 40% humidity).
- **Improper spectral matching** of the safelight and film results in artifacts.
- **Pressure marks add density** to the image and are caused by the transport system.
- **Pick off** marks remove emulsion from the base, **decreasing density**, which can be caused by dirty transport rollers and misaligned guideshoes.

- **Pi lines add density** to the image in a linear pattern **opposite film travel 3.14 inches apart.**
- Pi lines are caused by poor alignment or increased pressure between transport rollers.
- **Wet pressure sensitization marks increase density** caused by dirty rollers in the developer.
- With **hypo retention**, over time film becomes brown-yellow in color.

B. Screen–film

- Often **artifacts are objects left on a patient during imaging,** i.e., jewelry or eyeglasses.
- **Patient motion** is considered an artifact that can be minimized by using clear patient instructions and use of an appropriate **immobilization device.**
- **Backscatter artifacts** may be seen in examinations where high-intensity backscatter will expose the imaging plate.
- Misalignment of the tube to the grid or incorrect SID results in **grid cutoff.**
- Poor **film/screen contact** will cause areas of blur on an image.
- **Screen-film mammography** is performed with a single screen and single-emulsion film.
- Single-emulsion film has a **thicker emulsion layer** and is prone to more processor artifacts.
- Dirt or debris in the image receptor can mimic microcalcifications.
- **Table 12.5** lists common screen-film system artifacts and examples are shown in **Figure 12.4.**

Table 12.5
Common artifacts and their cause

Artifact source	Artifact	Cause	Appearance
Film Handling	Static	Low humidity	Positive density: artifact shown as crown, smudge, or tree patterns
	Scratches	Improper handling of film	Positive density artifact with no pattern
Processor	Pi Lines	Pressure from rollers	Positive density linear artifact perpendicular to film travel
	Guideshoe marks	Scratch from guide shoe	Negative density linear artifact parallel to film travel
Exposure	Fog	Exposure to x-ray/light/ heat	Positive density may or may not have a pattern
	Double exposure	Use of same image receptor for two exposures	Positive density: artifact showing two anatomical images superimposed

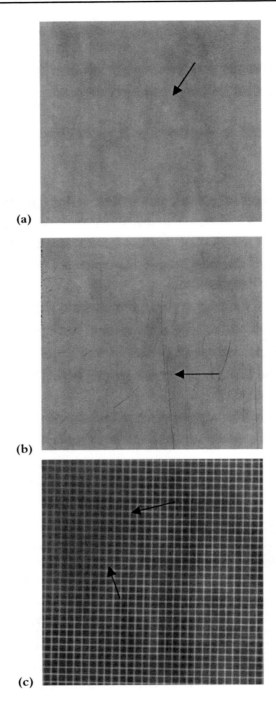

Figure 12.4
Medley of screen film artifacts:
(a) shows debris in a film/screen cassette;
(b) demonstrates scratches to film emulsion;
and (c) illustrates poor film/screen contact (blur).

C. Digital

- CR imaging plates are prone to **ghosting**, a slight residual image of prior exposures.
- A complete **erasure cycle** is required to remove residual image data from the imaging plate.
- Daily erasure of all cassettes is required to maintain a satisfactory performance.
- CR plates have an unlimited life span if maintained properly.
- **Figure 12.5** shows examples of the common digital system artifacts.
- **Software artifacts** are specific to **digital imaging**.
- **Dead pixels** or rows of pixels will cause artifact in an image.
- **Irregular intensity** at the image receptor will induce artifact.
- Calibration images are taken to correct for such variation.
- Each radiographic projection has a **characteristic histogram** and must be processed by an algorithm that is specific to this histogram.
- If the incorrect histogram is selected, the **raw data are processed incorrectly**, which results in **poor image quality**.

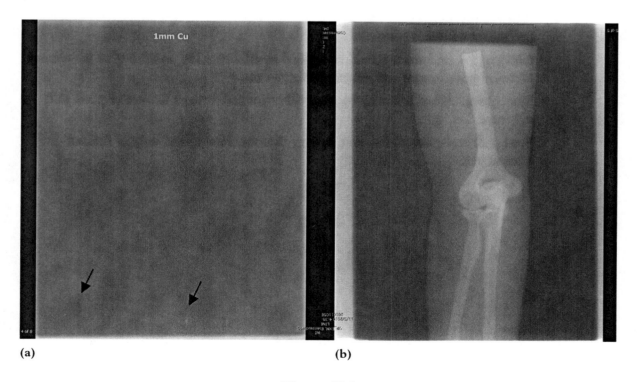

(a)   (b)

Figure 12.5

Digital imaging artifacts: (a) scratches on a CR imaging plate; (b) image processing error.

D. Fluoroscopy

- **Pincushion distortion** results from an image captured on a curved surface but displayed on a flat surface.
- Pincushion distortion appears like one looking at a fun house mirror.
- **Veiling glare** occurs when moving from a low attenuating part to a high attenuating part, i.e., chest to abdomen.
- **Vignetting** is a loss of brightness at the periphery of an image.
- **S distortion** creates a wavelike artifact in the image.
- External magnetic fields affect the electrons crossing the II, resulting in S distortion.

E. Interventional Radiology

- The use of **DSA** in Interventional Radiology (IR) is **highly susceptible to motion artifacts**.
- Patient motion such as breathing, cardiac motion, and gross patient movement lead to misregistration.
- **Misregistration** occurs when the mask image and the resulting image's anatomy do not align.
- When performing DSA with a portable C-arm, such as in operating room imaging, equipment motion is possible.
- Locks to the equipment should be applied to **minimize the possibility of movement** between mask images and subsequent exposures.
- Misregistration artifacts may be removed or limited through the use of **pixel shift software**.
- Pixel shift realignment, however, is **very time consuming** and **only of limited clinical use**.

QUESTIONS

Chapter 12: Image Quality

12.1   High spatial frequencies (line pairs per mm) most likely represent features that are:
   A. small.
   B. intermediate.
   C. large.
   D. any size.

12.2   The limiting resolution would most likely correspond to an MTF value of _____%.
   A. 100
   B. 75
   C. 50
   D. 10

12.3   Motion blur is best minimized by reducing the:
   A. focal spot size.
   B. exposure time.
   C. tube current.
   D. tube voltage.

12.4   Which type of radiograph is most likely to have the least magnification?
   A. Chest
   B. Extremity
   C. Abdomen
   D. Skull

12.5   Which is least likely to affect spatial resolution?
   A. Receptor thickness
   B. Patient motion
   C. X-ray intensity
   D. Focal size

12.6   Which would result in the worst spatial resolution?
   A. Screen-film mammography
   B. Screen-film radiography
   C. DR mammography
   D. CR radiography

12.7   What is most likely to limit the visibility of small details in digital radiographs?
   A. Pixel size
   B. Window width
   C. Window level
   D. Bit depth

12.8   For a fixed matrix size, the best spatial resolution will be for a CR cassette size of:
   A. 20 cm × 24 cm
   B. 30 cm × 20 cm
   C. 35 cm × 43 cm
   D. Independent of cassette size

12.9   The effect on spatial resolution by increased *collimation* in fluoroscopy is most likely:
   A. an improvement.
   B. no change.
   C. deterioration.
   D. cannot be determined.

12.10   Doubling the image matrix size in digital radiography will reduce the pixel size by _____ %.
   A. 10
   B. 20
   C. 30
   D. 50

12.11   Doubling the image matrix size in digital radiography will reduce the pixel area by _____ %.
   A. 4
   B. 25
   C. 50
   D. 75

12.12   Subject contrast is best increased by increasing the lesion:
   A. area.
   B. thickness.
   C. density.
   D. atomic number.

12.13   Subject contrast is independent of:
A. x-ray intensity.
B. tube voltage.
C. voltage ripple.
D. beam filtration.

12.14   If a lesion has a density of D_l, and the surrounding tissues have a density of D_b, the lesion contrast is:
A. $D_b + D_l$.
B. $(D_b + D_l)^{0.5}$.
C. $D_b - D_l$.
D. $(D_b - D_l)^{0.5}$.

12.15   Film contrast is most likely influenced by:
A. film gamma.
B. base + fog.
C. max density.
D. film thickness.

12.16   Image contrast is best increased (improved) by decreasing:
A. exposure time.
B. tube current.
C. SID.
D. tube voltage.

12.17   Which technique factor is most likely to affect image contrast?
A. mA
B. kVp
C. s
D. mAs

12.18   If the average pixel absorbs 100 x-rays, the standard deviation is most likely _____ .
A. 1
B. 10
C. 100
D. 1000

12.19   The least likely source of noise in a screen-film radiograph is:
A. film graininess.
B. structure mottle.
C. digitization noise.
D. quantum mottle.

12.20   Photostimulable phosphors require _____ exposure levels compared to screen-film systems displaying the same image noise.
A. increased
B. decreased
C. equivalent
D. none of the above

12.21   Improvements in image quality are best described by an increase in:
A. contrast.
B. noise.
C. noise/contrast.
D. contrast/noise.

12.22   When the tube current and exposure time are both doubled, the resultant increase in contrast-to-noise ratio (%) is most likely:
A. 50% higher.
B. doubled.
C. tripled.
D. quadrupled.

12.23.   A contrast detail phantom most likely has lesions that have varying:
A. size and contrast.
B. size and shape.
C. contrast and shape.
D. none of the above.

12.24   Which is least likely a film processing artifact?
A. Pressure mark
B. Pick off
C. Pi line
D. Double exposure

12.25   Static artifacts are minimized by keeping a humidity of _____ %.
A. 0
B. 10
C. 40
D. 80

12.26   Single-emulsion film is most susceptible to which of the following?
A.   Static artifacts
B.   Processor artifacts
C.   Poor film/screen contact
D.   Grid cutoff

12.27   The maximum cumulative radiation exposure for a CR plate is most likely _____ Gy.
A.   100
B.   1000
C.   10,000
D.   Unlimited

12.28   Histogram error is most likely to be encountered in:
A.   CT.
B.   fluoroscopy.
C.   digital radiography.
D.   screen-film.

12.29   Pixel shift image processing is most likely encountered in:
A.   Interventional Radiology.
B.   mammography.
C.   extremity radiography.
D.   CT

12.30   External magnetic fields may induce which of the following artifacts?
A.   Pincushion distortion
B.   S distortion
C.   Veiling glare
D.   Vignetting

ANSWERS[1]

Chapter 12: Image Quality

12.1   A   High spatial frequencies represent small objects.
p. 450 Bushong
p. 438 Carlton/Adler

12.2   D   Limiting resolution is measured at an MTF of 0.1.
p. 452 Bushong
p. 441 Carlton/Adler

12.3   B   Patient motion may be involuntary and can be minimized with short exposure times.
p. 293 Bushong
p. 451 Carlton/Adler

12.4   B   Extremities have the lowest OID, therefore the least amount of magnification.
p. 284 Bushong
p. 445 Carlton/Adler

12.5   C   Spatial resolution is not affected by exposure (intensity).
p. 284 Bushong
p. 444 Carlton/Adler

12.6   D   Computed radiography (CR) has a resolution of ~3 lp/mm, which is lower than screen-film systems and digital mammography.
p. 453 Bushong
p. 367 Carlton/Adler

12.7   A   Digital imaging resolution is limited by the pixel size.
p. 431 Bushong
p. 359 Carlton/Adler

12.8   A   The smallest image receptor size should be used in CR imaging as it uses smaller pixels and offers better spatial resolution.
n/a Bushong
n/a Carlton/Adler

12.9   B   Simply collimating the x-ray beam in fluoroscopy has no effect on special resolution.
n/a Bushong
n/a Carlton/Adler

12.10   D   Doubling the matrix size halves the pixel size.
p. 376 Bushong
p. 346 Carlton/Adler

12.11   D   Doubling the matrix size reduces the pixel size by 50% and pixel area by 75%. For example, a 2-mm pixel has an area of 4 mm^2, whereas a 1-mm pixel has an area of 1 mm^2.
p. 376 Bushong
p. 346 Carlton/Adler

---

[1] As a study aid, page numbers for additional study are given for the following references:
Bushong SC: *Radiologic Science for Technologists,* 9th ed. St. Louis, MO: Mosby, 2008.
Carlton RR, Adler AM: *Principles of Radiographic Imaging: An Art and a Science,* 4th ed. Albany, NY: Delmar Publishing Inc., 2005.

12.12	D	Atomic number is the most important determinant of x-ray attenuation and has the greatest impact on subject contrast.	*p. 168 Bushong* *p. 188 Carlton/Adler*
12.13	A	X-ray beam intensity does not affect subject contrast.	*p. 169 Bushong* *p. 188 Carlton/Adler*
12.14	C	The lesion contrast is the difference from the background to that of the lesion.	*p. 290 Bushong* *p. 423 Carlton/Adler*
12.15	A	Film contrast is affected by the film gradient and film gamma.	*p. 279 Bushong* *p. 311 Carlton/Adler*
12.16	D	Decreasing kVp increases differential absorption and leads to a higher image contrast.	*p. 172 Bushong* *p. 430 Carlton/Adler*
12.17	B	kVp affects the attenuation within the patient, thus influencing image contrast.	*p. 279 Bushong* *p. 430 Carlton/Adler*
12.18	B	The **standard deviation** of the number of x-ray photons is the square root of the average value. The square root of 100 is 10.	*n/a Bushong* *n/a Carlton/Adler*
12.19	C	Image mottle in film/screen systems may come from the film, structure mottle, and quantum mottle, but cannot occur due to digitization noise (no digitization in film/screen).	*p. 274 Bushong* *pp. 347 & 442 Carlton/Adler*
12.20	A	CR systems require increased exposure compared to screen-film for equivalent noise levels.	*p. 422 Bushong* *p. 367 Carlton/Adler*
12.21	D	Contrast-to-noise ratio is a practical indicator of relative image quality for a given type of lesion.	*p. 457 Bushong* *p. 347 Carlton/Adler*
12.22	B	When both the exposure time and mA are doubled, it is equivalent to a 4× increase in exposure or halving of the noise.	*p. 457 Bushong* *p. 347 Carlton/Adler*
12.23	A	A contrast detail phantom has different lesion sizes and has different contrast.	*p. 457 Bushong* *n/a Carlton/Adler*
12.24	D	Double exposures are independent of film processing and processing artifacts.	*p. 298 Bushong* *n/a Carlton/Adler*
12.25	C	Humidity levels above 40% will minimize static artifacts.	*p. 190 Bushong* *p. 279 Carlton/Adler*
12.26	B	Single-emulsion film is highly susceptible to processor artifacts because they use thicker emulsions.	*n/a Bushong* *n/a Carlton/Adler*

12.27	D	CR imaging plates do not have a specific useful life span; they may be used indefinitely or until they are deemed damaged (e.g., scratched).	*n/a Bushong* *n/a Carlton/Adler*
12.28	C	Histogram errors occur in digital imaging when the wrong examination is selected at the workstation and incorrect algorithms are applied to the image data.	*p. 494 Bushong* *p. 364 Carlton/Adler*
12.29	A	Pixel shift is used to eliminate misregistration in a digitally subtracted image.	*p. 473 Bushong* *p. 634 Carlton/Adler*
12.30	B	External magnetic fields disrupt electron direction within the CRT, causing S distortion.	*p. 352 Bushong* *n/a Carlton/Adler*

Chapter 13

QUALITY CONTROL

13.1 Overview
13.2 Image Receptors
13.3 X-Ray Systems
13.4 Computed Tomography (CT)

13.1 OVERVIEW

A. Quality assurance

- **Quality assurance (QA)** deals with policy centered on the human aspects of a department and also addresses procedures.
- **QA involves the technologist, physicist, and radiologist.**
- **Technologists** participate in policy and procedure development, scheduling activities, and record maintenance.
- **Physicists** act as advisors on policies and procedures, technique management, and adherence to regulatory and accreditation guidelines.
- **Radiologists** act as advisors on policies and procedures, provide staff/patient education, and maintain appropriate report practices.

B. Quality control

- **Quality control (QC)** is involved with the testing of radiographic systems, as well as ancillary equipment (e.g., processor).
- QC testing is done upon **installation of equipment**.
- Tests are also performed **after major part replacement**.
- QC programs require testing at predetermined time intervals.
- **QC testing** ranges from simple to fairly complex (i.e., that is characterized by **Levels I, II, and III**) as shown in **Table 13.1**.
- Level I testing can be performed by most technologists.
- Level II testing requires a technologist with additional education and experience.
- **Figure 13.1** shows examples of equipment used by the technologist for QC activities.

Table 13.1
Levels of testing, who performs task with examples

Level of testing	Performed by	Description
I	Technologist	Non invasive and simple, e.g., hyporetention
II	Specially trained technologist	Non invasive and complex, i.e., linearity
III	Physicist or Service Engineer	Invasive and complex, i.e., voltage waveform

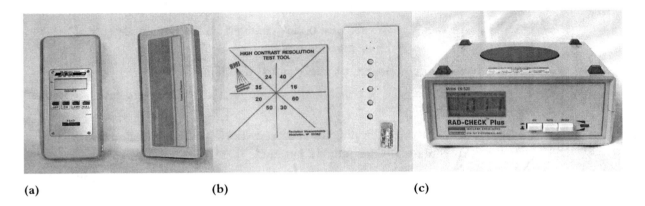

(a)   (b)   (c)

Figure 13.1
Examples of QC test tools used in radiography: (a) densitometer/sensitometer;
(b) resolution test tool/grid alignment tool; and (c) a dosimeter.

- Physicists or service engineers perform Level III testing.
- Level III testing requires disassembly of the equipment and use of specialized equipment.
- **A physicist reviews all QC results.**

C. Professional bodies

- The **American Registry of Radiologic Technologists (ARRT)** is a credentialing organization.
- ARRT tests and **certifies technologists** in Radiography, Computed Tomography, Mammography, and Magnetic Resonance.

- ARRT requires **continuing education** and **adherence to a code of ethics** for registered technologists.

- The **American Association of Physicists in Medicine (AAPM)** is a professional organization focused on scientific investigation and education.

- AAPM holds symposiums and annual meetings that present scientific research and the latest in educational programs in medical physics.

- The **Conference of Radiation Control Program Directors (CRCPD)** is a professional organization dedicated to radiation protection.

- CRCPD membership consists of **state** and **local government radiation professionals.**

- **CRCPD provides consistency** in radiation protection standards.

D. Accreditation organizations

- The **American College of Radiology (ACR)** includes **radiologists, radiation oncologists,** and **medical physicists.**

- The **ACR provides accreditation programs for many imaging modalities, including Mammography, CT, and MR.**

- ACR accreditation is based on a **3-year cycle.**

- ACR accreditation may be used for facility licensure and reimbursement purposes.

- The **Joint Commission, previously known as JCAHO,** is a private accrediting organization.

- The Joint Commission provides accreditation programs for hospitals and other health care organizations.

- Many states utilize Joint Commission accreditation for **licensure** and **reimbursement.**

- **The Joint Commission accreditation cycle is every 3 years, and results are made public.**

E. Mammography Quality Standards Act

- Mammography QC is a legal requirement under the **Mammography Quality Standards Act (MQSA) passed in 1992.**

- MQSA was updated in 1998 with the **Mammography Quality Standards Reauthorization Act (MQSRA).**

- **Mammography is the only x-ray imaging modality regulated by the federal government.**

- **Figure 13.2** shows examples of the FDA certificate and the ACR accreditation certificate.

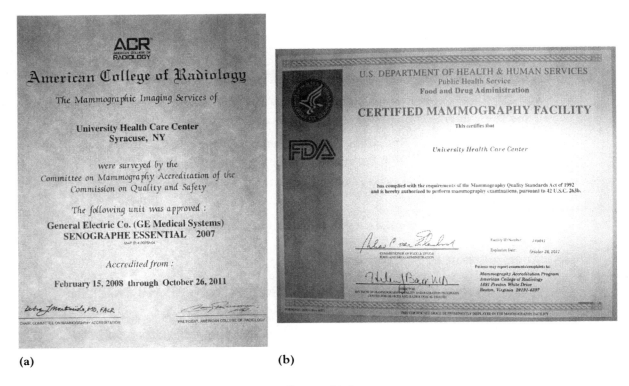

(a)   **(b)**

Figure 13.2
ACR accreditation certificate (a); FDA certification (b).

- MQSRA has explicit requirements for all participants in the performance of mammography.

- MQRSA contains continuing education and experience requirements for each participant.

- The **radiologist is the leader** of the mammography QC team and holds ultimate responsibility for compliance.

- The **medical physicist** is responsible for the testing of the mammography equipment annually and after service to or replacement of major components.

- The physicist also provides dose information and assists in review of the overall QA program.

- The **technologist** is responsible for the daily QC and the maintenance of the logs and charts.

- One technologist should be identified to perform the QC duties.

- **MQSRA also has explicit requirements for radiation dose and image quality.**

13.2 IMAGE RECEPTORS

A. Screens

- **Screens are susceptible to damage** through rough handling.
- Open cassettes should not be stacked on top of one another.
- Set film in the cassette as opposed to sliding it into the cassette.
- **Cleaning of the cassettes is essential,** and can be done with the use of **lint-less cloths** and a special cleaning solution.
- **Camel hair brushes** may also be used.
- **Mammography** cassettes must be **cleaned weekly.**
- **Radiography** screens must be cleaned **every other month.**
- **Mammography** cassettes require **film/screen contact** testing **semiannually,** and **radiography cassettes annually.**
- Resulting image, with an optical density of 1.5, is analyzed for **areas of increased/decreased density and blurring.**
- **Cassettes demonstrating areas of excessive blur are removed from service.**

B. Sensitometry

- **Sensitometry testing** uses a consistent and precise light source, a sensitometer, to expose a sheet of film.
- A dedicated box of film, **control film,** is identified for consistency.
- The process is known as **sensitometry testing** or **a sensitometry strip** and is done **daily.**
- Several measurements are taken and recorded daily including base + fog (B+F), speed, and contrast.
- The **contrast** is calculated from the reading of the **min density** or the **step closest to 0.2 + B+F,** subtracted from the **max density** or the **step closest to 2.0 + B+F.**
- **Figure 13.3** illustrates a sensitometry strip and a control chart for daily recording.
- **Table 13.2** details tolerance levels.
- A **fixer retention test,** or a hypo retention test, is performed **quarterly.**
- A sheet of unexposed film is processed, then a drop of testing solution is placed on it.
- After 2 min, the excess solution is removed and the **film is compared to a control strip.**
- The resulting **fixer retention must be below 0.05 g/m^2.**
- A **film crossover** must be done whenever a new box of control film is opened.
- Crossover is **performed because** each batch of **emulsion is slightly different.**

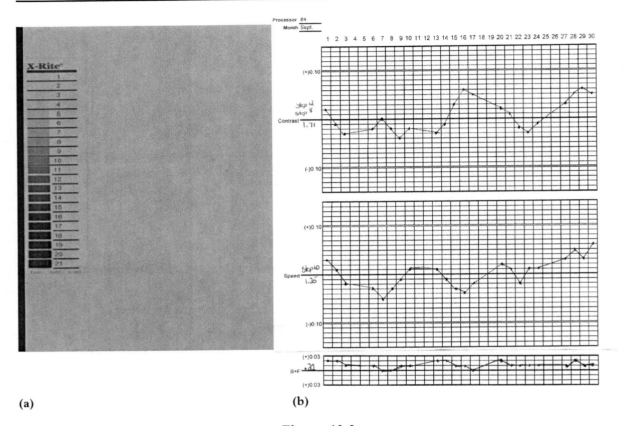

(a)   (b)

Figure 13.3
Photograph of a sensitometry strip (a), and a processor quality control chart (b) showing variation in sensitometry results (base + fog; speed; contrast) with tolerance levels.

Table 13.2
Tolerance levels for sensitometry testing

Factor	Tolerance	Comment
Temperature	±0.5 °F	95 °F is common for a 90-second processor
Base + fog	±0.03	May vary by ±0.05 for dual-emulsion film
Speed	±0.15	Also known as mid density (MD)
Contrast	±0.15	Also known as density difference (DD)

C. Film processor

- **Processor QC** is performed to ensure consistent image quality.
- The darkroom should be **wiped down daily**, starting with the highest shelf and working one's way down to the counters and then the floor.
- **Evaluate for light leaks** around doors, processor, and pass boxes.
- **Developer temperatures are checked daily**, with an acceptable variance of ±0.3 °C (0.5 °F).
- **Solution temperatures** and **replenishment rates are checked weekly**.
- **Darkroom fog testing** is required to ensure safelights are not causing excessive fog during handling.
- Fog testing is performed **semiannually**.
- **Film fog has a limit of no more than 0.05 OD**.

D. CR receptors

- **Proper handling** of the digital image receptor **prevents common artifacts (scratches and dust)**.
- **CR plates** are prone to **dust artifacts**, from dust within the reader or imaging plate.
- **Poor reader optics** may also induce artifacts.
- CR plates may be cleaned by the technologist, but dealing with readers requires service engineers.
- **Scratched CR plates** must be removed from service if a defect is realized.
- There is an **unlimited lifetime for CR and DR plates** if maintained properly.
- Radiation fatigue does not occur with CR/DR.
- CR is prone to **ghosting artifacts** due to **incomplete erasure** of an image and **fog from background radiation**.
- **Daily erasure** of all CR plates is necessary to **prevent fog**.

E. Digital detectors (flat panels)

- Due to the variation in systems **there is not a standardized QC program to cover flat-panel detectors**.
- Technologist must follow the guidelines established by the manufacturer.

- **A typical program for digital radiographic systems** would include the following:
  - Technologist to **verify all digital interfaces and network transmission daily.**
  - Testing of **laser printers and/or processors** to be performed **daily.**
  - **Weekly phantom images** to be compared with standard and analyzed for variation.
  - System to be thoroughly cleaned of dirt, debris, and contrast media.
  - **Annual performance testing by a medical physicist** that includes evaluation of image quality and a repeat of acceptance tests.
- **Medical physicists also need to evaluate QC records and service history.**

13.3 X-RAY SYSTEMS

A. X-ray tubes

- A diagnostic radiography tube must have **2.5 mm Al equivalent filtration.**
- **HVL** testing is performed **annually** and is **~2.5 mm Al at 80 kVp.**
- **kVp accuracy** is tested **annually** and must be within **5%.**
- **Timer circuits are tested annually.** For exposure times **greater than 10 ms, the accuracy must be 5%,** and **20% for exposure times less than 10 ms.**
- Reciprocity is tested to assure that regardless of the mA and time selected, output is proportional to the resultant mAs.
- **Reciprocity** is tested **annually,** and a variance of **±10%** being acceptable.
- **Linearity** is tested **annually** or after major part replacement and **must be within 10%.**
- **Reproducibility** of exposure is also important and is tested **annually** with a **5% variance.**
- **Radiation output** is tested **annually** and must be within **10% of value at installation.**

B. Radiography

- The **irradiated field/light field** of the collimator may have a misalignment **<2% of the SID.**
- **Positive Beam Limitation (PBL)** must be **within 3% of the SID,** and the **centering of the irradiated field to the cassette within 1%.**
- Collimated area on **PBL must not exceed the image receptor size.**
- Beam restriction systems must be tested **semiannually.**

- A pinhole camera, a star pattern, or a slit camera may be used to measure **focal spot size (annually)**.

- **Focal spot must be within 50% of the established size at acceptance testing.**

- **AEC testing** includes **variance with changing mA, kVp, cell selection, field size,** and **part thickness**.

- AEC testing is performed **annually** or after service of the AEC system.

- **Backup time** must be tested and terminate at **6 seconds or 600 mAs**.

- **Table 13.3** lists radiography specific QC activities.

Table 13.3
Radiography QC activities and frequency

Frequency	Activity
Daily	Darkroom cleaning Sensitometry Erasure of CR imaging plates (D★)
Weekly	Image receptor cleaning CRT monitor cleaning/evaluation (D★) Phantom image (D★)
Quarterly	Repeat/Reject analysis Fixer retention
Semiannually	Darkroom fog Collimator accuracy/alignment
Annually	Visual inspection AEC evaluation KVP accuracy Linearity/Reproducibility Timer evaluation FS evaluation HVL/Filtration Film/Screen contact Radiation output

★Digital equipment only, suggested QC activities.

C. Mammography

- **Phantom images** are evaluated **weekly for quality, artifact,** and **technical information.**
- **Figure 13.4** is a photograph of the mammography phantom and a radiograph of the phantom.
- **Compression device testing** is performed **semiannually** and **cannot exceed 40 lb.**
- **Generator, collimator,** and **x-ray tube testing,** such as that described in radiographic QC, are also performed **annually.**
- An **analysis of films that have been repeated** is performed **quarterly,** or after a **minimum of 250 patients.**
- All **repeat/reject images are categorized as to the reason for repeat,** i.e., mechanical, motion, positioning, etc.
- **Total repeat rate is (repeat films/total images)** $\times$ **100%,** and **should be less than 2%.**
- **Causal repeat rates** are those **calculated for each category,** such as positioning errors.
- Causal repeat rates assist in identifying areas of high repeats for corrective action.
- **Table 13.4** contains a comprehensive list of mammography-specific QC activities.

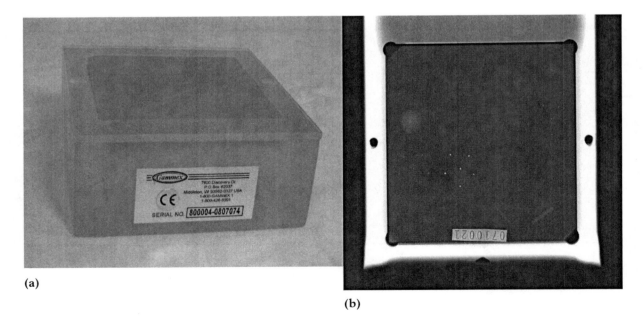

(a)

(b)

Figure 13.4
Photograph of the Gammex mammography phantom (a) and a radiograph
of the phantom (b) showing the fibers, specks, and masses.

Table 13.4
Mammography QC activities and frequency

Frequency	Activity
Daily	Darkroom cleaning Sensitometry Monitor cleaning/Evaluation (D★) Phantom image (D★)
Weekly	Screen cleaning Viewing conditions Phantom image Detector calibration (D★) SNR/CNR evaluation (D★)
Monthly	Visual check list System resolution (D★)
Quarterly	Repeat/Reject analysis Fixer retention
Semiannually	Darkroom fog Film/Screen contact Compression
Annually	AEC evaluation/Reproducibility KVP accuracy/Reproducibility FSS testing HVL Collimator alignment System artifact evaluation Screen uniformity Radiation output Entrance Air Kerma

★Digital equipment only, suggested QC activities.

D. Fluoroscopy

- **A visual inspection is performed semiannually to ensure proper function of all locks, lights, meters, protective devices, and exposure switches.**

- Fluoroscopic equipment must have a **timer to alert** the radiologist **after 5 minutes** of exposure.

- **Collimators** must restrict the beam to the input phosphor diameter within **3% of the SID**.

- **HVL testing** is performed at the kVp commonly used for that equipment.
- **kVp accuracy** is tested **semiannually** and must be **within 5%**.
- **Linearity is tested semiannually** or after major part replacement and **must be within 10%**.
- **Automatic Brightness Control (ABC) systems are tested semiannually.**
- Maximum Exposure Rate at the tabletop **using ABC** must be **100 mGy/min (10 R/min) or less.**
- **Digital fluoroscopy** systems should be evaluated **semiannually following the procedures in AAPM Report No. 15**, Performance Evaluation and Quality Assurance in Digital Subtraction Angiography (1985).
- **Protective apparel** must be evaluated for cracks, holes, or other damage.
- Testing is **performed semiannually** on all personnel and patient protective apparel.

E. Interventional Radiology

- **Interventional Radiology systems should be evaluated at acceptance and then semiannually.**
- **AAPM Report No. 15 (1985) specifies the type of phantom to be used.**
- Evaluation of **high contrast, low contrast,** and **spatial resolution** are performed.
- Interventional Radiology also requires **evaluation of subtraction effectiveness, image uniformity,** and **image registration**.
- **AAPM Report No. 70,** Cardiac Catheterization Equipment Performance (2001) describes cardiac catheterization evaluation.
- **Cinefluorography** requires **semiannual** evaluation and cleaning of optical components.
- Specialized phantoms are available for cinefluorography testing.
- Viewing of cinefluorography typically requires a 500W lamp.
- **Projector quality** is evaluated through the **display of a SMPTE pattern.**
- Quality indicators include **distortion** and **low-contrast visibility.**

13.4 COMPUTED TOMOGRAPHY (CT)

A. ACR Accreditation

- ACR accreditation is widely sought as a means of meeting regulatory and reimbursement requirements.
- The accreditation process includes **educational and clinical requirements** for the **technologist, radiologist, and physicist.**

- In addition, protocol review, clinical image review, phantom image analysis, and patient dose limits are required.
- The accreditation process operates on a **3-year cycle.**
- Detailed information regarding the CT accreditation process through the ACR can be found at www.acr.org/accreditation/computed.

B. Gantry

- **Couch incrimination** describes couch **movement in the longitudinal direction** (z-axis).
- CT table movement must be accurate and consistent.
- **Couch movement should be assessed monthly.**
- Both start and end table positions are recorded when scanning with a "patient-like" weight on the couch.
- Compare this table movement distance with that measured using a tape measure; the two distances **should not vary by more than ±2 mm.**
- **Laser lights are used for patient positioning,** and for CT interventional procedures.
- Many scanners have **both internal and external lasers.**
- Both sets of lasers should be **tested semiannually.**
- **Laser light accuracy cannot vary more than ±3 mm.**

C. Noise and Uniformity

- **Noise is the random fluctuation of HU when imaging a homogeneous object.**
- Noise is measured by **scanning a water phantom,** usually a 20-cm phantom.
- An **ROI** is place at the **center of the image,** measuring the **HU** and **standard deviation.**
- The **standard deviation indicates the level of noise** in an image.
- Noise testing should be performed at **weekly intervals.**
- **Uniformity is the consistency of HU** at various locations within a homogeneous object.
- Uniformity is measured weekly by **scanning a water phantom,** usually a 20-cm phantom.
- **ROIs are placed at the center and at 3, 6, 9, and 12 o'clock of the object.**
- The **HU of water** should not vary more than **±7 HU from zero at the center.**
- The **HU of water** should not vary more than **±5 HU from the center value at the periphery.**

D. Linearity

- **Linearity describes the relationship between the HU and the linear attenuation of a material at a fixed kVp.**
- **AAPM 5-pin phantom can be used for linearity,** where each pin contains a different material.
- **Each pin is measured for HU and standard deviation.**
- **Table 13.5** details the materials used, their respective HU, and tolerance levels.
- A linear relationship should be seen when material linear attenuation coefficients are plotted against measured HU.
- **Linearity testing is performed semiannually.**

Table 13.5
Table of HU linearity test materials

Material	Typical value (HU)	ACR tolerances (HU)
Polyethylene	−97	±10
Water	0	±7★
Acrylic	120	±10
Bone	910	±60

★Note that ±5 is preferred.

E. Resolution/Slice thickness

- **High contrast or spatial resolution is defined as the ability to differentiate two high-contrast objects as separate.**
- Spatial resolution testing is performed **semiannually** using the manufacturer's phantom and specifications.
- A **bar pattern or hole pattern** is imaged.
- **ACR acceptance criteria require at least 5 lp/cm for an adult abdomen and 6 lp/cm for an adult high-resolution chest exam.**
- **Figure 13.5** shows the ACR phantom and an image of the high-contrast portion of the phantom.
- **Low-contrast visibility describes a system's ability to differentiate two objects with similar linear attenuations.**
- Low-contrast visibility is sometimes referred to as **contrast resolution.**

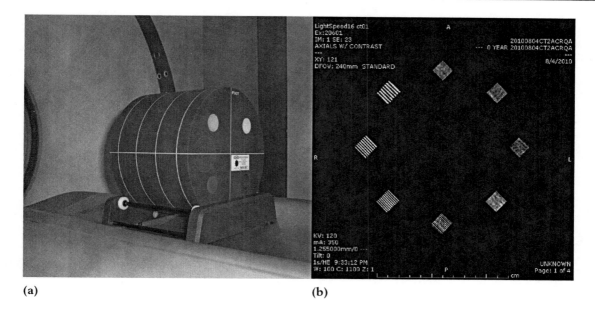

Figure 13.5
Photograph of an ACR CT accreditation phantom (a)
and CT image of the spatial resolution section (b).

- Low-contrast visibility is performed **semiannually** using a **hole-pattern phantom**.
- The **5-mm 0.5% pattern** must be visible.
- **All four of the 6-mm cylinders** must be visible to meet **ACR** acceptance criteria.
- **Slice thickness** testing is performed **semiannually using a ramp, spiral,** or **wedge phantom** provided by the manufacturer.
- Slices of **5 mm or greater must be within ±1 mm**, and for slices **less than 5 mm, the tolerance levels are ±0.5 mm**.

QUESTIONS

Chapter 13: Quality Control

13.1   Who is least likely to be involved in a Radiology QA program?
   A. Radiological technologist
   B. Service engineer
   C. Medical physicist
   D. Diagnostic radiologist

13.2   Equipment testing is least likely to be performed:
   A. prior to purchase.
   B. after installation.
   C. annually.
   D. post maintenance.

13.3   Level III testing would most likely be performed by a:
   A. general technologist.
   B. QC technologist.
   C. service engineer.
   D. radiology administrator.

13.4   Hospitals are most likely to be accredited by:
   A. JCAHO.
   B. CRCPD.
   C. ACR.
   D. ARRT.

13.5   Which of the following organizations accredits medical imaging equipment?
   A. CRCPD
   B. ACR
   C. AAPM
   D. ARRT

13.6   Mammography is regulated by the:
   A. American College of Radiology.
   B. American Association of Physicists in Medicine.
   C. federal government.
   D. state government.

13.7   Under MQSA, responsibility for annual equipment tests are with the:
   A. radiological technologist.
   B. medical physicist.
   C. diagnostic radiologist.
   D. radiology administrator.

13.8   Mammography cassettes would most likely be cleaned:
   A. daily.
   B. weekly.
   C. monthly.
   D. every 3 months.

13.9   Mammography screen-contact tests are most likely performed:
   A. weekly.
   B. monthly.
   C. semiannually.
   D. annually.

13.10   The optimal film density in a screen contact test is most likely _____ .
   A. 0.5
   B. 1.0
   C. 1.5
   D. 2.0

13.11   Film strips are most likely to be exposed to a standard amount of light using a:
   A. sensitometer.
   B. densitometer.
   C. photometer.
   D. hot light.

13.12   When a new box of film is opened for film processor QC, one should perform a:
   A. film crossover.
   B. speed assessment.
   C. processor service.
   D. darkroom cleaning.

13.13   An acceptable variation in film developer temperature (°C) is most likely _____ .
   A. ±0.1
   B. ±0.3
   C. ±1
   D. ±3

13.14   CR plates should likely be erased:
    A. hourly.
    B. daily.
    C. weekly.
    D. monthly.

13.15   The likely lifetime of a properly maintained CR plate is most likely:
    A. 6 months.
    B. 1 year.
    C. 2 years.
    D. unlimited.

13.16   The minimum filtrationon an x-ray tube is most likely _____ mm Al.
    A. 0.5
    B. 1.5
    C. 2.5
    D. 3.5

13.17   The limit on x-ray tube linearity is most likely _____ %.
    A. 1
    B. 3
    C. 10
    D. 30

13.18   The acceptable tolerance on a focal spot size is most likely _____ %.
    A. 10
    B. 20
    C. 30
    D. 50

13.19   Mammography phantom images are generally taken:
    A. daily.
    B. weekly.
    C. monthly.
    D. every 3 months.

13.20   In mammography, repeat analysis is most likely performed:
    A. weekly.
    B. monthly.
    C. quarterly.
    D. annually.

13.21   In fluoroscopy, a timer sounds a warning after an exposure of _____ minutes.
    A. 2
    B. 5
    C. 10
    D. 30

13.22   Patient and personnel protective apparel in fluoroscopy should be tested:
    A. monthly.
    B. every 3 months.
    C. every 6 months.
    D. annually.

13.23   In fluoroscopy, kVp accuracy must be within _____ %.
    A. 1
    B. 2
    C. 5
    D. 10

13.24   An acceptable CT table increment accuracy is most likely _____ mm.
    A. ±0.5
    B. ±1
    C. ±2
    D. ±4

13.25   Accuracy of laser lights on a CT scanner (mm) is most likely _____ mm.
    A. ±0.5
    B. ±1
    C. ±3
    D. ±5

13.26   Acceptable HU for water, from the value of zero, is most likely _____.
    A. ±1
    B. ±2
    C. ±4
    D. ±7

13.27   The uniformity of water HU from the center to the periphery should not exceed _____ .
    A. ±1
    B. ±2
    C. ±3
    D. ±5

13.28 Linearity tests the relationship between HU value and material:
A. linear attenuation.
B. mass attenuation.
C. atomic number.
D. physical density.

13.29 The spatial resolution required by the ACR for an adult phantom image is likely _____ lp/cm.
A. 1
B. 2
C. 5
D. 10

13.30 Which part of a QC phantom is *least* likely to be used to measure slice thickness?
A. Ramp
B. Spiral
C. Wedge
D. Bar

ANSWERS[1]

Chapter 13: Quality Control

13.1   B   A QA program is generally composed of technologists, a physicist, and radiologists, but not service engineers.

p. 306 Bushong
p. 481 Carlton/Adler

13.2   A   Equipment testing is performed at installation, annually, and after a major component is replaced.

p. 306 Bushong
p. 481 Carlton/Adler

13.3   C   Level I testing is performed by a general technologist, level II by a trained technologist, and level III by a physicist or service engineer.

n/a Bushong
n/a Carlton/Adler

13.4   A   The Joint Commission on Accreditation of Health Care Organizations (now the Joint Commission) is one of the most common accreditation processes used by hospitals.

p. 305 Bushong
p. 461 Carlton/Adler

13.5   B   ACR accredits many areas of imaging, including mammography.

p. 332 Bushong
n/a Carlton/Adler

13.6   C   MQSA and MQSRA are federal regulations covering the use of mammography in the United States.

p. 332 Bushong
p. 481 Carlton/Adler

13.7   B   A physicist must inspect mammography equipment annually under MQSA.

p. 332 Bushong
n/a Carlton/Adler

13.8   B   Screens must be cleaned weekly under MQSA regulations.

p. 334 Bushong
p. 624 Carlton/Adler

13.9   C   Screen-film contact testing is required every 6 months in mammography under MQSA.

p. 342 Bushong
p. 624 Carlton/Adler

13.10   C   An optical density of about 1.5 should be used.

n/a Bushong
n/a Carlton/Adler

13.11   A   Sensitometers consistently deliver a step-wedge pattern of light intensities to a film for testing.

p. 334 Bushong
p. 304 Carlton/Adler

13.12   A   Film crossover is needed whenever a new box of QC film is opened because of slight differences in film emulsions.

p. 344 Bushong
n/a Carlton/Adler

---

[1] As a study aid, page numbers for additional study are given for the following references:
Bushong SC: *Radiologic Science for Technologists,* 9th ed. St. Louis, MO: Mosby, 2008.
Carlton RR, Adler AM: *Principles of Radiographic Imaging: An Art and a Science,* 4th ed. Albany, NY: Delmar Publishing Inc., 2005.

13.13	B	The acceptable variation in film developer temperature is ±0.3°.	*p. 334 Bushong* *p. 295 Carlton/Adler*
13.14	B	CR plates are erased daily to remove any fogging.	*n/a Bushong* *p. 369 Carlton/Adler*
13.15	D	CR cassettes have an unlimited lifetime if properly cared for and not damaged.	*p. 487 Bushong* *n/a Carlton/Adler*
13.16	C	Diagnostic radiography tubes contain a window with 0.5 mm Al, inherent filtration of 1.0 mm Al and 1.0 mm of added filtration for a total of 2.5 mm Al.	*p. 306 Bushong* *p. 169 Carlton/Adler*
13.17	C	Linearity has an acceptable variance of 10%.	*p. 306 Bushong* *p. 485 Carlton/Adler*
13.18	D	A 50% increase in focal spot size is acceptable.	*p. 306 Bushong* *p. 484 Carlton/Adler*
13.19	B	MQSA requires a weekly phantom image be performed.	*p. 335 Bushong* *p. 624 Carlton/Adler*
13.20	C	Quarterly repeat/reject analysis is performed every 3 months.	*p. 340 Bushong* *p. 624 Carlton/Adler*
13.21	B	A fluoroscopy timer signals at 5-minute intervals as a patient and personnel safety measure.	*p. 572 Bushong* *p. 579 Carlton/Adler*
13.22	C	All protective apparel should be fluoroscoped at 100 kVp every 6 months to ensure there are not cracks or holes.	*p. 310 Bushong* *n/a Carlton/Adler*
13.23	C	The acceptable variance for kVp is 5%.	*p. 308 Bushong* *p. 485 Carlton/Adler*
13.24	C	Table increment must be ±2 mm, as it has implications on image quality and patient dose.	*p. 391 Bushong* *n/a Carlton/Adler*
13.25	C	Laser light accuracy is important when performing invasive examinations and must be accurate to within ±3 mm.	*p. 392 Bushong* *n/a Carlton/Adler*
13.26	D	A variance of ±7 HU from zero is acceptable for the HU of water in CT.	*p. 390 Bushong* *n/a Carlton/Adler*
13.27	D	Uniformity testing requires measurement at the periphery of a scan and center be within ±5 HU.	*p. 390 Bushong* *n/a Carlton/Adler*
13.28	A	Linearity tests the relationship between HU and the material linear attenuation coefficient.	*p. 390 Bushong* *n/a Carlton/Adler*

13.29   C   5 lp/mm is required by ACR for adult abdomen protocols,   *p. 391 Bushong*
              6 lp/mm for high-resolution CT (HRCT) protocols.   *n/a Carlton/Adler*

13.30   D   A bar pattern cannot be used to measure slice thickness.   *p. 391 Bushong*
                                                                              n/a Carlton/Adler

Chapter 14

RADIATION BIOLOGY

14.1 Cell Biology
14.2 Radiation and Cells
14.3 High-Dose Effects
14.4 Stochastic Effects
14.5 Pregnancy and Radiation

14.1 CELL BIOLOGY

A. Cell function

- **DNA** provides **genetic information** for a cell and controls growth/development.
- **Radiation damage** during this process may result in **cell death** or **late effects of radiation**.
- Irradiation may damage DNA, resulting in visible changes to its structure.
- Damage that is not detected may result in cell death.
- Extensive cell death results in destruction of tissues and organs.

B. Cell division

- Cells divide through mitosis and meiosis.
- **Mitosis** is any division of a cell, except those of sperm and eggs.
- **Mitosis** has four phases: **prophase, metaphase, anaphase,** and **telophase**.
- The **metaphase** is where **damage by radiation** to the chromosome is visible.
- **Figure 14.1** shows cell division via mitosis.
- **Meiosis is the division of genetic cells.**
- The process of meiosis begins with a genetic cell containing **46 chromosomes**.
- These cells produce **two daughter cells** with **46 chromosomes**.
- The daughter cells divide for a second time, without duplicating DNA, resulting in **granddaughter cells** with **23 chromosomes**.

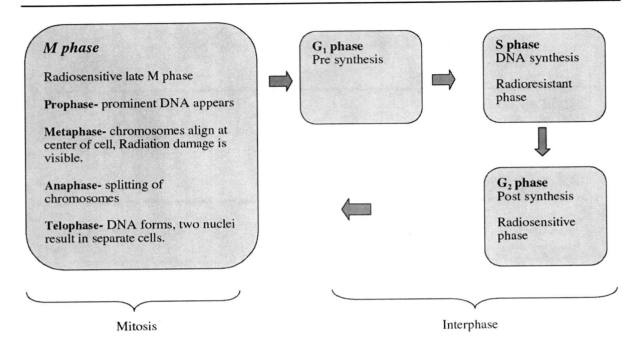

Figure 14.1

Cell cycle (M, G_1, S, and G_2) indicating radiosensitive and resistant parts.

C. Energy deposition in cells

- Ionizing radiations deposit energy in tissue.
- The amount of **radiation absorbed** by a tissue (Gy) determines the **damage** to the tissue.
- **Altered molecules may not respond appropriately, lose their function, or die.**
- The human body is ~80% water-based solution with less than 1% DNA.
- **Direct effects** are seen when the ionization occurs on a target molecule (**DNA**).
- **Indirect effects transfer energy** to the target molecule resulting from the ionization of other molecules.
- Most **damage is considered the result of indirect effects through free radical interaction.**

D. Free radicals

- Radiation of the human body is much like radiation of a water solution.
- **Irradiation of water** molecules will **form two ions.**
- **Irradiation of a water** molecule creates ion pairs H+ and OH–, in addition to **two free radicals H• and OH•.**

- Free radicals possess additional energy, are highly reactive, and remain for ~1 ms.
- This **excessive energy may transfer** to another molecule creating **point lesions**.
- Free radicals may also combine with other molecules **creating toxins**.
- The resulting toxic substances are the **damaging byproducts of water irradiation**.

E. Radiation damage

- **Macromolecules** irradiated in solution result in three different types of damage (i.e., main-chain scission, cross-linking, and point lesions).
- **Main-chain scission** results in a fracture to the structure of the macromolecule.
- The macromolecule will decrease in size and viscosity.
- Macromolecules have structures off the main chain and when these appendages attach to other macromolecules, **cross-linking** has occurred.
- Cross-linking results in an increased viscosity.
- **Point lesions** are damage to a single chemical bond and are not evident.
- Point lesions alter the molecule and can cause the cell to function improperly.
- **Late radiation effects** are caused by **point lesion** damage to cells.
- **Macromolecule damage** by irradiation **is generally repairable**.

14.2 RADIATION AND CELLS

A. Cell survival curves

- The effects of radiation are measured in terms of cell survival.
- Irradiation of cell groups or a colony provides data on the number of cells surviving a given dose.
- **Figure 14.2** shows a typical cell survival curve in radiobiology.
- D_{35} represents the radiation dose at which 35% of cells survive and 65% die.
- A dose of $2 \times D_{35}$ results in a survival of 12% of cells.
- A **high Dx suggests radiation resistance**, while a low Dx indicates radiosensitivity.
- Cell recovery begins moments after injury.
- Injury may be classified by the time frame in which damage is evident.
- **Early effects** of radiation occur within **minutes of exposure**.
- **Late effects** of radiation may take **months to years to develop**.

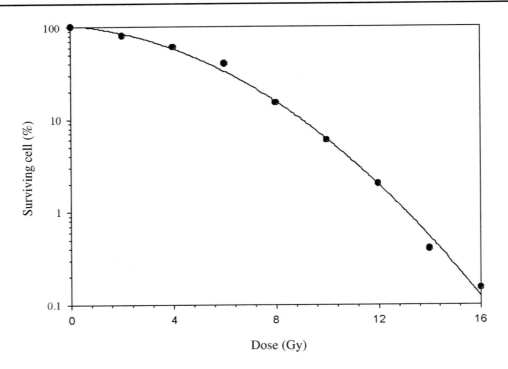

Figure 14.2
Typical cell survival curve showing percentage of cells
that will survive any given dose.

B. Cell sensitivity

- As the cell ages and regenerates, its radiosensitivity changes.
- Cells in **mitosis** are most **sensitive**, where increased cell death is seen during irradiation.
- **Late S phase** is the most **radioresistant** phase for human cells.
- **Bergonie** and **Tribondeau** discovered that maturity and metabolism affect tissue radiosensitivity.
- A fetus is more radiosensitive than a toddler or an adult.
- Stem cells are highly sensitive to radiation, whereas mature cells are more resistant to damage.
- **Table 14.1** lists **radiosensitivity for a range of cell types.**
- **Cell sensitivity to radiation increases with increased oxygen.**

Table 14.1
Relative sensitivity of cells to radiation

Cell sensitivity	Cell type
High	Lymphocytes, spermatogonia, intestinal crypt cells
Intermediate	Endothelial cells, osteoblasts, and fibroblasts
Low	Muscle cells and nerve cells

C. Fractionation/Dose rate

- **Radiation** given in a very **short amount of time** can **result in radiation damage.**
- The same radiation dose given over a long time period might result in *no* damage.
- This difference in response is due to the **body's ability to repair** radiation damage.
- If creating damage was the goal, the dose would need to be increased for longer exposures to overcome the body's ability to repair damage.
- The lengthening of time frames for radiation exposure is known as **protracted exposure.**
- **Fractionation** is the process of giving the same total dose, but in equal parts separated by a specific time frame.
- Fractionation is used in **radiation therapy.**
- This process allows for normal tissue repair between fractions or treatment days.

D. Chromosome aberrations

- Cells contain 22 pairs of autosomes and one pair of sex chromosomes.
- **The Y chromosome is from the female and the X from the male.**
- Individual chromosomes damaged by radiation can be seen.
- **Radiation exposure** is capable of causing of **chromosome aberrations.**
- **Chromosome aberrations** caused by radiation follow a **non-threshold dose-response relationship.**
- Occupationally induced chromosome aberrations have been realized at 20+ years post industrial exposure.
- **Ring chromosomes** result from two hits to the same chromosome in the G_1 phase.
- When two adjacent chromosomes are hit, dicentrics may be produced.
- A multi-hit with no loss of genetic material is a **reciprocal translocation.**
- **Single hit aberrations** take place at exposure levels below **1 Gy (100 rad).**
- As radiation exposure increases, so does the frequency of multi-hit aberrations.

E. LET and RBE

- **Linear Energy Transfer (LET)** describes the rate or how much energy is deposited per unit distance in a tissue.
- Diagnostic x-rays have a **LET of ~3 keV/μm.**
- As the LET increases, so does the radiation's ability to cause tissue damage.
- LET provides an understanding of radiation quality and **radiation weighting factor (w_R)** used in radiation protection.
- Calculation for **Relative Biological Effectiveness (RBE)** is based on a standard x-ray beam of 250 kVp.
- Diagnostic x-rays have an **RBE of 1.**
- As the **RBE increases,** so does the radiation's **ability to induce damage** to tissue.

14.3 HIGH-DOSE EFFECTS

A. Whole body irradiation

- **1 Gy (100 rad)** or more exposure to the whole body will **result in radiation sickness,
within hours.**
- High radiation doses result in vomiting, diarrhea and decreased white blood cell count.
- **10 Gy (1000 rad) exposure results in violent radiation sickness.**
- **High doses of radiation delivered to the whole body can kill individuals through three syndromes called hematological, GI, and CNS.**
- These syndromes exhibit a **nonlinear threshold response,** which represents **acute radiation lethality.**
- **LD$_{50/60}$** represents the whole body dose that **will kill 50% of a population in 60 days.**
- A dose of **~3.5 Gy (350 rad) is currently believed to be LD$_{50/60}$ for humans.**
- If medical care is available to the radiation victim, **~6 Gy (600 rad) is the LD$_{50/60}$ for humans.**
- The time between exposure and death is known as the **mean survival time,** which generally decreases with increasing dose.

B. Radiation syndromes

- Radiation decreases the number of blood cells circulating within the system due to cell death and the time needed to replace with new cells.

- **Hematologic syndrome** results from doses of **~2–10 Gy (200–1000 rad)** with a mild illness.

- **Latent period may be 4 weeks** where a decrease in the number of red/white blood cells and platelets occurs.

- **Lethal doses** leave the body unable to fight infection due to **loss of white blood cells**.

- **Gastrointestinal (GI) syndrome** results from doses of **~10–50 Gy (1000–5000 rad)** with vomiting and diarrhea within hours.

- The **latent period is 3 to 5 days** without symptoms.

- In the late stage the intestinal lining is damaged, causing **massive fluid loss and infection**.

- **Central Nervous System (CNS) syndrome** results from doses of **50⁺ Gy (5000⁺ rad)** and leads to death within hours.

- Nausea and vomiting begin within minutes of exposure, with patients often confused and disoriented.

- **Table 14.2** lists the key characteristics of all three radiation syndromes.

Table 14.2
Radiation induced syndromes

Syndrome	Dose threshold (Gy)	Latent period
Hematologic	2–10	4 weeks
Gastrointestinal	10–50	3–5 days
Central Nervous System	50+	12 hours

C. Skin effects

- Skin burns are an example of a **deterministic radiation response**.

- **Figure 14.3** shows a graph of deterministic effects that are also known as harmful tissue reactions.

- Skin's stem cells are **basal cells**, and damage to basal cells is the **earliest manifest injury** to the organ.

- A dose of **3–10 Gy (300–1000 rad)** will induce mild erythema with 48 hours.

- A latent period is seen with a second phase of erythema being more severe and peaking at 2 weeks.

- **Moist desquamation** occurs **after the second erythema** in high-dose exposures.

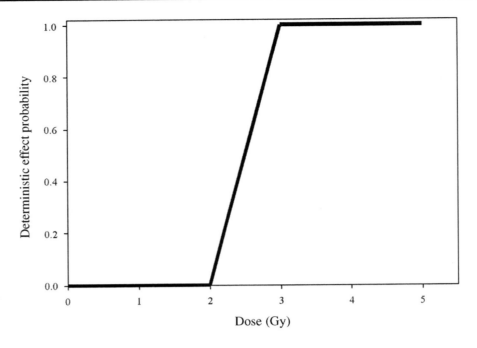

Figure 14.3
Sigmoid response to radiation for deterministic effects
(i.e., erythema, epilation, etc.) with threshold dose
below which these effects do not occur.

- **Loss of hair, or epilation,** may also occur at doses of 3 Gy (300 rad).
- The **higher the dose**, the more likely the **damage is permanent.**

D. Cataracts

- Radiation can induce cataracts in the eye lens.
- Cataract induction is associated with a **threshold dose**, and exhibits a **nonlinear** dose response curve.
- The **lens' radiosensitivity increases with age**, and has a **latent period** for cataract induction of between **5–20 years.**
- Acute exposures to the lens of the eye have a threshold dose of **2 Gy (200 rad).**
- For **protracted occupational exposures** over several years, the threshold dose is taken to be **5 Gy (500 rad).**
- Occupational doses in diagnostic radiology are well below the threshold doses for cataract induction.

- Radiologic technologists do not normally need special eye protection.
- Patients undergoing high-dose imaging such as **IR head/neck studies** can exceed the **threshold dose** for cataract induction.
- Patients in Interventional Neuroradiology may **benefit from eye protection**.

E. Sterility

- **Human gonads are highly radiosensitive.**
- Ovary stem cells are **oogonia** and multiply prior to birth.
- The **most radiosensitive** germ cell is the **oocyte** in a mature follicle.
- Doses ~0.1 Gy (10 rad) will cause disruption/delay of menstruation.
- Doses ~2 Gy (200 rad) will cause temporary sterility, with doses of ~6 Gy (600 rad) resulting in permanent sterility in women.
- Testes stem cells are **spermatogonia**, mature into **spermatocytes**, spermatids, and differentiate to become spermatozoa, taking 3–5 weeks.
- **Spermatogonia are the most radiosensitive phase**, with mature spermatocytes and spermatozoa the least sensitive phases.
- Doses of ~0.1 Gy (10 rad) have been shown to decrease sperm count.
- Doses of ~0.2 Gy (20 rad) will cause temporary sterility, with doses of ~ 5 Gy (500 rad) resulting in permanent sterility for men.

14.4 STOCHASTIC EFFECTS

A. Stochastic effects

- Diagnostic radiology is most concerned with stochastic effects caused by low-dose radiation.
- **Leukemia, solid tumors, and genetic effects** are examples of stochastic effects.
- Response is directly proportional to dose.
- Data for high doses are available and are extrapolated to low dose situations for radiation protection purposes.
- This extrapolation produces a linear, non-threshold relationship.
- **Stochastic effects** are currently believed to have **no threshold** or safe dose level.
- **Current radiation protection practices** are based on the linear, no threshold dose response.

B. Carcinogenesis (medical)

- **Acute and chronic myeloid leukemia** has been observed in patients treated for ankylosing spondylitis.
- **Thyroid cancer** has been observed in children treated for enlarged thymus, acne, tonsillitis, and ringworm.
- **Breast cancer** has been observed in patients treated with x-rays for postpartum mastitis and patients fluoroscoped for tuberculosis treatment.
- Excess cancers have been observed after radiotherapy for Hodgkin's lymphoma, prostate cancer, and carcinoma of the cervix.
- **Radiation therapy for childhood malignancies has resulted in secondary cancers.**
- Patients who had injections of radium for tuberculosis or ankylosing spondylitis have shown an excess of **bone cancers.**

C. Carcinogenesis (non–medical)

- **Radiation-induced skin cancers** were reported in radiologists, dentists, technologists working in the early 20th century when radiation safety was lax.
- Radiation-induced cancers and leukemia have been observed in survivors of the atomic bomb in Hiroshima and Nagasaki.
- Uranium miners **exposed to radon** and radon daughter products show an **excess of lung cancer.**
- Dial painters who **ingested radium** show an **excess of bone sarcomas** and carcinomas of the **epithelial cells lining the nasopharynx.**
- Ongoing studies of registries of radiation workers have now also shown increased cancer risk with occupational exposures.

D. Quantitative radiation risks

- About 42% of the U.S. populations will get cancer in their lifetimes.
- A **relative risk of 1** shows **no increase in radiation risk.**
- Values higher than 1 indicate an **increased risk in an exposed population.**
- For example, a relative risk of 1.5 would equate to a 50% increase in the exposed population.
- The relative risk quantifies the increase in risk that is attributed to radiation.
- **Solid tumors** show an excess of cancer incidence that is **a linear function of dose.**
- **Leukemia** appears to depend in a **linear-quadratic manner with radiation dose.**
- **Table 14.3** shows the relative sensitivity of organs to radiation-induced carcinogenesis.

Table 14.3
Relative sensitivity of organs to radiation-induced cancer

Organ sensitivity	Organs susceptible to radiation-induced cancer
High	Red bone marrow; lungs; breast (female); stomach; colon
Moderate	Liver; esophagus; bladder; thyroid
Low	Bone; brain; salivary glands; skin

- The **Biologic Effects of Ionizing Radiation (BEIR)** committee estimates cancer induction risks at about **10% per Sv** when averaged over age and sex.

- **Figure 14.4** shows how radiation risks vary with age and sex, and **Table 14.4** shows relative risks as a function of age.

- The radiosensitivity of infants and young children is especially high.

- **On average, radiation-induced malignancies have a 50% mortality rate.**

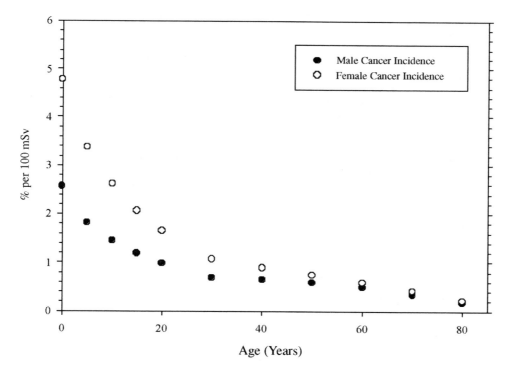

Figure 14.4
Radiation risk from whole body exposure (males and females)
as a function of exposure age for a uniform whole body exposure.

Table 14.4
Relative radiosensitivity as a function of age

Age	Cancer incidence (%)
0 (newborn)	100
20	21
40	13
60	8.9
80	3.2

E. Genetic effects

- **Damage to a germ cell** will result in abnormalities realized in the following generation.

- Large-scale animal studies suggest that genetic effects do occur.

- **No genetic effects** have been observed **in any groups of humans** exposed to radiation.

- Nowadays, concern about hereditary effects is much lower than concerns about cancer.

- **1 Gy (100 rad) to the gonads is estimated to produce one genetic effect per 500 live births.**

- Hereditary risks for a working population are lower than a general population because they exclude children.

- The doubling dose is one that would double the *spontaneous* mutation incidence in any exposed population.

- Current estimates of the doubling dose are about ~2 Gy (200 rad).

- Few of the spontaneous mutations in humans could be ascribed to background radiation.

14.5 PREGNANCY AND RADIATION

A. Congenital abnormalities

- The fetal risk depends on the gestation period.

- The **embryo** is present from **conception through week 7**, when **organogenesis** occurs.

- The **fetus** is present from **week 8 to delivery**.

- High radiation doses during the first 2 weeks post conception may result in a spontaneous abortion.

- A **high dose** would be in excess of **100 mGy (10 rad)**.

- The fetus is considered most vulnerable to congenital abnormalities from x-ray exposure during the first trimester.

- **Mental retardation** could occur at **8 to 15 weeks** post conception.

- A much smaller risk of mental retardation is also possible between 16 and 25 weeks.

- **Congenital abnormalities** are reported to occur in approximately 5% of live births.

- The high natural background of congenital abnormalities makes the effect of medical x-rays difficult to evaluate.

- **Risks of congenital abnormalities are negligible at radiation doses below 50 mGy (5 rad).**

- **Table 14.5** lists fetal age and the dose to induce deterministic radiation effects.

Table 14.5
Current knowledge of the deterministic effects (i.e., fetal death, malformations, and growth retardation or impairment of mental facility) of irradiation of the embryo and fetus, where the conceptus age is post–conception

Dose range (mGy)	Deterministic radiation effects
<50	None
50 to 100	Scientifically uncertain★
>100	Fetal death possible (1st to 2nd weeks)
	Malformation possible (3rd to 8th weeks)
	Growth retardation or impairment of mental facility possible (9th to 15th weeks)

★Most likely too subtle to be clinically detected.

B. Fetal cancer risks

- The greatest effect of exposure in late pregnancy is an increased risk of childhood cancers.

- Studies have shown that **diagnostic x-rays in utero increase childhood cancers**.

- X-rays appear to primarily increase **childhood leukemia**.

- Fetal dose as low as **10 mGy (1 rad)** appear to elevate childhood cancers.
- A fetal dose of **25 mGy (2.5 rad)** is believed to result in a childhood cancer risk of **1 in 500**.
- The natural background incidence of childhood cancer is also 1 in 500.
- At an incidence of 1 in 500 (0.2%), childhood cancer is a relatively rare event.
- **Childhood cancer rates are thus doubled following a fetal exposure of 25 mGy.**
- **Figure 14.5** shows the relationship between dose to the fetus and induction of childhood cancer.

C. Exposures of pregnant patients

- Up to 100 mGy (10 rad), any **fetal radiation risks are low** compared to normal risks of pregnancy.
- When the conceptus **dose exceeds 100 mGy** during the period 2 to 15 weeks post conception, risks of development **deficits are believed to start to appear**.

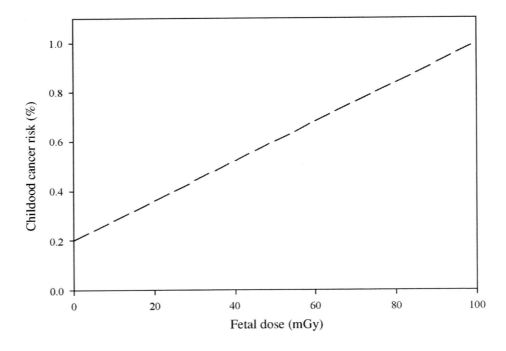

Figure 14.5
Childhood cancer risk as a function of dose to fetus, showing the low
natural incidence (i.e., 0.2%) and 25 mGy as the risk-doubling dose.

- **After 15 weeks, the primary concern is an elevated cancer risk.**

- Any cancer risks from medical x-rays would be too small to justify consideration of any medical intervention.

- Most x-ray examinations result in **embryo/fetal doses less than 50 mGy (5 rad)**.

- An abdominal and pelvic CT would likely result in an embryo dose of **35 mGy (3.5 rad)**.

- It is unlikely that a diagnostic x-ray examination could warrant consideration of any medical intervention.

D. Protecting pregnant patients

- Exposure of a pregnant patient to radiation should be avoided whenever possible.

- The **conceptus dose** will be very low when the x-ray beam does not directly irradiate it.

- In general, **exposure to scattered radiation** will be of **little practical importance**.

- Examinations resulting in **direct irradiation of the fetus or embryo require a dose estimate**.

- Any radiation-related risks must be quantified and taken into consideration.

- Decision to proceed with x-ray examinations requires a risk-benefit analysis.

- Benefit of the information obtained in the diagnostic examination must exceed any risks.

QUESTIONS

Chapter 14: Radiation Biology

14.1 Which type of cell is least likely to divide by mitosis?
A. Liver
B. Kidney
C. Lung
D. Sperm

14.2 In humans, a cell that has undergone meiosis division has _____ chromosomes.
A. 17
B. 23
C. 31
D. 46

14.3 Energy deposition in radiobiology is best quantified by:
A. equivalent dose.
B. effective dose.
C. absorbed dose.
D. relative dose.

14.4 The most radiosensitive part of a cell is most likely:
A. DNA.
B. mRNA.
C. tRNA.
D. mRNA and tRNA.

14.5 The percentage of the human body that is water is most likely _____%.
A. <10
B. 10
C. 40
D. 80

14.6 Irradiation of water by x-rays is most likely to result in the production of:
A. oxygen.
B. free radicals.
C. hydrogen.
D. steam.

14.7　　The most sensitive part of the cell cycle is:
　　　　A. S (Synthesis).
　　　　B. M (Mitosis).
　　　　C. G1.
　　　　D. G2.

14.8　　The most radioresistant phase of the cell cycle is the _____.
　　　　A. G
　　　　B. M
　　　　C. S
　　　　D. G and M

14.9　　The percentage of cells a D_{35} dose is likely to kill is _____.
　　　　A. 10
　　　　B. 35
　　　　C. 65
　　　　D. 90

14.10　　The most radiosensitive cells are most likely to be found in the:
　　　　A. newborn.
　　　　B. child.
　　　　C. adolescent.
　　　　D. adult.

14.11.　　Which of the following is most radiosensitive?
　　　　A. Erythroblasts
　　　　B. Muscle
　　　　C. Nerve
　　　　D. Epidermis

14.12　　Cell sensitivity is most likely increased by the addition of:
　　　　A. nitrogen.
　　　　B. oxygen.
　　　　C. carbon dioxide.
　　　　D. water vapor.

14.13　　Radiation-induced chromosome aberrations may be observed after a period of:
　　　　A. days.
　　　　B. weeks.
　　　　C. months.
　　　　D. years.

14.14   The Relative Biological Effectiveness (RBE) of diagnostic x-rays is most likely _____.
A. 1
B. 2
C. 5
D. >5

14.15   The LD$_{50/60}$ *whole body* dose in humans is most likely _____ Gy.
A. 1
B. 3
C. 10
D. 30

14.16   Acute radiation syndromes are not seen following a uniform whole body exposure of _____ Gy.
A. 0.1
B. 1
C. 10
D. 100

14.17   The latent period for the central nervous syndrome is most likely a few:
A. days.
B. weeks.
C. minutes.
D. hours.

14.18   The likely threshold dose for inducing a skin reaction is _____ Gy.
A. None (no threshold)
B. 0.3
C. 3
D. 30

14.19   The likely threshold dose for inducing cataracts following occupational exposure is _____ Gy.
A. None (no threshold)
B. 0.5
C. 5
D. 50

14.20   The lowest dose at which sperm count might be reduced is most likely _____ Gy.
A. 0.001
B. 0.01
C. 0.1
D. 1

14.21   Permanent sterility in males most likely requires a single dose of _____ Gy.
A. 1
B. 2
C. 6
D. 10

14.22   The threshold dose for stochastic effects of radiation is most likely _____ mGy.
A. None (no threshold)
B. 0.01
C. 0.1
D. 1

14.23   Which organ listed below is *least* sensitive to cancer induction by x-rays?
A. Lung
B. Colon
C. Bone marrow
D. Kidney

14.24   Which organ listed below is *most* sensitive to cancer induction by x-rays?
A. Stomach
B. Brain
C. Spleen
D. Heart

14.25   Genetic effects of radiation have been observed in:
A. A-bomb survivors.
B. radium dial painters.
C. uranium miners.
D. none of the above.

14.26   The mortality rate for radiation-induced cancers is most likely _____%.
A. 1
B. 10
C. 50
D. 90

14.27 Cancer induction radiation risks from occupational uniform whole body irradiation are most likely _____% per Sv.
A. 0.01
B. 0.1
C. 1
D. 10

14.28 Elevated leukemia rates have been observed in which of the following populations?
A. A-bomb survivors
B. ^{226}Ra dial painters
C. Radiologic technologist
D. All of the above

14.29 Congenital abnormalities are most likely to occur when radiation exposure occurs during:
A. preconception.
B. first 10 days.
C. organogenesis.
D. fetal period.

14.30 Elevated childhood cancer risk is most likely to occur when exposure occurs during:
A. preconception.
B. 10 days.
C. organogenesis.
D. fetal period.

ANSWERS[1]

Chapter 14: Radiation Biology

14.1   D   Genetic cells undergo meiosis, whereas somatic cells undergo mitosis.   *p. 507 Bushong*
n/a Carlton/Adler

14.2   B   The process of meiosis results in a cell with 23 chromosomes, which occurs in sperm cells and ovaries.   *p. 509 Bushong*
n/a Carlton/Adler

14.3   C   Absorbed dose is used in radiology.   *p. 34 Bushong*
p. 140 Carlton/Adler

14.4   A   Cell damage from radiation occurs in DNA molecules.   *p. 509 Bushong*
n/a Carlton/Adler

14.5   D   About 80% of the human body is water.   *p. 523 Bushong*
n/a Carlton/Adler

14.6   B   Irradiated water produces free radicals.   *p. 524 Bushong*
n/a Carlton/Adler

14.7   B   Cells are most radiosensitive during mitosis (M phase).   *p. 531 Bushong*
n/a Carlton/Adler

14.8   C   Cells are most radioresistant during the S phase.   *p. 531 Bushong*
n/a Carlton/Adler

14.9   C D_{35} means that 65% of the cells irradiated are killed and 35% survive.   *p. 537 Bushong*
n/a Carlton Adler

14.10   A   Newborns are the most radiosensitive.   *p. 513 Bushong*
p. 138 Carlton/Adler

14.11   A   Erythroblasts are the most radiosensitive.   *p. 510 Bushong*
n/a Carlton/Adler

14.12   B   Addition of oxygen increases cell radiosensitivity.   *p. 514 Bushong*
n/a Carlton/Adler

---

[1] As a study aid, page numbers for additional study are given for the following references:
Bushong SC: *Radiologic Science for Technologists,* 9th ed. St. Louis, MO: Mosby, 2008.
Carlton RR, Adler AM: *Principles of Radiographic Imaging: An Art and a Science,* 4th ed. Albany, NY: Delmar Publishing Inc., 2005.

14.13	D	Chromosome damage can be observed decades after radiation exposure.	*p. 545 Bushong* *n/a Carlton/Adler*
14.14	A	Diagnostic x-rays have an RBE of 1.	*pp. 503 Bushong* *n/a Carlton/Adler*
14.15	B	LD$_{50/60}$ represents the dose needed to kill 50% of the population in 60 days and is beleived to be ~3.5 Gy, or 350 rad.	*p. 538 Bushong* *n/a Carlton/Adler*
14.16	B	At doses above 1 Gy, radiation syndromes are seen. A dose of 0.1 Gy would not produce an effect.	*p. 536 Bushong* *n/a Carlton/Adler*
14.17	D	Central nervous syndrome occurs at exposures above 50 Gy (5000$^+$ rad) and has a latent period of several hours.	*p. 536 Bushong* *n/a Carlton/Adler*
14.18	C	Erythema can occur after a dose of 3–10 Gy (300–1000 rad).	*p. 539 Bushong* *n/a Carlton/Adler*
14.19	B	Cataract induction threshold for occupational exposure is ~5 Gy (500 rad).	*p. 552 Bushong* *n/a Carlton/Adler*
14.20	C	Doses as low as 0.1 Gy (10 rad) have resulted in a decreased sperm count.	*p. 541 Bushong* *n/a Carlton/Adler*
14.21	C	A testicular dose as low as 6 Gy (600 rad) will result in a permanent sterility in males.	*p. 541 Bushong* *n/a Carlton/Adler*
14.22	A	Stochastic effects are taken to have no threshold.	*p. 517 Bushong* *n/a Carlton/Adler*
14.23	D	Exposure of the kidney is least likely to result in cancer.	*p. 510 Bushong* *n/a Carlton/Adler*
14.24	A	Exposure of the stomach is most likely to result in cancer induction.	*p. 510 Bushong* *n/a Carlton/Adler*
14.25	D	Currently there is no evidence in humans of genetic effects caused by radiation.	*p. 564 Bushong* *n/a Carlton/Adler*
14.26	C	Half of radiation-induced cancers will result in death.	*p. 560 Bushong* *n/a Carlton/Adler*
14.27	D	Cancer induction by radiation is about 10% per sievert (effective dose).	*n/a Bushong* *n/a Carlton/Adler*
14.28	A	Atomic bomb survivors have increased leukemia rates, whereas ^{226}Ra dial painters have elevated bone cancer rates.	*p. 555 Bushong* *n/a Carlton/Adler*

14.29   C   Congenital abnormalities from radiation exposure occur
during organogenesis.

p. 564 Bushong
n/a Carlton/Adler

14.30   D   Elevated childhood cancer risks are believed to be in the
fetal period.

p. 564 Bushong
n/a Carlton/Adler

Chapter 15

RADIATION PROTECTION

15.1 **Radiation Measurement**
15.2 **Protection Devices**
15.3 **Protecting Patients**
15.4 **Workers and Public**
15.5 **Population Exposures**

15.1 RADIATION MEASUREMENT

A. Gas–filled detectors

- **Ionization chambers** and **Geiger-Mueller (G-M) detectors** are gas-filled detectors.

- Radiation traveling through the gas-filled space will ionize the gas and the displaced electrons can be collected and measured.

- Ionization chambers are used to measure radiation intensity in fluoroscopy and radionuclide imaging.

- **Ionization chambers are generally small and portable.**

- The sensitivity of **ionization chambers** used in radiology is about **0.01 mGy/hour (1 mR/hour)**.

- Nuclear medicine employs G-M detectors for contamination inspections.

- G-M detectors are capable of identifying one ionizing event; they are highly sensitive.

- **Pocket dosimeters** used in radiology departments are usually **ionization chambers**.

- Parents or those assisting with positioning of a child during exposure wear pocket dosimeters.

B. Thermoluminescent dosimetry

- Materials that glow when heated are termed **thermoluminescent**.

- Of those materials, a smaller portion will glow even brighter if exposed to radiation prior to heating.

- Such materials have been adapted for use in occupational dose monitoring and measurement of patient doses.

- After exposure, thermoluminescent detectors (TLDs) are loaded into a planchet, and placed in special ovens for heating.

- A **photomultiplier tube (PMT)** (light detector) records the emission of light from the TLD.

- TLDs are reusable after the reading process.

- **Lithium fluoride (LiF)** is commonly used in medical dosimetry.

- **Calcium fluoride (CaF)** is more sensitive.

C. Optically stimulated luminescence dosimetry

- **Optically stimulated luminescence (OSL)** is used for **personnel monitoring** and has replaced the traditional film badge.

- **Aluminum oxide (Al$_2$O$_3$)** maintains electrons in an excited state after the absorption of radiation.

- Once exposed to laser light, the excess energy is released as visible light, with an intensity proportional to the radiation incident at the detector.

- **OSL detectors are the most sensitive detectors currently available.**

- OSL monitors may be read more than once for verification of results and are extremely stable.

- **Figure 15.1** shows a commercial OSL system.

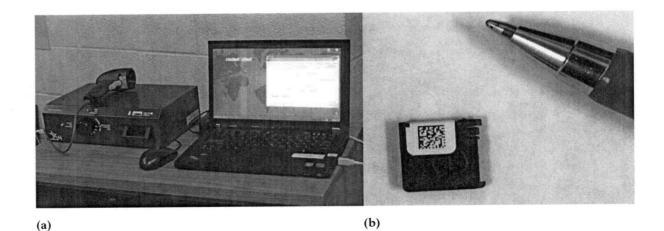

(a)   (b)

Figure 15.1
OSL reader/computer workstation (a) and OSL chip with a pen tip to illustrate chip size (b).

D. Scintillation detectors

- Scintillation detectors emit light when irradiated proportionally to the incident intensity of radiation.
- Radiation is absorbed and light is emitted, allowing a PMT to absorb the light and convert to an electrical signal.
- Scintillators used to detect radiation in a radiology department **are sodium iodide (NaI).**
- **Scintillation detectors are used to identify the photon energy of any contamination in nuclear medicine.**
- **The photon energy can be identified because the amount of light produced is directly proportional to the photon energy.**
- **Table 15.1** lists commonly used detectors in diagnostic radiology.

Table 15.1
Radiation detectors used in diagnostic radiography and their applications

Radiation detector	Detector material	Application
Ionization chamber	Air	Measure x-ray tube output
Pocket dosimeter	Air	Monitor dose of parent holding an infant (x-ray)
Thermoluminescent dosimeter	Lithium fluoride	Measure patient doses
Optically stimulated luminescent detector	Aluminum oxide	Record technologists' occupational exposure
Scintillation detector	Sodium iodide	Identify radioactive contamination

15.2 PROTECTION DEVICES

A. Protective shields

- **Lead (Pb)** may be used in construction for shielding.
- Material such as **concrete** can also be used.
- The tenth-value layer (TVL) is the amount of a material that will reduce the intensity of a beam to one-tenth the original.
- **1 TVL is equivalent to 3.3 HVL.**

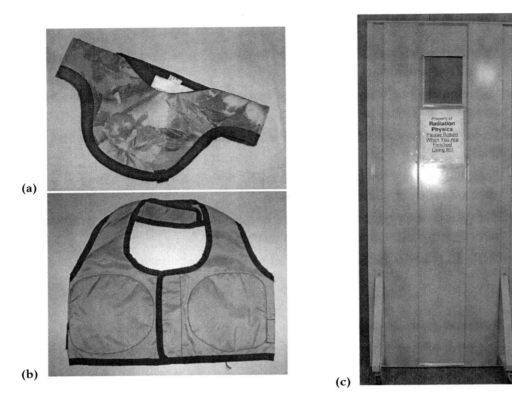

Figure 15.2
Protective devices: (a) thyroid shield; (b) breast shield; (c) mobile lead wall.

- Shielding for personnel is usually a lead apron (**~0.5 mm Pb**).
- A material similar in attenuation to lead may also be used (lead equivalent).
- **Protective apparel** should always be stored properly, hung usually, to prevent folding and cracking of the attenuating materials.
- All protective shields must be evaluated annually for cracks, holes, or tears through radiographic or fluoroscopic review.
- If there is a crack/hole in any shield, it must be taken out of service.
- The same **high-attenuation materials** used in **lead aprons** are used in **gonad** and **breast shields**.
- **Figure 15.2** shows protective devices commonly used in diagnostic radiology.

B. Room shielding design

- Radiography rooms must be shielded to prevent leakage of radiation into other areas.

- Room shielding is calculated using work loads (W), use factors (U), and occupancy factors (T).

- The **workload (W)** is a measure of the number of exams performed each week.

- Workload is measured in **milliampere-minutes per week (mA-min/wk)**.

- **Table 15.2** provides common values of workloads in radiography rooms.

- **Use factor (U)** refers to the percentage of time that the primary x-ray source is directed at a barrier.

- The **occupancy factor (T)** relates to the essential time an area is considered as being occupied.

Table 15.2
Weekly workload in mA-min for an average and busy radiology exam room (a 5-day workweek). Data based on values listed in NCRP Report No. 147

Room type	Average	Busy
Radiography room	40	60
Chest room	50	100
Fluoroscopy room	250	400
Mammography	500	1000
Angiography (cardiac)	3000	5000

C. Room shielding construction

- Room shielding may be accomplished through lead sheets affixed to the walls and floors/ceilings where necessary.

- Planning is based on the types of exams, equipment used, and areas that border the exam room.

- **Primary protective barriers** are used to intercept the primary x-ray beam.

- **Lead-lined sheetrock (1/16 in. of Pb)** or **~4 in. of concrete** may be used as a primary barrier.

- **Secondary protective barriers** shield against scatter and leakage radiation.

- Secondary protective barriers may be **sheetrock, acrylic,** or **glass** as the secondary radiation has less intensity.

- The **operating console** is located behind a protective barrier

- A **leaded-glass window** is incorporated for observation of the patient.

- The **protective barrier should be 7 feet in height** and have a protective window for patient safety.

D. X-ray equipment

- The **x-ray tube housing** is designed to limit leakage radiation to **<1 mGy/h (100 mR/h) at 1 m**.
- **Total filtration of 2.5 mm Al** is required in all diagnostic x-ray tubes.
- The **housing for the fluoroscopic image receptor** must be **2 mm Pb** or equivalent.
- Fluoroscopy systems must contain an **interlock** that prevents exposure while the tower is in the "parked" position.
- Fluoroscopic controls must be the **dead man type**.
- **Bucky slot** coverings must be available and used, **0.25 mm Pb** equivalent.
- A **protective curtain of 0.25 mm Pb** equivalent or greater is used in fluoroscopy to reduce occupational exposure.

15.3 PROTECTING PATIENTS

A. Equipment

- **Filtration** absorbs low-energy x-rays that would reach the patient but provides no useful purpose (i.e., only increases patient dose).
- **Collimation** controls the area of irradiation, or **field of view (FOV)**.
- **Source-to-skin distance (SSD)** must be at least **38 cm for traditional units** and **30 cm for portable units**.
- Proper use of automatic exposure control (AEC) should be employed to prevent overexposures and repeat images.
- A **timer** that signals after **5 min** of fluoroscopy must be in place.
- The **exposure rate in fluoroscopy** is not to exceed **100 mGy/min (10 R/min)**.
- Exposure rate must be tested in both the manual and automatic brightness control (ABC) technique.

B. Operational

- Decreasing the exposed area to that clinically necessary prevents unnecessary exposure.
- **Persons of childbearing age** can be provided with **gonad shielding** when the gonads are in or near the useful x-ray beam.
- Shielding must never obscure pertinent anatomical information.

- All women of childbearing age will be asked if there is a possibility of pregnancy.
- A pregnant patient should only be imaged after discussion with a radiologist and appropriate dose-conserving techniques have been determined.
- Select **low mAs, high kVp techniques** when appropriate.
- Use **posterior-anterior (PA)** positioning when appropriate.
- **Breast dose** may be **reduced by 99%** when utilizing the posterior-anterior (PA) position compared to the anterior-posterior (AP) position.
- Utilization of **pulsed fluoroscopy** will decrease dose and should be used when this does not detract from diagnostic information.

C. Dose monitoring

- Patient doses are often monitored in real time in IR using **Kerma Area Product (KAP) meters**.
- Kerma Area Product (KAP) systems are often referred to as **Dose Area Product (DAP)**.
- KAP meters measure in units of **Gy-cm²** in the SI system and **R-cm²** in the non-SI system.
- One Gy-cm² is approximately 100 R-cm².
- **KAP** provides an accurate characterization of the total radiation incident on the patient.
- For any given examination and patient, the **KAP value is directly related to the patient risk** and can be converted into patient effective dose.
- KAP meters in IR frequently provide additional information on the radiation intensity at the Interventional Reference Point (IRP).
- The IRP Air Kerma value is a surrogate for the patient skin dose and used to predict the likelihood of a deterministic effect (i.e., skin burn or epilation).
- **Figure 15.3** illustrates a KAP (DAP) meter found in an Interventional Suite for biplane imaging.

D. Patient dose limits

- **For most diagnostic radiological examinations, there are no regulatory dose limits.**
- The radiologist is responsible for ensuring that no more radiation is used to perform each radiological examination than is necessary.
- **Regulatory dose limits apply to fluoroscopy (state) and mammography (federal).**

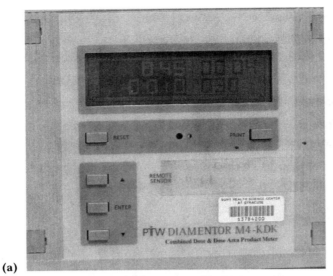

(a)

(b)

Figure 15.3

Kerma Area Product (KAP) (DAP) meter used in angiography suite (a) and
a closeup of the meter (b) showing dose values. A KAP of 0.45 mGy-cm^2
is shown indicating total radiation incident on the patient as well as an
Interventional Reference Point (IRP) value of 0.010 mGy.

- A **maximum entrance Air Kerma rate of 100 mGy/min (10 R/min)** in fluoroscopy is a regulatory requirement in most U.S. states.

- For large patients, up to **200 mGy/min (20 R/min)** may be used, provided visible and audible alarms show that the **"high dose" mode** is in operation.

- In **mammography**, the legal dose limit for an average-sized breast with 50% glandularity is **3 mGy per view (MQSA) when a grid is used.**

- The MQSA dose limit is **1 mGy per view with no grid.**

- MQSA limits apply to the dose to a **standard-size breast phantom with 50% glandularity (i.e., not a patient).**

E. Protecting the fetus

- All female patients of **childbearing age** (10–60 years of age) are questioned regarding the **possibility of pregnancy**.

- Patients that may be pregnant should have a pregnancy test prior to imaging procedures.

- If pregnant, consultation between the radiologist and ordering practitioner will determine if **alternative non-ionizing imaging procedures are appropriate**.

- When ionizing radiation procedures are determined to be appropriate, **both anterior and posterior shielding of the pregnant patient is performed**.

- **Limited examinations** may also be performed, i.e., only a AP/Lat (lateral) ankle exam.

- Shielding and limiting exposures reduce patient and fetal exposures.

15.4 WORKERS AND PUBLIC

A. Protection philosophy

- In the United States, the **National Council on Radiation Protection and Measurements (NCRP)** recommends the best radiation protection practice.

- Internationally, the **International Commission on Radiological Protection (ICRP)** also makes similar recommendations.

- ICRP and NCRP recommendations are reviewed on a regular basis, and used by national governments to develop appropriate regulations.

- ICRP/NCRP requires all exposures to be justified by a net benefit.

- Justified exposures also need to be optimized.

- All doses are required to be **As Low As Reasonably Achievable (ALARA)**.

- **ALARA** simply means that no more radiation should be used than is necessary to generate the required diagnostic information.

- In addition, regulatory dose limits in fluoroscopy and mammography must not be exceeded.

B. Worker dose limits

- A **radiation monitoring device** should be **worn at the collar**.

- Monitoring devices should be worn **outside of protective apparel**.

- Data collected from the monitors is used to estimate dose for the individual.

- **50 mSv/year (5 rem/year)** is the current U.S. regulatory occupational dose limit.

- **Eye lens dose** limit is 150 mSv/year (15 rem/year).
- **Table 15.3** provides a summary of occupational dose limits in the United States.
- Pregnant radiation workers will be provided with an **additional monitoring device** to be **worn under protective apparel.**

Table 15.3
Regulatory dose limits for radiation workers

Type of exposure	U.S. regulatory limit	Comments
Whole body	50 mSv/year	May be worn at waist or chest level for ease of use
Eyes	150 mSv/year	Best worn at collar level outside apron in fluoroscopy
Extremities	500 mSv/year	Ring device used for IR procedures and NM
Fetus	0.5 mSv/month	Monitoring device worn under apron at waist level

C. Minimizing occupational doses

- **Radiation protection principles** include limiting exposure **time**, increasing **distance** from the source of radiation, and the use of **shielding.**
- **Figure 15.4** shows average yearly occupational exposures for several types of technologists.
- At a distance **1 m from a patient** the scatter radiation is **~0.1% the intensity** of the original beam.
- In fluoroscopy, exposure times should be minimized, provided this does not detract from diagnostic performance.
- Use of Last Image Hold minimizes exposure times.
- **Immobilization devices** are used for patients who require assistance in maintaining positioning for examination.
- Under some circumstances, such devices are inadequate and a patient may require the assistance of a person.
- A radiation worker **shall not** be used, and a family member or other medical staff should always be chosen.
- Radiographic control panels should have an **exposure switch** that **prevents entrance into the room** during exposure.

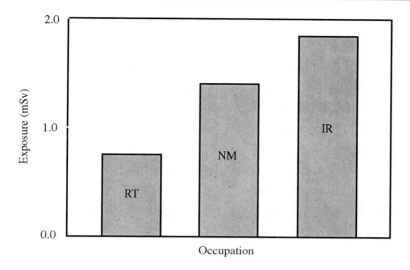

Figure 15.4
Average yearly occupational effective doses for Radiologic Technologists (RT),
Nuclear Medicine Technologists (NM), and Interventional Procedure Technologist (IR).
Typically, operators are well below the occupational dose limit of 50 mSv (5 rem).

- Portable radiography equipment is equipped with exposure switches that can be
  engaged at a minimum distance of 2 m.
- **Portable radiography** equipment requires a **protective apron** for the technologist.

D. Protecting pregnant radiation workers

- After a pregnancy is declared, there is a regulatory **monthly limit of 0.5 mSv to the
  embryo** or fetus of a radiation worker.
- Pregnant radiation workers are monitored by **an additional dosimeter** on the
  abdomen to estimate fetal doses.
- A monthly dose limit minimizes radiation risks to the fetus.
- A regulatory fetal dose rate limit of 0.5 mSv/month implies a total **dose limit of
  about 5 mSv.**
- Fetal dose limits to radiation workers are thus *higher* than that of **members of the
  public (1 mSv).**
- A higher fetus legal dose limit allows women of reproductive capacity to be radiation
  workers.

E. Protecting members of the public

- Dose limit to members of the public is **1 mSv/year (100 mrem/year).**

- Radiology facility design must ensure that doses to the public do not exceed the limits.
- Primary and secondary barriers reduce exposure to the public.
- Warning signs are posted in areas where exposure to radiation may occur.
- Radiation caution signs have a **bright yellow background** with a **black or purple propeller design and writing.**
- **Caution Radiation Area** signs are posted if exposures of **0.5 mSv/hour (5 mrem/hour)** may occur.
- **Caution High Radiation Area** signs are used for areas exceeding **1 mSv/hour (100 mrem/hour) at 30 cm.**
- **Very High Radiation Area** signs are used for areas exceeding **5 Sv/hour (500 rad/hour) at 1 m.**

15.5 POPULATION EXPOSURES

A. Ubiquitous natural background radiation

- Ubiquitous natural background radiation includes **cosmic rays, terrestrial radiation, and internally deposited radioactivity.**
- Cosmic rays are energetic charged particles that originate in galaxies.
- In the United States, **cosmic rays** result in average doses of about **0.3 mSv/year.**
- A **transatlantic flight** results in an effective dose of about **0.03 mSv.**
- **Air crews** receive an additional **5 mSv each year.**
- **External radiation (gamma rays)** from naturally occurring radionuclides in the soil delivers **~0.3 mSv/year** in the United States.
- Internal radionuclides **including ^{40}K and ^{14}C are primordial radionuclides that result in ~0.4 mSv/year** to all U.S. inhabitants.
- Cosmic radiation, terrestrial radioactivity, and primordial radionuclides contribute an average annual effective dose of **~1 mSv** *to everyone* in the **United States each year.**
- Inhabitants of Leadville, CO, have higher average doses due to increased cosmic radiation and ores containing elevated levels of radioactivity.
- **Table 15.4** summarizes typical background exposures in the United States and in Leadville, CO.

B. Radon

- Domestic radon is the greatest contributor to natural background radiation.
- **Radon**, a radioactive gas, is the product of uranium decay.
- **Radon** is an **alpha emitter**, with a half-life of about 4 days.

Table 15.4
Population exposure (mSv/year) from background exposure

Exposure source	Average annual dose (mSv) in U.S.	Annual dose in Leadville, CO (10,000 ft elevation)
Terrestrial	0.3	1.0
Primordial radionuclides	0.4	0.4
Cosmic	0.3	0.9
Radon	2	3.5
Total	**3**	**5.8**

- Alpha particles are of **high LET** and **high RBE** and are therefore very damaging.

- The **progeny of radon** are also radioactive and include alpha emitters.

- **Radon daughters** attach to aerosols and can be deposited in the **lungs**.

- **The risk from radon is from alpha irradiation** of the bronchial mucosa, which can induce bronchogenic cancer.

- Uranium deposits vary by geographical location, resulting in markedly different doses in different regions (i.e., radon exposure is not ubiquitous).

- Average annual **effective doses** from **radon in the United States** are **estimated about 2 mSv/year**.

- However, there are *very wide* variations in radon exposure.

- Radon levels **can be high in poorly ventilated basements**, but low in high-rise buildings.

C. Medical x-ray examinations in the United States

- In the United States in 2006, a total of 550 million medical examinations were performed that used ionizing radiations.

- 280 millions examinations were categorized as radiographic, and include basic fluoroscopy.

- Dental x-rays accounted for 125 million examinations, primarily bitewing intraoral studies.

- 70 million CT examinations were performed, primarily in hospital settings.

- Mammography accounted for a total of 35 million examinations.

- 20 million nuclear medicine studies were performed, primarily in cardiac imaging.

- Interventional Radiology had approximately 15 million examinations.

D. Medical radiation doses

- The U.S. population average dose from diagnostic medical examinations was **0.6 mSv in 1980.**

- By the year **2006,** diagnostic **medical** examination doses to the U.S. population had increased to **3 mSv.**

- **U.S. population doses** from **medical imaging** have thus increased **sixfold** in a single generation.

- Diagnostic **medical imaging** currently accounts for most of the **U.S. population dose**, and continues to increase.

- Medical doses in the United States are now beginning to exceed doses from natural background.

- Only **12%** of all **diagnostic exams** are **CT** scans, which accounts for **half** the **population medical dose.**

- **Figure 15.5** illustrates the increase seen in CT examinations from 1993–2006.

- Use of CT has been increasing at a rate of **~10% per year over the last decade**, whereas population growth over the same period has been <1% per year.

- **Table 15.5** summarizes data for U.S. medical exposures in 2006.

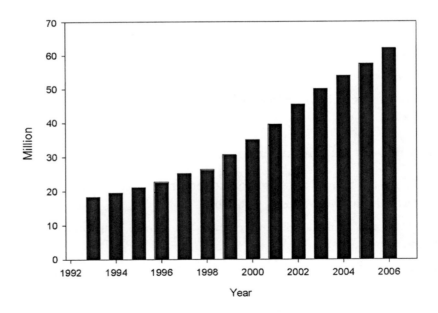

Figure 15.5
Total number of CT procedures performed in the United States from 1993–2006.

Table 15.5
Medical x-ray examinations performed in the U.S. in 2006

Type of examination	Number of examinations (millions)	Average patient effective dose	Population average dose
Radiography/Fluoroscopy	290	0.7	0.6
Computed Tomography	67	7	1.5
Interventional Radiology	17	9	0.4
Nuclear Medicine	17	11	0.7

E. Man-made radiation (non-medical)

- Nuclear power contributes less than 1% of the total dose to the U.S. population.
- **Consumer products** contribute about 0.1 mSv/year (10 mrem/year).
- Airport surveillance, smoke detectors, and watch dials are radiation-emitting consumer products.
- Occupational exposure includes medical, nuclear power, and industry.
- Medical workers average 1.5 mSv/year (150 mrem/year).
- Nuclear power employees average 5 mSv/year (500 mrem/year).
- Industrial workers are exposed to ~2.5 mSv/year (250 mrem/year).
- **Occupational doses contribute very little** to the total exposure of the U.S. population doses.

QUESTIONS

Chapter 15: Radiation Protection Questions

15.1   Geiger-Mueller tubes most likely contain a:
A. gas.
B. scintillator.
C. photoconductor.
D. fluid.

15.2   Which of the following detectors is best for detecting one single x-ray photon?
A. Scintillator
B. Geiger-Mueller
C. Ionization chamber
D. Photostimulable phosphor

15.3   When a thermoluminescent dosimeter is heated, it emits:
A. light.
B. charge.
C. x-rays.
D. RF radiation.

15.4   The radiation detection property of aluminum oxide is best described as:
A. triboluminescence.
B. fluorescence.
C. phosphorescence.
D. optically stimulated luminescence.

15.5   OSL dosimeters are stimulated using:
A. heat.
B. light.
C. charge.
D. voltage.

15.6   Which of the following is the most sensitive radiation detector used for occupational dose monitoring?
A. Film badge
B. OSL
C. TLD
D. Pocket dosimeter

15.7   One TVL is equivalent to how many HVLs?
A. 1.3
B. 2.3
C. 3.3
D. 4.3

15.8   The radiation intensity transmitted through two tenth-value layers is most likely _____%.
A. 10
B. 1
C. 0.1
D. 0.01

15.9   The occupancy factor of the office of an x-ray technologist is most likely _____.
A. 1
B. 0.9
C. 0.5
D. 0.1

15.10   Which is *least* likely needed to design the shielding for an x-ray room?
A. Occupancy factor
B. Use factor
C. X-ray beam filtration
D. Workload

15.11   The dose rate limit in the operator's booth of a CT scanner is most likely _____ mSv/week.
A. 0.001
B. 0.01
C. 0.1
D. 1

15.12   The height from the floor of shielding in an x-ray room would likely be _____ feet.
A. 5
B. 7
C. 9
D. >9

15.13   The lead equivalence of the housing of an image receptor is most likely _____ mm.
A. 0.5
B. 1
C. 2
D. 4

15.14   The protective curtain placed between the fluoroscopy unit and the practitioner is likely to have a lead equivalence of _____ mm.
      A. 0.05
      B. 0.1
      C. 0.15
      D. 0.25

15.15   The timer in fluoroscopy would most likely sound every _____ minutes.
      A. 2
      B. 5
      C. 10
      D. 20

15.16   The maximum Air Kerma rate in conventional fluoroscopy should not exceed _____ mGy/min.
      A. 0.1
      B. 1
      C. 10
      D. 100

15.17   The minimum source to skin distance for a portable radiographic unit is _____ mm.
      A. 20
      B. 30
      C. 38
      D. 48

15.18   Which of the following techniques is most appropriate for minimizing patient breast dose during a scoliosis series?
      A. PA positioning
      B. Pulsed fluoroscopy
      C. High mAs, low kVp
      D. Use of a wedge filter

15.19   The units of a Kerma Area Product (AKA Dose Area Product) meters are most likely _____ .
      A. Gy
      B. cm^2
      C. $Gy\text{-}cm^2$
      D. $Gy\text{-}cm$

15.20 If the area of the patient exposed to x-rays is A, patient risk is most likely proportional to _____.
   A. A
   B. 1/A
   C. A^2
   D. $A^{0.5}$

15.21 Activation of high-level control in fluoroscopy increases the maximum Air Kerma rate by _____%.
   A. 50
   B. 100
   C. 200
   D. >200

15.22 The maximum dose to a standard breast in mammography is most likely _____ mGy per image.
   A. 1
   B. 2
   C. 3
   D. No dose limit

15.23 The current whole body regulatory dose limit for radiation workers is most likely _____ mSv/year.
   A. 0.05
   B. 0.5
   C. 5
   D. 50

15.24 The current extremity regulatory dose limit for radiation workers is _____ mSv/year.
   A. 0.5
   B. 5
   C. 50
   D. 500

15.25 Which of the following is least likely to affect the dose to an x-ray technologist?
   A. Time
   B. Image receptor
   C. Distance
   D. Shielding

15.26   At a distance of 1 m from a patient, the scatter intensity is most likely _____%.
A. 10
B. 1
C. 0.1
D. 0.01

15.27   In the United States, annual natural background exposure is most likely _____ mSv/year.
A. 1
B. 2
C. 3
D. 5

15.28   The largest source of natural background exposure is from:
A. Cosmic radiation.
B. Terrestrial radioactivity.
C. Primordial radionuclides (^{40}K).
D. Radon (+ daughters).

15.29   Consumer products that emit ionizing radiations are least likely to include:
A. MR scanners.
B. airport surveillance.
C. smoke detectors.
D. watches.

15.30   The percentage (%) of the U.S. population medical dose attributed to CT is most likely _____.
A. 90
B. 50
C. 25
D. 10

ANSWERS[1]

Chapter 15: Radiation Protection

15.1 A G-M tubes contain a gas.

p. 590 Bushong
p. 142 Carlton/Adler

15.2 B G-M tubes are used in nuclear medicine, are very sensitive, and are capable of detecting a single photon.

p. 590 Bushong
p. 142 Carlton/Adler

15.3 A TLDs release light when heated whose intensity is proportional to the radiation exposure.

p. 593 Bushong
p. 144 Carlton/Adler

15.4 D Optically Stimulated Luminesence (OSL) detectors are made of aluminum oxide.

p. 594 Bushong
p. 143 Carlton/Adler

15.5 B OSL detectors are read by exposing them to a light source, similar to TLD detectors and heat.

p. 594 Bushong
p. 143 Carlton/Adler

15.6 B OSL detectors are more sensitive than film or TLD badges.

p. 594 Bushong
p. 143 Carlton/Adler

15.7 C One tenth-value layer (TVL) reduces the radiation beam to one-tenth its original value and is equivalent to ~0.3 HVLs.

p. 574 Bushong
n/a Carlton/Adler

15.8 B One tenth-value layer reduces the radiation beam to one-tenth its original value.

p. 574 Bushong
n/a Carlton/Adler

15.9 A Areas such as offices, labs, or living space have an occupancy factor of 1.0.

p. 587 Bushong
n/a Carlton/Adler

15.10 C When planning a room, the occupancy factor, workload, kVp, and use factor are required, whereas beam filtration is not.

p. 587 Bushong
n/a Carlton/Adler

15.11 D Controlled areas are limited to 1 mSv/wk (100 mrem/wk).

p. 586 Bushong
n/a Carlton/Adler

15.12 B The height of a barrier needs to be at least 7 feet, the potential height of a person.

n/a Bushong
n/a Carlton/Adler

---

[1] As a study aid, page numbers for additional study are given for the following references:
Bushong SC: *Radiologic Science for Technologists,* 9th ed. St. Louis, MO: Mosby, 2008.
Carlton RR, Adler AM: *Principles of Radiographic Imaging: An Art and a Science,* 4th ed. Albany, NY: Delmar Publishing Inc., 2005.

15.13	C	An equivalent of ~2 mm lead is used as a primary barrier in most radiography rooms.	*p. 585 Bushong* *n/a Carlton/Adler*
15.14	D	Protective curtains and Bucky slot covers used in fluoroscopy have a lead equivalent of 0.25 mm.	*p. 583 Bushong* *p. 580 Carlton/Adler*
15.15	B	Fluoroscopy systems have a 5-minute exposure timer.	*p. 572 Bushong* *p. 579 Carlton/Adler*
15.16	D	Regulation limit conventional fluoroscopy entrance Air Kerma to 100 mGy/min (10 R/min).	*p. 311 Bushong* *p. 579 Carlton/Adler*
15.17	B	The minimum SID in portable radiography is 30 cm (12 in.).	*n/a Bushong* *p. 579 Carlton/Adler*
15.18	A	The use of PA positioning will substantially decrease dose to the breast relative to an AP projection.	*p. 606 Bushong* *p. 203 Carlton/Adler*
15.19	C	KAP (DAP) meters read out in Gy-cm^2.	*p. 606 Bushong* *n/a Carlton/Adler*
15.20	A	Patient risk is proportional to exposed area.	*p. 584 Bushong* *n/a Carlton/Adler*
15.21	B	Regulations limit conventional fluoroscopy entrance Air Kerma to 100 mGy/min (10 R/min) but 200 mGy/min (20 R/min) for high-dose fluoroscopy (i.e., 100%).	*p. 311 Bushong* *n/a Carlton/Adler*
15.22	C	A single mammography image should not exceed 3 mGy (300 mrad).	*p. 328 Bushong* *n/a Carlton/Adler*
15.23	D	Occupational dose limit is 50 mSv/year or 5 rem/year.	*p. 606 Bushong* *p. 151 Carlton/Adler*
15.24	D	Occupational dose limit for extremities is 500 mSv/year or 50 rem/year.	*p. 606 Bushong* *p. 151 Carlton/Adler*
15.25	B	Imaging receptor used, film/screen, CR, or DR will have negligible effect on operator dose.	*p. 12 Bushong* *n/a Carlton/Adler*
15.26	C	At a distance of 1 m, the scatter radiation intensity is about 0.1% of the patient entrance Air Kerma.	*p. 585 Bushong* *n/a Carlton/Adler*
15.27	C	The average background dose from natural sources in the United States is ~3 mSv (300 mrem).	*p. 5 Bushong* *p. 139 Carlton/Adler*
15.28	D	Radon is the largest source of natural background exposure.	*p. 5 Bushong* *p. 139 Carlton/Adler*

15.29   A   MR scanners do not use ionizing radiation.

p. 5 Bushong
p. 138 Carlton/Adler

15.30   B   About half the U.S. medical dose is from CT.

p. 602 Bushong
n/a Carlton/Adler

TEST A

TEST A

1. Which of the following is a unit of energy?
   A. Electron volt
   B. Watt
   C. Ampere
   D. Coulomb

2. The ratio of the proton mass to the electron mass is most likely _____ .
   A. 2:1
   B. 20:1
   C. 200:1
   D. 2000:1

3. For waves, the relationship between velocity (v), frequency (f), and wavelength (λ) is:
   A. $v = f / \lambda$.
   B. $v = f \times \lambda$.
   C. $v = \lambda / f$.
   D. $v = f + \lambda$.

4. Increasing the distance from an electromagnetic source of radiation from 1 m to 4 m would reduce the radiation intensity by a factor of _____ .
   A. 4
   B. 8
   C. 16
   D. 64

5. Velocity is measured in:
   A. meters.
   B. seconds.
   C. meters/second.
   D. meters/second/second.

6. An object is *least* likely to become charged by:
   A. friction.
   B. induction.
   C. batteries.
   D. magnets.

7. In the United States, the domestic electrical power supply voltage (V) is most likely _____ .
   A. 110
   B. 220
   C. 330
   D. 440

8. Electricity is most likely to be produced in a(n):
   A. generator.
   B. electromagnet.
   C. electrical motor.
   D. transformer.

9. The frequency of the AC electricity supply to an x-ray generator is most likely:
   A. 0 (DC).
   B. 6 Hz.
   C. 12 Hz.
   D. 60 Hz.

10. The maximum power (kW) of an x-ray generator is most likely _____ .
    A. 3
    B. 10
    C. 30
    D. 100

11. Increasing the x-ray tube voltage to 95 kVp increases the maximum photon energy to _____ keV.
    A. 40
    B. 60
    C. 70
    D. 95

12. Air Kerma is measured in:
    A. roentgen.
    B. gray.
    C. sievert.
    D. coulomb.

13. When the energy of an x-ray photon doubles, the chance of a Compton scatter interaction is reduced by _____%.
    A. 400
    B. 200
    C. 50
    D. 25

14. In a photoelectric effect, x-ray interactions are most likely to occur with:
    A. inner shell electrons.
    B. outer shell electrons.
    C. middle shell electrons.
    D. all atomic electrons.

15. Use of a grid with a Bucky factor of 5 would likely require an increase in mAs of _____%.
    A. 100
    B. 200
    C. 500
    D. 1000

16. If the attenuation coefficient is 0.1 cm^{-1}, the percentage of x-rays transmitted through 1 cm is most likely _____%.
    A. 0.09
    B. 0.9
    C. 9
    D. 90

17. The physical principle underlying the functioning of x-ray tube filaments is best described as:
    A. thermionic emission.
    B. quantum tunneling.
    C. radiative heating.
    D. internal conversion.

18. Anode rotation is *least* likely to make use of:
    A. electromagnets.
    B. stators.
    C. rotors.
    D. rectifiers.

19. Restricting the size of an x-ray beam is most likely to reduce:
    A. x-ray production.
    B. scattered radiation.
    C. primary transmission.
    D. anode heating.

20. Which SID (cm) is most likely to result in the highest heel effect?
    A. 30
    B. 50
    C. 75
    D. 100

21. All grains found in film emulsions are likely to contain:
    A. lead.
    B. tungsten.
    C. silver.
    D. barium.

22. The thickness of a film emulsion is most likely _____ mm.
    A. 0.005
    B. 0.05
    C. 0.5
    D. 5.0

23. When a photoelectron migrates to a sensitivity center, the resultant charge is most likely:
    A. positive.
    B. negative.
    C. neutral.
    D. positive or negative.

24. Which is *least* likely an integral component of an automatic film processor?
    A. Fixer
    B. Washer
    C. Dryer
    D. Cooler

25. The percentage of x-rays absorbed by a phosphor is best referred to as the:
    A. detection efficiency.
    B. fluorescence yield.
    C. conversion efficiency.
    D. primary transmission.

26. Material for the rear of a cassette would most likely have a high:
    A. conversion efficiency.
    B. atomic number.
    C. melting point.
    D. physical density.

27. A screen-film combination used for extremity radiography would likely be classified as having a speed of _____ .
    A. 0.5
    B. 5
    C. 50
    D. 500

28. The light color emitted by photostimulable phosphors is most likely:
    A. blue.
    B. yellow.
    C. orange.
    D. red.

29. A motherboard would be least likely to include a:
    A. microprocessor.
    B. RAM.
    C. ROM.
    D. modem.

30. Which of the following is most likely used to perform filtered back projections in CT imaging?
    A. Array processors
    B. Modem
    C. RAID
    D. Microprocessor

31. Which would likely be slowest in transmitting a digital chest x-ray?
    A. ISDN line
    B. Phone line
    C. DSL line
    D. Cable modem

32. How many shades of gray can a byte display?
    A. 2
    B. 8
    C. 64
    D. 256

33. Which of the following is *least* likely to relate to post processing raw x-ray image data?
    A. Windowing
    B. Leveling
    C. Flat field
    C. Inversion

34. The brightness of a conventional viewbox for radiographs is most likely _____ nits.
    A. 1.5
    B. 15
    C. 150
    D. 1500

35. How many (horizontal) lines are most likely to be used on a digital monitor showing a chest x-ray?
    A. 800
    B. 1600
    C. 3200
    D. 6400

36. Compared to CRTs, LCDs are more likely to have a greater:
    A. gray scale.
    B. refresh rate.
    C. number of lines.
    D. noise level.

37. X-ray beam quality is most likely to be independent of:
    A. x-ray tube voltage.
    B. voltage ripple.
    C. tube current.
    D. filtration.

38. An average patient would likely be called:
    A. sthenic.
    B. hyposthenic.
    C. hypersthenic.
    D. asthenic.

39. Which of the following is the most common technique chart?
    A. Automatic Exposure
    B. Variable kVp
    C. Fixed kVp
    D. All used equally

40. An electronic timer in an AEC system should be set at what percentage of the anticipated exposure time?
    A. 75%
    B. 150%
    C. 250%
    D. >250%

41. Which of the following is *least* likely a mammography system target/filter combination?
    A. Mo/Mo
    B. Mo/Rh
    C. Rh/Rh
    D. Rh/Mo

42. X-ray tube power requirements for an IR system is most likely _____ W.
    A. 100
    B. 1000
    C. 10,000
    D. 100,000

43. The tomographic angle is most likely to influence the slice:
    A. thickness.
    B. location.
    C. width.
    D. length.

44. Magnification radiography would always make use of a reduced:
    A. beam filtration.
    B. focal spot.
    C. tube current.
    D. tube voltage.

45. The housing of an II is most likely made of:
    A. acrylic.
    B. lead.
    C. metal.
    D. semiconductors.

46. Photocathode electron intensity is directly proportional to the phosphor:
    A. column diameter.
    B. light output.
    C. physical density.
    D. thickness.

47. Output phosphors on IIs are most likely made of:
    A. GdOS.
    B. CsI.
    C. BaFBr.
    D. ZnCdS.

48. The electron gun in a CRT is most likely to be modulated by a(n):
    A. video signal.
    B. x-ray beam.
    C. focusing coils.
    D. focusing lens.

49. The number of TV lines on a standard fluoroscopy display is most likely _____ .
    A. 250
    B. 500
    C. 1000
    D. 2000

50. In the fluoroscopy imaging chain, a charge-coupled device (CCD) could replace the:
    A. CRT display.
    B. lens system.
    C. TV camera.
    D. output phosphor.

51. Automatic Brightness Control in fluoroscopy makes use of the light produced in the:
    A. CCD camera.
    B. input phosphor.
    C. photocathode.
    D. output phosphor.

52. Doubling the magnification in fluoroscopy with image intensifiers will likely increase the entrance Air Kerma by a factor of _____ .
    A. 2
    B. 3
    C. 4
    D. 8

53. A CT fan beam angle is most likely _____ degrees.
   A. 5
   B. 15
   C. 50
   D. 150

54. A graphical plot of projections as a function of x-ray tube angles is called a:
   A. sinogram.
   B. back projection.
   C. projection.
   D. ray-sum.

55. What is the likely pixel size (mm) when the head CT field of view is 25 cm?
   A. 0.25
   B. 0.5
   C. 1
   D. 2

56. The Hounsfield Unit of fat is most likely:
   A. 0
   B. 50
   C. −200
   D. −100

57. If the window width is 100, and the level is 50, which pixel value will appear gray?
   A. 0
   B. 50
   C. 100
   D. 150

58. Use of helical scanning most likely improves image:
   A. acquisition speed.
   B. quantum mottle.
   C. spatial resolution.
   D. scatter rejection.

59. The spatial resolution on a 64-slice CT scanner is best described as being:
   A. isocentric.
   B. isomorphic.
   C. isotropic.
   D. none of the above.

60. Which is *least* likely to be a CT artifact?
    A. Partial volume
    B. Streak
    C. Beam hardening
    D. π-line

61. The units of Air Kerma are _____ .
    A. J
    B. J/kg
    C. J-s/kg
    D. J/s-kg

62. The energy imparted to a patient in a chest radiograph is most likely _____ mJ.
    A. 0.02
    B. 2
    C. 200
    D. 20,000

63. Entrance Air Kerma for an AP abdominal radiograph is most likely _____ mGy.
    A. 0.03
    B. 0.3
    C. 3
    D. 30

64. Entrance Air Kerma for a lateral skull radiograph is most likely _____ mGy.
    A. 0.15
    B. 1.5
    C. 15
    D. 150

65. Volume CTDI (CTDI$_{vol}$) is measured in units of:
    A. joule.
    B. watt.
    C. gray.
    D. sievert.

66. The effective dose is an indicator of the patient risk of:
    A. stochastic effects.
    B. genetic effects.
    D. deterministic effects.
    D. all of the above.

67. The typical adult effective dose from a body CT examination is most likely _____ mSv.
    A. 0.1
    B. 1
    C. 10
    D. 100

68. The typical adult effective dose from an abdominal radiograph is most likely _____ mSv.
    A. 0.5
    B. 5
    C. 50
    D. 500

69. High contrast films are most likely to have a:
    A. high speed.
    B. low speed.
    C. good resolution.
    D. limited latitude.

70. The best measure of spatial resolution is most likely:
    A. mm per line pair.
    B. mm.
    C. line pairs per mm.
    D. line pairs.

71. For a given source-to-image-receptor distance (SID) and source-to-object distance (SOD), magnification is given by:
    A. SID/SOD.
    B. SID + SOD.
    C. SID – SOD.
    D. SOD/SID.

72. The dynamic range of an 8-bit digital detector is _____ .
    A. 64
    B. 128
    C. 256
    D. 512

73. A contrast detail curve would plot lesion contrast as a function of lesion:
    A. detail.
    B. diameter.
    C. atomic number.
    D. density.

74. Hypo retention is likely to turn films:
    A. black.
    B. white.
    C. red.
    D. brown.

75. CR is least likely to be susceptible to artifacts due to:
    A. fog.
    B. dust.
    C. overexposure.
    D. ghosting.

76. CR plates should be erased every:
    A. day.
    B. week.
    C. month.
    D. year.

77. Quality control (QC) primarily involves equipment:
    A. purchase.
    B. testing.
    C. maintenance.
    D. repair.

78. Under MQSA, responsibility for daily QC is most likely with the:
    A. radiologic technologist.
    B. medical physicist.
    C. diagnostic radiologist.
    D. radiology administrator.

79. In a film QC program, the limits on speed fluctuations are most likely:
    A. ±0.01.
    B. ±0.05.
    C. ±0.15.
    D. ±0.50.

80. Incomplete image erasure on a CR plate would likely result in:
    A. ghosting.
    B. aliasing.
    C. overexposure.
    D. underexposure.

81. Which of the following is least likely to be used to measure the focal spot size?
   A. Pinhole camera
   B. Star pattern
   C. Slit camera
   D. Digital camera

82. Maximum entrance Air Kerma rates in routine fluoroscopy are most likely _____ mGy/min.
   A. 0.1
   B. 1
   C. 10
   D. 100

83. CT image noise is most likely measured using a:
   A. water phantom.
   B. linearity insert.
   C. resolution test pattern.
   D. low contrast resolution test pattern.

84. High contrast resolution is most likely measured using a:
   A. water phantom.
   B. bar pattern.
   C. dosimetry phantom.
   D. low-contrast lesions.

85. How many chromosomes do most human cells contain?
   A. 23
   B. 32
   C. 46
   D. 64

86. The fraction of radiobiological damage arising from indirect effects of radiation
   is likely _____ .
   A. 1/4
   B. 1/3
   C. 1/2
   D. 2/3

87. Late radiation effects are most likely due to:
   A. main-chain scission.
   B. cross-linking.
   C. point lesions.
   D. all of the above.

88. Fractionation is most likely used in radiation therapy because this allows for tissue:
    A. repair.
    B. reoxygenation.
    C. recycling.
    D. all of the above.

89. The most likely relative biological effectiveness of diagnostic x-ray is _____ .
    A. 1
    B. 1.5
    C. 5
    D. 20

90. Hematological syndrome is most likely to be observed in a matter of:
    A. minutes.
    B. hours.
    C. days.
    D. weeks.

91. Which of the following is most likely a stochastic radiation effect?
    A. Lung cancer
    B. Erythema
    C. Sterility
    D. Cataract

92. The fetal radiation dose that most likely doubles the risk of childhood cancer is _____ mGy.
    A. 0 (no risk)
    B. 25
    C. 100
    D. 500

93. The lowest dose that a medical TLD is most likely to measure is _____ mGy.
    A. 0.05
    B. 0.5
    C. 5
    D. 50

94. The lead thickness equivalent of a lead apron in radiology is most likely _____ mm.
    A. 0.1
    B. 0.5
    C. 1
    D. 5

95. Cracks can best be prevented for protective apparel by placing these in(on):
    A. drawers.
    B. shelving.
    C. cupboards.
    D. hangers.

96. The most likely shielding of an x-ray room is _____ mm lead.
    A. 0.02
    B. 0.2
    C. 2
    D. 20

97. The minimum source–to-skin distance (SSD) for a conventional radiographic unit
    is _____ mm.
    A. 20
    B. 30
    C. 38
    D. 48

98. During fluoroscopy, radiation dose monitoring devices are normally worn close to the:
    A. collar.
    B. head.
    C. knees.
    D. waist.

99. The dose limit to the fetus of a pregnant radiation worker is _____ mSv/month.
    A. 0.005
    B. 0.05
    C. 0.5
    D. 5

100. Medical radiation doses in the United States, when averaged over the population, are
     about _____ mSv.
     A. 1
     B. 3
     C. 10
     D. 30

ANSWERS

1.   A   The unit for energy is an electron volt (eV).

   p. 4 Bushong
   p. 15 Carlton/Adler

2.   D   Protons and neutrons are ~2000 times the mass of an electron.

   p. 41 Bushong
   p. 23 Carlton/Adler

3.   B $v = f \times \lambda$, where v = velocity, f = frequency, and λ = wavelength.

   p. 60 Bushong
   p. 33 Carlton/Adler

4.   C   The inverse square law may be applied to calculate the effect, $(I_1/I_2) = (d_2/d_1)^2$. A 4× increase in distance will reduce intensity by a factor of 16.

   p. 67 Bushong
   p. 40 Carlton/Adler

5.   C   Velocity measures the rate of change of an object's position within a specific time period, meters/second.

   p. 19 Bushong
   p. 34 Carlton/Adler

6.   D   Objects may be electrified (charged) by contact, friction, or induction, but not by magnets.

   p. 73 Bushong
   p. 43 Carlton/Adler

7.   A   Electrical potential in the United States for homes/offices is 110 V.

   p. 77 Bushong
   p. 91 Carlton/Adler

8.   A   A generator uses the movement of a coil of wire in a magnetic field to produce electricity.

   p. 91 Bushong
   p. 68 Carlton/Adler

9.   D   Current from wall outlets in the United States is 60 Hz alternating current (AC).

   p. 110 Bushong
   p. 91 Carlton/Adler

10.   D   A radiography generator's maximum rating is ~100 kW.

   p. 116 Bushong
   p. 96 Carlton/Adler

11.   D   Maximum photon energy is numerically equal to the kVp applied to the x-ray tube. For example, when the kVp is 95, the resulting maximum keV of a photon is 95.

   p. 142 Bushong
   p. 172 Carlton/Adler

12.   B   Air Kerma is measured in gray (Gy).

   Front matter, Bushong
   p. 130 Carlton/Adler

---

[1] As a study aid, page numbers for additional study are given for the following references:
   Bushong SC: *Radiologic Science for Technologists,* 9th ed. St. Louis, MO: Mosby, 2008.
   Carlton RR, Adler AM: *Principles of Radiographic Imaging: An Art and a Science,* 4th ed. Albany, NY: Delmar Publishing Inc., 2005.

13.	C	Compton interactions are inversely proportional to x-ray energy (1/E). When the energy is doubled, the chance of an interaction is halved, or reduced by 50%.	*p. 165 Bushong* *p. 194 Carlton/Adler*
14.	A	Photoelectric interactions are between incident x-ray photons and inner shell electrons.	*p. 165 Bushong* *p. 186 Carlton/Adler*
15.	C	There is a direct relationship between the Bucky factor and the increase in mAs required to maintain image quality. With a Bucky factor of 5, an increase of five times, or 500%, is required to maintain a constant x-ray intensity at the image receptor.	*p. 235 Bushong* *p. 262 Carlton/Adler*
16.	D	An attenuation coefficient of 0.1 cm^{-1} results in an attenuation of 10% of the beam and transmission of 90% of the beam through 1 cm of tissue.	*p. 175 Bushong* *p. 239 Carlton/Adler*
17.	A	The process of boiling off electrons at the filament is termed thermionic emission.	*p. 122 Bushong* *p. 107 Carlton/Adler*
18.	D	Anode rotation is performed using an electromagnet, stator, to turn the rotor within the vacuum tube. Rectifiers are not used.	*p. 127 Bushong* *p. 116 Carlton/Adler*
19.	B	Reducing the FOV irradiates less tissue, thereby reducing scatter.	*p. 225 Bushong* *p. 229 Carlton/Adler*
20.	A	Anode heel effect increases as the SID is reduced, and will be greatest at the shortest SID (30 cm).	*p. 129 Bushong* *p. 114 Carlton/Adler*
21.	C	Film used in diagnostic radiology contains silver, often in the form of a silver halide crystal.	*p. 182 Bushong* *p. 273 Carlton/Adler*
22.	A	The film's emulsion layer is 0.005 mm (5 μm) in thickness.	*p. 182 Bushong* *p. 273 Carlton/Adler*
23.	B	Photoelectrons collect at the sensitivity center and have a negative charge.	*p. 184 Bushong* *p. 276 Carlton/Adler*
24.	D	The automatic film processor has four main stages: development, fixing, washing, and drying. There is no cooler.	*p. 200 Bushong* *p. 291 Carlton/Adler*
25.	A	Detection efficiency is the percentage of x-rays absorbed by a screen.	*p. 212 Bushong* *p. 319 Carlton/Adler*
26.	B	The posterior cover of a cassette is made of a high atomic number material to absorb any backscatter.	*p. 214 Bushong* *p. 325 Carlton/Adler*

27.   C   Detail film-screen combinations with a speed of 50 are used for extremity imaging.

p. 210 Bushong
p. 323 Carlton/Adler

28.   A   Photostimulable phosphors release a blue light that can be detected and differentiated from the red stimulating light using a filter.

p. 415 Bushong
p. 358 Carlton/Adler

29.   D   A motherboard is the main circuit board in a computer that contains the microprocessor, RAM chips, ROM chips, and expansion slots for additional equipment. A modem is not included.

p. 402 Bushong
n/a Carlton/Adler

30.   A   Array processors are used in CT reconstruction due to their computational speed.

p. 373 Bushong
p. 345 Carlton/Adler

31.   B   Cable can function at speeds of 1000 times that of phone lines, with ISDN and DSL lines somewhere in between those speeds.

p. 405 Bushong
n/a Carlton/Adler

32.   D   A bit can only represent one of two digits, a 0 or a 1. There are 8 bits in a byte, resulting in 256 possible combinations or shades of gray.

p. 403 Bushong
p. 379 Carlton/Adler

33.   C   Post processing includes annotation, windowing/leveling, and inversion, not flat fielding.

p. 472 Bushong
p. 348 Carlton/Adler

34.   D   Conventional viewboxes have a brightness of about 1500 nits.

p. 310 Bushong
p. 488 Carlton/Adler

35.   B   A digital monitor used to view a chest x-ray would have 1600 horizontal lines.

p. 470 Bushong
p. 345 Carlton/Adler

36.   A   LCD monitors have a greater gray scale range.

p. 470 Bushong
p. 384 Carlton/Adler

37.   C   Tube current (mA) is the prime factor controlling beam quantity and has no effect on beam quality.

p. 245 Bushong
p. 175 Carlton/Adler

38.   A   Sthenic patients are generally considered an average patient.

p. 251 Bushong
n/a Carlton/Adler

39.   C   Fixed kVp charts are the most used due to their ease of use.

p. 262 Bushong
p. 499 Carlton/Adler

40.   B   The timer should be set to 150% (1.5 times) the anticipated time of exposure.

p. 109 Bushong
p. 103 Carlton/Adler

41.	D	Target filter combinations used in mammography are: Mo/Mo, Mo/Rh, Rh/Rh, and W/Ag. Rh/Mo is not used.	*p. 322 Bushong* *p. 615 Carlton/Adler*
42.	D	IR generators must have a power rating on the order of 100,000 W, or 100 kW.	*p. 364 Bushong* *p. 631 Carlton/Adler*
43.	A	The larger the tomographic angle, the thinner the slice thickness.	*p. 267 Bushong* *p. 589 Carlton/Adler*
44.	B	Magnification requires the use of a small focal spot to reduce focal spot blur.	*p. 269 Bushong* *p. 616 Carlton/Adler*
45.	C	The image intensifier is a vacuum tube made of glass.	*p. 349 Bushong* *p. 568 Carlton/Adler*
46.	B	The intensity of photoelectrons is proportional to the light output of the input phosphor within the image intensifier.	*p. 352 Bushong* *p. 570 Carlton/Adler*
47.	D	The output phosphor of an image intensifier is composed of zinc cadmium sulfide.	*p. 350 Bushong* *p. 570 Carlton/Adler*
48.	A	The video signal from the TV camera tube modulates the electron gun of the CRT.	*p. 356 Bushong* *p. 576 Carlton/Adler*
49.	B	Standard CRT monitors have ~500 lines of data.	*p. 356 Bushong* *p. 576 Carlton/Adler*
50.	C	A CCD may replace a TV camera tube to view the II output.	*p. 439 Bushong* *p. 575 Carlton/Adler*
51.	D	ABC automatically adjusts the kVp, mA, or both to maintain a preset brightness at the output phosphor for viewing.	*p. 347 Bushong* *p. 572 Carlton/Adler*
52.	C	Doubling the magnification reduces the exposed area of an image intensifier by a factor of 4, and will therefore require a quadrupling of the entrance Air Kerma.	*p. 352 Bushong* *p. 570 Carlton/Adler*
53.	C	CT scanner fan beams are ~50 degrees, wide enough to cover an entire patient.	*p. 370 Bushong* *p. 645 Carlton/Adler*
54.	A	A sinogram is a graphical representation of profile data or measurements.	*p. 369 Bushong* *p. 660 Carlton/Adler*
55.	B	Pixel size is calculated by dividing the matrix size into the FOV, so a 250 mm FOV and a 512 matrix has a pixel size of 0.5 mm.	*p. 376 Bushong* *p. 663 Carlton/Adler*

56.   D   Fat has an HU of −100. It is less dense than water.

p. 377 Bushong
p. 659 Carlton/Adler

57.   B   With a level of 50 and a width of 100, pixels above 100 appear white and those below 0 will appear black. A pixel value of 50 would appear gray.

p. 456 Bushong
p. 349 Carlton/Adler

58.   A   Helical scanning allows for increased acquisition speed.

p. 370 Bushong
p. 648 Carlton/Adler

59.   C   Isotropic imaging results in a voxel of equal dimension in all directions and is achieved with 64-slice CT scanners.

p. 379 Bushong
n/a Carlton/Adler

60.   D   Partial volume, streak, and beam hardening are all common CT artifacts. π-lines are a processor-related artifact.

pp. 370, 379, & 384 Bushong
p. 665 Carlton/Adler

61.   A   Air Kerma is measured as joule/kg.

p. 34 Bushong
p. 140 Carlton/Adler

62.   B   A chest x-ray will impart 2 mJ to a patient.

n/a Bushong
n/a Carlton/Adler

63.   C   An abdominal radiograph has an EAK of 3 mGy.

p. 598 Bushong
p. 202 Carlton/Adler

64.   B   EAK for a lateral skull radiograph is 1.5 mGy.

n/a Bushong
p. 202 Carlton/Adler

65.   C   CTDI$_{vol}$ is measured in gray (Gy).

n/a Bushong
n/a Carlton/Adler

66.   A   The effective dose is an indicator of the patient stochastic risk.

p. 575 Bushong
p. 141 Carlton/Adler

67.   C   An adult abdomen CT has an effective dose of ~10 mSv.

n/a Bushong
n/a Carlton/Adler

68.   A   An adult abdomen radiograph has an effective dose of 0.5 mSv.

n/a Bushong
n/a Carlton/Adler

69.   D   Film contrast and latitude are inversely related, so a high film contrast has a narrow (i.e., limited) latitude.

p. 185 Bushong
p. 422 Carlton/Adler

70.   C   Spatial resolution is measured in lp/mm.

p. 450 Bushong
p. 438 Carlton/Adler

71.	A	Magnification is given by the equation SID/SOD.	*p. 285 Bushong* *p. 460 Carlton/Adler*
72.	C	Dynamic range is calculated using 2^n, where n represents the number of bits in the system, or 2^8 is 256.	*p. 454 Bushong* *p. 489 Carlton/Adler*
73.	B	A contrast detail curve shows the relationship between lesion diameter and contrast.	*p. 457 Bushong* *n/a Carlton/Adler*
74.	D	When hypo remains after processing, the stored films will turn brown.	*p. 302 Bushong* *n/a Carlton/Adler*
75.	C	Overexposure does not cause artifacts in CR imaging.	*p. 422 Bushong* *p. 366 Carlton/Adler*
76.	A	CR plates are erased once every day to ensure the removal of fog/ghost images.	*p. 487 Bushong* *n/a Carlton/Adler*
77.	B	QC pertains to the testing and monitoring of equipment.	*p. 306 Bushong* *p. 480 Carlton/Adler*
78.	A	Daily tasks in QC are performed by a trained radiologic technologist.	*p. 333 Bushong* *n/a Carlton/Adler*
79.	C	Both the speed and contrast indicators have an acceptable variance of ±0.15 OD.	*p. 334 Bushong* *n/a Carlton/Adler*
80.	A	Ghosting occurs when an image is taken and not fully erased.	*p. 487 Bushong* *p. 373 Carlton/Adler*
81.	D	A pinhole or slit camera and a star pattern can all be used to measure focal spot sizes, but not a digital camera.	*p. 308 Bushong* *p. 484 Carlton/Adler*
82.	D	100 mGy/min (10 R/min) is the limit for entrance Air Kerma conventional fluoroscopy.	*p. 311 Bushong* *p. 579 Carlton/Adler*
83.	A	A water phantom is used to assess CT image noise.	*p. 390 Bushong* *n/a Carlton/Adler*
84.	B	A bar pattern is used to assess high contrast resolution.	*p. 391 Bushong* *n/a Carlton/Adler*
85.	C	Most human cells each contain 46 chromosomes.	*p. 509 Bushong* *n/a Carlton/Adler*
86.	D	Two-thirds of radiobiological damage is a result of indirect effects of radiation.	*p. 524 Bushong* *n/a Carlton/Adler*

87.	C	Point lesions resulting from low exposures are believed to be responsible for late radiation effects.	*p. 521 Bushong* *n/a Carlton/Adler*
88.	B	A fractionation in radiation therapy permits the repair of normal tissues.	*p. 514 Bushong* *n/a Carlton/Adler*
89.	A	X-rays have an RBE of 1.	*p. 513 Bushong* *n/a Carlton/Adler*
90.	D	Hematological effects occur a few weeks after exposure.	*p. 536 Bushong* *n/a Carlton/Adler*
91.	A	Lung cancer is a stochastic effect of radiation.	*p. 516 Bushong* *n/a Carlton/Adler*
92.	B	A dose of 25 mGy (2.5 rad) doubles the risk of childhood cancer.	*n/a Bushong* *n/a Carlton/Adler*
93.	A	TLDs can measure as low as 0.05 mGy (5 mrad).	*p. 594 Bushong* *n/a Carlton/Adler*
94.	B	A lead equivalent of 0.5 mm is used for protective aprons.	*p. 624 Bushong* *p. 155 Carlton/Adler*
95.	D	Protective devices should be placed on hooks or hangers in the radiography suite to prevent folding, which may crack/breach the protective material.	*n/a Bushong* *n/a Carlton/Adler*
96.	C	An equivalent of ~2 mm (1/16 inch) lead is used as a primary barrier in most radiography rooms.	*p. 585 Bushong* *n/a Carlton/Adler*
97.	C	The minimum source-to-skin distance is 38 cm (15 in.).	*n/a Bushong* *p. 579 Carlton/Adler*
98.	A	Radiation monitors should be worn near the collar, specifically in fluoroscopy.	*p. 622 Bushong* *p. 143 Carlton/Adler*
99.	C	The dose limit for a fetus is 0.5 mSv (50 mrem) per month, which corresponds to 5 mSv (500 mrem) for the entire pregnancy.	*p. 625 Bushong* *p. 159 Carlton/Adler*
100.	B	Approximately 3 mSv (300 mrem) is attributed to medical radiation in the United States.	*p. 5 Bushong* *p. 139 Carlton/Adler*

TEST B

1. How many eV are there in 10 keV?
   A. 100
   B. 1000
   C. 10,000
   D. 100,000

2. Heat is best described as a form of:
   A. energy.
   B. power.
   C. electricity.
   D. temperature.

3. In which shell will an electron have the lowest binding energy?
   A. K
   B. L
   C. M
   D. N

4. Frequencies are measured in:
   A. hertz.
   B. tesla.
   C. gauss.
   D. ohm.

5. Ionization in air produced by x-rays is approximately _____ ions per cm.
   A. 0.1
   B. 1
   C. 10
   D. 100

6. How would halving the distance between electric charges affect the size of the electrostatic force?
   A. Halve it
   B. Reduce to a quarter
   C. Double it
   D. Quadruple it

7. The power dissipated in an electrical circuit with a current I and voltage V is:
   A. $I \times V$.
   B. I/V.
   C. $I^2 V$.
   D. IV^2.

8. A transformer with a turns ratio that is less than 1 would likely be known as a(an):
   A. autotransformer.
   B. step up transformer.
   C. isolation transformer.
   D. step down transformer.

9. Which component is *least* likely to be associated with a diagnostic x-ray generator?
   A. Three-phase power
   B. Single-phase power
   C. Transformer circuit
   D. Rectifier circuit

10. The minimum voltage required to generate tungsten characteristic x-rays is _____ kVp.
    A. 33
    B. 36
    C. 55
    D. 70

11. What percentage (%) of electrical energy is most likely converted into x-rays?
    A. 0.1
    B. 1
    C. 10
    D. 99

12. Doubling the x-ray tube mAs will increase the average photon energy by _____%.
    A. 0
    B. 10
    C. 50
    D. 100

13. What percentage (%) of x-ray interactions in a chest x-ray are most likely to be coherent scatter?
    A. <5
    B. 10
    C. 20
    D. 50

14. The probability of a photoelectric interaction with an atom that has an atomic number Z varies as:
    A. Independent of Z
    B. Z
    C. Z^2
    D. Z^3

15. If a grid has strip height h, and an interspace thickness D, the grid ratio is:
    A. h/D.
    B. D/h.
    C. 1/(D + h).
    D. 1/(D – h).

16. A typical HVL at 80 kV is most likely _____ mm Al.
    A. 0.025
    B. 0.25
    C. 2.5
    D. 25

17. Emission of electrons is most likely increased by increasing the x-ray tube filament:
    A. length.
    B. current.
    C. diameter.
    D. atomic number.

18. At 1 meter, leakage radiation through the tube housing should not exceed _____ mGy/h.
    A. 0.01
    B. 0.1
    C. 1
    D. 10

19. A Positive Beam Limitation (PBL) system uses a sensor in the Bucky tray to provide information on:
    A. image receptor size.
    B. radiation exposure.
    C. scatter radiation.
    D. scatter removal grids.

20. The anode angle of a typical diagnostic x-ray tube is most likely _____ degrees.
    A. 1
    B. 5
    C. 15
    D. 25

21. The minimum number of silver atoms required to sensitize a sensitivity center is most likely:
    A. one.
    B. two.
    C. three.
    D. four.

22. A film processor (developer) is most likely to have a temperature of about _____ °C.
    A. 35
    B. 40
    C. 45
    D. 50

23. The amount of light energy released by a phosphor is most closely related to the material:
    A. areal density.
    B. atomic number.
    C. conversion efficiency.
    D. physical density.

24. Prior to 1970, radiographic screens were most likely made of:
    A. calcium tungstate.
    B. barium sulphate.
    C. gadolinium oxysulfite.
    D. lanthanum (or yttrium).

25. Light produced in an x-ray screen phosphor is most likely to travel:
    A. forward.
    B. sideways.
    C. backwards.
    D. isotropically.

26. Photostimulable phosphors (PSPs) are most likely erased by the use of:
    B. light.
    A. heat.
    C. radiowaves.
    D. compression.

27. Photoconductors in x-ray imaging are most likely made of:
    A. Se.
    B. Ag.
    C. Na.
    D. Si.

28. Which of the following receptors would likely have the best spatial resolution?
    A. CsI flat-panel detector
    B. BaFBr photostimulable phosphor
    C. Se photoconductor
    D. Gd_2O_2S screen

29. The speed of a central processing unit (CPU) is most likely measured in:
    A. bytes.
    B. hertz.
    C. bits.
    D. bits/s.

30. Annual data storage for a radiology department is best measured in:
    A. kilobytes.
    B. megabytes.
    C. gigabytes.
    D. terabytes.

31. What effect will adding 1 bit to the coding for a pixel have on the number of gray shades?
    A. Halve
    B. Double
    C. Quadruple
    D. No effect

32. Lossless compression would most likely reduce data storage needs by about _____%.
    A. 1
    B. 5
    C. 10
    D. 50

33. The post processing function that alters image contrast is most likely:
    A. window center.
    B. window level.
    C. window width.
    D. dynamic range.

34. In thermography (TG), images are imparted to a film by applying:
    A. heat.
    B. pressure.
    C. charge.
    D. voltage.

35. Luminance is most likely measured in:
    A. lux.
    B. nits.
    C. candles.
    D. candela.

36. The best way of displaying a digital image is by use of:
    A. DICOM.
    B. SMPTE.
    C. GSDF.
    D. ACR/NEMA.

37. X-ray beam quantity is *unlikely* to be directly proportional to:
    A. mA.
    B. s.
    C. mAs.
    D. kV.

38. Imaging a patient with ascites would likely require technical factors to:
    A. increase (slightly).
    B. increase (a lot).
    C. decrease.
    D. remain constant.

39. Automatic Exposure Control (AEC) systems are most likely to control:
    A. exposure time.
    B. x-ray tube current.
    C. x-ray tube voltage.
    D. beam filtration.

40. In automatic exposure techniques, the choice of x-ray tube voltage is mainly based on:
    A. patient weight.
    B. patient age.
    C. projection used.
    D. anatomical region.

41. The signal-to-noise ratio (SNR) of a TV system in Interventional Radiology is most likely _____.
    A. 10
    B. 100
    C. 1000
    D. 10,000

42. The location of the fulcrum determines the:
    A. patient entrance.
    B. object plane.
    C. patient exit.
    D. none of the above.

43. The magnification factor can be expressed as:
    A. Image size/Object size.
    B. Image size/SID.
    C. Object size/Image size.
    D. Object size/SID.

44. Which of the following fluoroscopy imaging modes provides the least patient dose per frame?
    A. Spot image
    B. Photospot image
    C. Cinefluorography
    D. DSA

45. The voltage across an image intensifier (II) is most likely _____ V.
    A. 25
    B. 250
    C. 2500
    D. 25,000

46. If the II input diameter is 25 cm, and the II output diameter is 2.5 cm, the minification gain is _____.
    A. 1/100
    B. 1/10
    C. 10
    D. 100

47. Veiling glare of an image intensifier will most likely reduce:
    A. resolution.
    B. contrast.
    C. noise.
    D. dose.

48. Mirrors are most likely to be inserted after an II when obtaining:
    A. spot images.
    B. digital photospot images.
    C. photospot images.
    D. Last Image Hold (LIH).

49. The number of fields in a TV frame is most likely _____ .
    A. 2
    B. 4
    C. 30
    D. 60

50. The bandpass of a standard (500 line) fluoroscopy TV system is approximately _____ MHz.
    A. 5
    B. 10
    C. 20
    D. 40

51. The response of a CCD to light is best described as:
    A. constant.
    B. linear.
    C. quadratic.
    D. exponential.

52. The most important benefit of digital fluoroscopy is the ability to:
    A. increase frame rate.
    B. improve resolution.
    C. post process images.
    D. reduce kVp.

53. The transmitted intensity detected by a single CT detector is known as a:
    A. projection.
    B. sinogram.
    C. filter.
    D. ray sum.

54. The number of projections acquired by a CT scanner for a 360° x-ray tube rotation is likely _____ .
    A. 10
    B. 100
    C. 1000
    D. 100,000

55. CT images show values of relative:
    A. linear attenuation.
    B. mass attenuation.
    C. physical density.
    D. atomic number.

56. The Hounsfield Unit of tissue is most likely _____ .
    A. 0
    B. 50
    C. 100
    D. 200

57. The most likely x-ray tube rotation time in a head CT examination is _____ second(s).
    A. 0.1
    B. 0.3
    C. 1
    D. 3

58. X-ray detectors used in current CT scanners are best characterized as:
    A. scintillators.
    B. photoconductors.
    C. thermoluminescent dosimeters.
    D. ionization chambers.

59. The angle used for linear interpolation algorithms in helical CT is most likely _____ degrees.
    A. 45
    B. 90
    C. 180
    D. 360

60. To calculate CT pitch, one requires information on the speed of the:
    A. table.
    B. x-ray tube.
    C. table and x-ray tube.
    D. detector array.

61. The most likely unit to replace exposure (roentgen) is:
   A. air kerma (Gy).
   B. absorbed dose (Gy).
   C. equivalent dose (Sv).
   D. effective dose (Sv).

62. An absorbed dose of 1 rad corresponds to how many mGy?
   A. 0.1
   B. 1
   C. 10
   D. 100

63. Equivalent dose is best used as an indicator of:
   A. absorbed energy.
   B. biological harm.
   C. ionization events.
   D. radiation intensity.

64. The maximum Air Kerma rate in normal fluoroscopy is currently _____ mGy/min.
   A. 10
   B. 20
   C. 50
   D. 100

65. For a lateral projection, the ratio of the embryo dose to the entrance Air Kerma (EAK) is most likely _____ .
   A. 1/2
   B. 1/5
   C. 1/10
   D. 1/20

66. In an exposed population, the Genetically Significant Dose (GSD) is an indicator of potential:
   A. genetic harm.
   B. stochastic risk.
   C. carcinogenic risk.
   D. somatic damage.

67. Body CTDI doses are measured using an acrylic cylinder with a diameter of _____ cm.
   A. 8
   B. 16
   C. 24
   D. 32

68. A typical adult body $CTDI_{vol}$ would likely be _____ mGy.
    A. 2
    B. 6
    C. 20
    D. 60

69. Subject contrast is least likely to be affected by the lesion:
    A. size.
    B. chemical structure.
    C. density.
    D. atomic number.

70. The best resolution corresponds to an MTF value of _____ .
    A. 0
    B. 0.1
    C. 0.5
    D. 1

71. Focal spot blur is least likely to be affected by:
    A. beam filtration.
    B. focal size.
    C. object magnification.
    D. source to Image receptor distance.

72. Receptor blur would likely be minimized by using a:
    A. photostimulable phosphor.
    B. photoconductor.
    C. scintillator + TFT.
    D. scintillator + film.

73. The most important source of noise in a screen-film radiograph is:
    A. film graininess.
    B. structure mottle.
    C. quantum mottle.
    D. film graininess + structure mottle.

74. Which is most likely to result in repeat (consistent) artifacts?
    A. Patient dentures
    B. Double exposures
    C. Patient motion
    D. Off-center tubes

75. Which is *least* likely to be deemed a distortion issue?
    A. Magnification
    B. Elongation
    C. Foreshortening
    D. Shape

76. QC test results are most likely to be reviewed by a:
    A. radiology administrator.
    B. medical physicist.
    C. diagnostic radiologist.
    D. service engineer.

77. Under MQSA, the leader of the Quality Control team will be the:
    A. radiological technologist.
    B. medical physicist.
    C. diagnostic radiologist.
    D. radiology administrator.

78. Radiography cassettes are most likely cleaned:
    A. daily.
    B. weekly.
    C. monthly.
    D. annually.

79. Which of the following tests is not performed on a radiographic unit?
    A. X-ray beam filtration
    B. Focal spot size
    C. Exposure linearity
    D. Film sensitometry

80. The most appropriate test of a fixer solution is likely:
    A. temperature.
    B. retention.
    C. replenishment.
    D. specific gravity.

81. Testing of flat-panel detectors by a medical physicist is most likely to be performed:
    A. weekly.
    B. monthly.
    C. every 6 months.
    D. annually.

82. The half-value layer (HVL) for a fluoroscopy unit at 80 kVp is most likely _____ kV.
    A. 0.5
    B. 1.5
    C. 2.5
    D. 3.5

83. Accuracy of the light field to the irradiated area in diagnostic radiography is most likely _____ of SID.
    A. 1%
    B. 2%
    C. 5%
    D. 10%

84. The backup for an AEC must terminate the exposure after no more than _____ mAs.
    A. 6
    B. 60
    C. 600
    D. no limit

85. Which type of cell is least likely to divide by meiosis?
    A. Colon
    B. Egg
    C. Sperm
    D. None of the above

86. Irradiation of macromolecules is *least* likely to result in:
    A. main-chain scission.
    B. cross-linking.
    C. point lesions.
    D. duplicate deletion.

87. Which of the following cells is least radiosensitive?
    A. Lymphocyte
    B. Spermatogonia
    C. Neuronal
    D. Intestinal crypt

88. The linear energy transfer for diagnostic x-rays is most likely _____ keV/μm.
    A. 0.3
    B. 3
    C. 30
    D. 300

89. After radiation exposure, the appearance of gastrointestinal syndrome is most likely after three:
    A. hours.
    B. days.
    C. weeks.
    D. months.

90. Stochastic radiation effects are unlikely to include:
    A. leukemia.
    B. genetic effects.
    C. breast cancer.
    D. epilation.

91. Embryonic death is most likely to occur during:
    A. pre-conception.
    B. 10 days post conception.
    C. organogenesis.
    D. fetal period.

92. The fetal period is taken to commence, post conception, at week _____ .
    A. 1
    B. 3
    C. 7
    D. 15

93. Which of the following is a thermoluminescent dosimeter material?
    A. LiF
    B. NaI
    C. Se
    D. CsI

94. The most common scintillator used in x-ray imaging is most likely:
    A. NaI.
    B. NaCl.
    C. Se.
    D. CsI.

95. Bucky slot coverings are most likely to have a Pb equivalent thickness of _____ mm.
    A. 0.25
    B. 0.5
    C. 1
    D. 2

96. The dose rate limit in an area open to the public is most likely _____ mSv/week.
    A. 0.002
    B. 0.02
    C. 0.2
    D. 2

97. Leakage radiation from an x-ray tube at 1 m is required to be no greater than _____ mGy/hour.
    A. 0.01
    B. 0.1
    C. 1
    D. 10

98. Which projection would likely reduce patient doses and radiation risk?
    A. PA
    B. AP
    C. Lateral (Right)
    D. Lateral (Left)

99. Operators are advised to stand a distance greater than _____ meter(s) from a portable x-ray exam.
    A. 0.5
    B. 1
    C. 2
    D. 4

100. When an infant needs to be held for a radiographic examination, the most appropriate person would be:
    A. family member.
    B. radiologic technologist.
    C. attending radiologist.
    D. department secretary.

ANSWERS

1.   C   1 keV = 1000 eV, so 10 keV = 10,000 eV.

p. 34 Bushong
p. 15 Carlton/Adler

2.   A   Heat is a type of energy.

p. 24 Bushong
p. 30 Carlton/Adler

3.   D   Binding energies decrease with increasing distance from the nucleus, so the N-shell has the lowest binding energy.

p. 44 Bushong
p. 27 Carlton/Adler

4.   A   One cycle per second equals one hertz (Hz).

p. 58 Bushong
p. 34 Carlton/Adler

5.   D   X-rays produce ~100 ion pairs/cm in air.

p. 53 Bushong
p. 137 Carlton/Adler

6.   D   Halving the distance would quadruple the force between electric charges.

p. 76 Bushong
p. 39 Carlton/Adler

7.   A   Power = I × V (current × voltage).

p. 116 Bushong
p. 50 Carlton/Adler

8.   D   When the number of turns in the secondary coil is less than in the primary coil, the voltage decreases on the secondary side of the transformer (step down).

p. 94 Bushong
p. 74 Carlton/Adler

9.   B   Single-phase generators are not currently found in radiology departments.

p. 115 Bushong
p. 91 Carlton/Adler

10.   D   A projectile electron would need a keV of 70 or higher to create a K-shell characteristic x-ray.

p. 142 Bushong
p. 131 Carlton/Adler

11.   B   Approximately 1% of the electrical energy is converted into x-rays.

p. 140 Bushong
p. 127 Carlton/Adler

12.   A   mAs has no effect on average photon energy.

p. 246 Bushong
p. 173 Carlton/Adler

13.   A   In diagnostic radiology, less than 5% of interactions are coherent.

p. 164 Bushong
p. 189 Carlton/Adler

---

[1] As a study aid, page numbers for additional study are given for the following references:

Bushong SC: *Radiologic Science for Technologists,* 9th ed. St. Louis, MO: Mosby, 2008.

Carlton RR, Adler AM: *Principles of Radiographic Imaging: An Art and a Science,* 4th ed. Albany, NY: Delmar Publishing Inc., 2005.

14.	D	The probability of a photoelectric interaction is directly proportional to the third power of the atomic number of the material (Z^3).	*p. 167 Bushong* *p. 189 Carlton/Adler*
15.	A	The grid ratio is the grid lines' height divided by the width of the interspace, h/D.	*p. 233 Bushong* *p. 257 Carlton/Adler*
16.	C	The HVL in the diagnostic energy range is ~2.5 mm Al.	*p. 157 Bushong* *p. 166 Carlton/Adler*
17.	B	Increasing the tube current directly affects the number of electrons emitted from the filament.	*p. 106 Bushong* *p. 107 Carlton/Adler*
18.	C	Leakage radiation should not exceed 1 mGy/h (100 mR/h).	*p. 121 Bushong* *p. 118 Carlton/Adler*
19.	A	PBL systems provide automated collimation based on image receptor size using sensors located in the Bucky tray.	*p. 232 Bushong* *p. 232 Carlton/Adler*
20.	C	Diagnostic x-ray systems have target angles of about 15 degrees.	*p. 128 Bushong* *p. 113 Carlton/Adler*
21.	D	A sensitized grain requires a minimum of four or more silver atoms at the sensitivity center.	*p. 184 Bushong* *p. 276 Carlton/Adler*
22.	A	Developer temperature is generally 35 °C, or 95 °F.	*p. 202 Bushong* *p. 295 Carlton/Adler*
23.	C	Conversion efficiency is defined as the amount of light emitted for each x-ray absorbed.	*p. 212 Bushong* *p. 319 Carlton/Adler*
24.	A	Up to the 1970s, original screens in radiography were composed of calcium tungstate.	*p. 208 Bushong* *p. 320 Carlton/Adler*
25.	D	Screens emit light isotropically, or in all directions, when stimulated.	*p. 209 Bushong* *p. 319 Carlton/Adler*
26.	B	Erasure of the PSP is needed to prevent ghosting or artifacts from prior exposures. An intense white light source is used.	*p. 416 Bushong* *p. 358 Carlton/Adler*
27.	A	Amorphous selenium (a-Se) is a photoconductor.	*p. 430 Bushong* *p. 371 Carlton/Adler*
28.	C	Amorphous selenium (a-Se) has the best spatial resolution.	*p. 432 Bushong* *p. 371 Carlton/Adler*
29.	B	Computer processing speeds are quantified using hertz (Hz).	*p. 401 Bushong* *n/a Carlton/Adler*

30.	D	A radiology department measures its data storage in terabytes.	*p. 475 Bushong* *p. 384 Carlton/Adler*
31.	B	Increasing the coding of a pixel by 1 bit will double the number of gray shades.	*p. 403 Bushong* *p. 344 Carlton/Adler*
32.	D	Lossless compression will decrease a file size by 50% of the original without loss of quality.	*p. 490 Bushong* *n/a Carlton/Adler*
33.	C	Window width controls the range of values visualized in an image (contrast), whereas window level controls the image brightness.	*p. 472 Bushong* *p. 349 Carlton/Adler*
34.	A	TG film utilizes a heated source to "expose" the film, creating an instant image.	*p. 206 Bushong* *p. 381 Carlton/Adler*
35.	B	Luminance is measured in candela per meter squared (c/m^2), or nits.	*p. 467 Bushong* *p. 488 Carlton/Adler*
36.	C	The Gray Scale Display Function (GSDF) was developed for consistent gray scale representation.	*p. 479 Bushong* *n/a Carlton/Adler*
37.	D	mAs (mA × seconds) is directly proportional to x-ray beam quantity, whereas x-ray intensity is proportional to kVp^2.	*p. 247 Bushong* *p. 177 Carlton/Adler*
38.	B	Ascites is an additive disease process, requiring a significant increase in technical factors.	*p. 252 Bushong* *p. 250 Carlton/Adler*
39.	A	AEC is used to ensure the exposure time results in a satisfactory image.	*p. 108 Bushong* *p. 101 Carlton/Adler*
40.	D	Automatic exposure techniques select the x-ray tube voltage (kVp) on the basis of the anatomical region being exposed.	*p. 264 Bushong* *p. 538 Carlton/Adler*
41.	C	An SNR of 1000 is most likely used in Interventional Radiology.	*p. 443 Bushong* *p. 347 Carlton/Adler*
42.	B	The fulcrum is the center of the object plane or area that is "in focus" in a tomographic image.	*p. 267 Bushong* *p. 588 Carlton/Adler*
43.	A	Magnification is Image size/Object size.	*p. 285 Bushong* *p. 459 Carlton/Adler*
44.	C	Cinefluoroscopy has the lowest dose per image frame.	*p. 357 Bushong* *p. 577 Carlton/Adler*
45.	D	A voltage of 25,000 V (25 kV) across the image intensifier accelerates the electrons from the photocathode to the anode.	*p. 350 Bushong* *p. 570 Carlton/Adler*

46.	D	Minification gain equals the input diameter divided by the output diameter, all squared. In this example, $(25/2.5)^2$ corresponds to a minification gain of 100.	*p. 351 Bushong* *p. 571 Carlton/Adler*
47.	B	Veiling glare reduces image contrast.	*p. 352 Bushong* *p. 572 Carlton/Adler*
48.	C	The mirror assembly will enter the light field between the II and the TV camera tube when photospot imaging is utilized.	*p. 352 Bushong* *p. 570 Carlton/Adler*
49.	A	There are two TV fields in a TV frame.	*p. 356 Bushong* *p. 575 Carlton/Adler*
50.	A	Traditional fluoroscopy TV systems have a bandpass of ~5 MHz.	*p. 357 Bushong* *n/a Carlton/Adler*
51.	B	CCD cameras respond to light in a linear manner.	*p. 441 Bushong* *p. 575 Carlton/Adler*
52.	C	Digital fluoroscopy is superior to traditional fluoroscopy because of the post processing abilities.	*p. 437 Bushong* *pp. 576 & 578 Carlton/Adler*
53.	D	A single-detector reading will provide a ray sum, where the detector array information will create a projection.	*p. 369 Bushong* *p. 643 Carlton/Adler*
54.	C	One rotation of the CT x-ray tube results in ~1000 projections.	*n/a Bushong* *p. 645 Carlton/Adler*
55.	A	Hounsfield Units or CT numbers are calculated using the linear attenuation coefficient (μ) of water and that of the material to be measured. $HU = 1000 \times (\mu_x - \mu_{water})/\mu_{water}$.	*p. 376 Bushong* *p. 657 Carlton/Adler*
56.	B	Tissue, i.e., muscle, has an HU of 50.	*p. 377 Bushong* *p. 659 Carlton/Adler*
57.	C	Rotation time of 1 second is often used in head imaging.	*n/a Bushong* *p. 651 Carlton/Adler*
58.	A	Scintillator crystals with photodiodes are currently used in CT detectors; often cadmium tungstate or ceramic materials are used.	*p. 374 Bushong* *p. 654 Carlton/Adler*
59.	C	180° interpolation is typically used in modern CT scanners.	*p. 385 Bushong* *n/a Carlton/Adler*
60.	C	Pitch is calculated by dividing the beam width into the distance the table travels per rotation of the x-ray tube.	*p. 386 Bushong* *p. 648 Carlton/Adler*

61.	A	SI system uses Air Kerma, measured in gray (Gy) in place of intensity, measured in roentgen (R).	*p. 34 Bushong* *p. 140 Carlton/Adler*
62.	C	1 rad equals 0.01 Gy, or 10 mGy.	*p. 34 Bushong* *p. 140 Carlton/Adler*
63.	B	Equivalent dose quantifies biological damage.	*p. 513 Bushong* *p. 140 Carlton/Adler*
64.	D	An Air Kerma regulatory limit of 100 mGy/min (10 R/min) has been set for fluoroscopy in the United States.	*p. 311 Bushong* *p. 202 Carlton/Adler*
65.	D	Attenuation in the patient results in an embryo dose 1/20 of the EAK.	*p. 610 Bushong* *n/a Carlton/Adler*
66.	A	GSD is a predictor of potential genetic damage in an exposed population.	*p. 601 Bushong* *p. 139 Carlton/Adler*
67.	D	A 32-cm acrylic phantom is used for CTDI measurements of the adult body scan protocols.	*n/a Bushong* *n/a Carlton/Adler*
68.	C	A typical adult body CTDI$_{vol}$ is 20 mGy.	*p. 603 Bushong* *p. 667 Carlton/Adler*
69.	B	The size, mass density, and atomic number affect the ability to see a lesion. Chemical structure has no effect.	*p. 457 Bushong* *p. 423 Carlton/Adler*
70.	D	A perfect representation of an object has a modulation transfer function (MTF) of 1.	*p. 335 Bushong* *p. 441 Carlton/Adler*
71.	A	Focal spot blur is not affected by x-ray beam filtration.	*p. 288 Bushong* *p. 446 Carlton/Adler*
72.	B	A photoconductor would have the best resolution.	*p. 432 Bushong* *pp. 364 & 371 Carlton/Adler*
73.	C	Quantum mottle is the greatest source of noise in screen-film systems.	*p. 212 Bushong* *p. 322 Carlton/Adler*
74.	D	An off-center x-ray tube would result in multiple repeat exams.	*n/a Bushong* *n/a Carlton/Adler*
75.	A	Magnification is an increase in overall size, and is not a distortion.	*pp. 485 & 486 Bushong* *pp. 446 & 467 Carlton/Adler*
76.	B	QC tests performed by a trained technologist are reviewed by a medical physicist.	*p. 306 Bushong* *p. 481 Carlton/Adler*

77.	C	The diagnostic radiologist is the leader of the Quality Control team (MQSA requirement).	*p. 332 Bushong* *n/a Carlton/Adler*
78.	C	Radiography cassettes are cleaned monthly.	*p. 310 Bushong* *p. 488 Carlton/Adler*
79.	D	Film sensitometry is performed on a film processor, not a radiographic unit.	*p. 314 Bushong* *p. 303 Carlton/Adler*
80.	B	Fixer solutions are tested for retention.	*p. 302 Bushong* *p. 289 Carlton/Adler*
81.	D	Digital radiographic rooms are inspected by a medical physicist once a year, similarly to analog radiography rooms.	*p. 306 Bushong* *n/a Carlton/Adler*
82.	C	An HVL of ~2.5 is appropriate for 80 kVp.	*p. 307 Bushong* *p. 307 Carlton/Adler*
83.	B	The light field may deviate from the irradiated field by 2% of the SID, or 2 cm (0.8 in.) when using 100 cm (40 in.) SID.	*p. 307 Bushong* *p. 484 Carlton/Adler*
84.	C	AEC systems must have a safety backup to terminate exposure at 600 mAs.	*p. 264 Bushong* *p. 542 Carlton/Adler*
85.	A	Genetic cells undergo meiosis, whereas somatic cells undergo mitosis.	*p. 507 Bushong* *n/a Carlton/Adler*
86.	D	Irradiation of macromolecules may result in main chain scission, cross linking, or point lesions, but not duplicate deletion.	*p. 521 Bushong* *n/a Carlton/Adler*
87.	C	Nerve tissue is considered to be highly radioresistant.	*p. 510 Bushong* *n/a Carlton/Adler*
88.	B	X-ray LET is about 3 keV/μm.	*p. 513 Bushong* *n/a Carlton/Adler*
89.	B	Gastrointestinal syndrome occurs at exposures between 10–50 Gy (1000–5000 rad) with a latent period of several days.	*p. 536 Bushong* *n/a Carlton/Adler*
90.	D	Stochastic effects do not include epilation.	*p. 516 Bushong* *n/a Carlton/Adler*
91.	B	Fetal death from radiation exposure is most likely to occur in the first 10 days post conception.	*p. 564 Bushong* *n/a Carlton/Adler*

92.   C   The fetal period begins 7 weeks post conception.   *n/a Bushong*
                                                                n/a Carlton/Adler

93.   A   Lithium fluoride (LiF) is a common TLD material.   *p. 593 Bushong*
                                                                p. 144 Carlton/Adler

94.   D   CsI is used as a detector material in many indirect DR systems,   *n/a Bushong*
            as well as the input phosphor in II tubes used for fluoroscopy.   *n/a Carlton/Adler*

95.   A   Bucky slot covers used in fluoroscopy have a lead equivalent   *p. 583 Bushong*
            of 0.25 mm.   *p. 580 Carlton/Adler*

96.   B   Uncontrolled areas are limited to 1 mSv/y (100 mrem/y), or   *p. 586 Bushong*
            0.02 mSv/wk (2 mrem/wk).   *p. 152 Carlton/Adler*

97.   C   The regulatory limit for leakage radiation is 1 mGy/h   *p. 585 Bushong*
            (100 mR/h) at 1 meter.   *p. 118 Carlton/Adler*

98.   A   PA positioning reduces patient doses and radiation risk.   *p. 606 Bushong*
                                                                       p. 203 Carlton/Adler

99.   C   Portable radiography equipment must have an exposure cord   *p. 582 Bushong*
            of at least 2 meters for appropriate distance from the primary   *p. 155 Carlton/Adler*
            beam.

100.   A   An immobilization device should be used to secure an infant.   *p. 625 Bushong*
            If this is not possible, a member of the family or other health   *n/a Carlton/Adler*
            care professionals should be used, whereas technologists should
            never hold patients.

APPENDIX A

SUMMARY OF PREFIX NAMES AND MAGNITUDES

Prefix Name	Symbol	Magnitude
exa	E	10^{18}
peta	P	10^{15}
tera	T	10^{12}
giga	G	10^{9}
mega	M	10^{6}
kilo	k	10^{3}
hecta	h	10^{2}
deca	da	10
deci	d	10^{-1}
centi	c	10^{-2}
milli	m	10^{-3}
micro	μ	10^{-6}
nano	n	10^{-9}
pico	p	10^{-12}
femto	f	10^{-15}
atto	a	10^{-18}

APPENDIX B

RADIOLOGIC QUANTITIES AND UNITS

Quantity	SI Unit	SI to Non-SI Non-SI Unit	Non-SI to SI Conversion	Conversion
Exposure	C/kg	roentgen	1 C/kg = 3876 R	1 R = 2.58×10^{-4} C/kg
Air Kerma	gray (J/kg)	roentgen	1 Gy = 115 R	1 R = 8.73 mGy
Absorbed dose	gray (J/kg)	rad (100 erg/g)	1 Gy = 100 rad	1 rad = 10 mGy
Equivalent dose	sievert	rem	1 Sv = 100 rem	1 rem = 10 mSv

APPENDIX C

SI AND NON-SI UNITS FOR QUANTITIES USED IN RADIOLOGICAL PHYSICS

Quantity	SI Unit	Non-SI Unit
Length	meter (m)	centimeter (cm)
Mass	kilogram (kg)	gram (g)
Time	second (s)	minute (min)
Electrical current	ampere (A)	electrostatic unit (ESU) per second (s)
Frequency	hertz (Hz)	revolutions per minute (rpm)
Force	newton (N)	dyne
Energy	joule (J)	erg
Power	watt (W)	erg/s
Electrical charge	coulomb (C)	ESU

APPENDIX D

UNITS FOR PHOTOMETRIC QUANTITIES

Quantity	SI Unit	Non-SI Unit	To Convert Non-SI Units to SI Units
Luminance*	cd/m² (nit)	foot-lambert	foot-lambert × 3.4261 = cd/m²
Illuminance**	lumen/m² (lux)	foot-candle	foot-candle × 10.761 = lumen/m²

*Light scattered or emitted by a surface.
**Light falling on a surface.

APPENDIX E

SELECTED RADIOLOGICAL PHYSICS WEB SITES

American Association of Physicists in Medicine (AAPM)	www.aapm.org
American College of Radiology (ACR)	www.acr.org
American Journal of Roentgenology (AJR)	www.ajronline.org
American Registry of Radiologic Technologists (ARRT)	www.arrt.org
American Roentgen Ray Society (ARRS)	www.arrs.org
American Society of Radiologic Technologists (ASRT)	www.asrt.org
Conference of Radiation Control Program Directors (CRCPD)	www.crcpd.org
CTISUS Advanced Diagnostic Imaging	www.ctisus.com
Health Physics Society (HPS)	www.hps.org
Huda Physics Review	www.HudaPhysicsReview.com
Image Gently	www.imagegently.org
Image Wisely	www.imagewisely.org
International Commission on Radiation Units and Measurements (ICRU)	www.icru.org
International Commission on Radiological Protection (ICRP)	www.icrp.org
Joint Commission for Accreditation of Healthcare Organizations (JCAHO) (now Joint Commission)	www.jcaho.org
National Council on Radiation Protection and Measurements (NCRP)	www.ncrponline.org
Radiological Society of North America (RSNA)	www.rsna.org
Society for Imaging and Informatics in Medicine (SIIM)	www.siim.web.org
U.S. Food and Drug Administration (FDA)	www.fda.gov
U.S. Nuclear Regulatory Commission (NRC)	www.nrc.gov

BIBLIOGRAPHY

GENERAL RADIOLOGIC IMAGING

AAPM Report No. 15: Performance Evaluation and Quality Assurance in Digital Subtraction Angiography. New York: American Institute of Physics, 1985. www.aapm.org/pubs/reports/RPT_15.pdf.

AAPM Report No. 70: Cardiac Catheterization Equipment Performance. Report of AAPM Task Group No. 17. Madison, WI: Medical Physics Publishing, 2001. www.aapm.org/pubs/reports/RPT_70.pdf.

Ball J, Moore AD, Turner S: *Ball and Moore's Essential Physics for Radiographers*, 4th ed. Hoboken, NJ: Wiley-Blackwell, 2008.

Bushong SC: *Radiologic Science for Technologists*, 9th ed. St. Louis, MO: Mosby, 2008.

Carlton RR, Adler AM: *Principles of Radiographic Imaging: An Art and a Science*, 4th ed. Albany, NY: Delmar Publishing Inc., 2005.

Carter C: *Digital Radiography and PACS*. St. Louis, MO: Mosby, 2008.

Cullinan AM, Cullinan JE: *Producing Quality Radiographs*, 2nd ed. Baltimore, MD: Lippincott William & Wilkins, 1994.

Daniels C: Fundamentals of Diagnostic Radiology (CD-ROM). Madison, WI: Medical Physics Publishing, 1996.

Fosbinder R, Kelsey CA: *Essentials of Radiologic Science*. New York: McGraw-Hill, 2011.

Graham TG: *Principles of Radiological Physics*. 5th ed. New York: Churchill Livingstone, 2007.

Papp J: *Quality Management in the Imaging Sciences*, 4th ed. St. Louis, MO: Mosby, 2010.

Samei E, Badano A, Chakraborty D, Compton K, Cornelius C, Corrigan K, Flynn MJ, Hemminger B, Hangiandreou N, Johnson J, Moxley M, Pavlicek W, Roehrig H, Rutz L, Shepard J, Uzenoff R, Wang J, Willis C: Assessment of Display Performance for Medical Imaging Systems. Report of the American Association of Physicists in Medicine (AAPM) Task Group 18, Medical Physics Publishing, Madison, WI, AAPM On-Line Report No. O3, April 2005. www.aapm.org/pubs/reports/OR_03.pdf.

Selman J: *The Fundamentals of Imaging Physics and Radiobiology: For the Radiologic Technologist*, 9th ed. Springfield, IL: Charles C Thomas, 2000.

Stevens AT: *Quality Management for radiographic imaging*. New York: McGraw-Hill, 2001.

EXAMINATION REVIEW BOOKS

Carlton RR: *Delmar's Radiography Exam Review*. Albany, NY: Delmar Cengage Learning, 2010.

Bonsignore K, Maiellaro D, Kudlas M, Thengampallil A, Thengampallil S: *Kaplan's Radiography Exam with CD-ROM*, 2nd ed. New York: Kaplan Publishing, 2009.

Huda W: *Review of Radiologic Physics*, 3rd edition. Philadelphia: Lippincott Williams & Wilkins, 2010.

Leonard WL: *Radiography Examination Review*, 10th ed. Holly Springs, NC: JLW Publications, 2004.

Saia DA: *Appleton and Lange's Review for the Radiography Examination*, 7th ed. New York: McGraw-Hill, 2008.

Saia DA: *Radiography PREP: Program Review and Exam Preparation*, 5th ed. New York: McGraw-Hill, 2008.

BREAST IMAGING

American College of Radiology (ACR). *Mammography Quality Control Manual*. Reston, VA: ACR, 1999.

Andolina V, Lillé L: *Mammographic Imaging: A Practical Guide*, 3rd ed. Philadelphia: Lippincott Williams & Wilkins, 2010.

Myers CP: *Mammography Quality Control: The Why and How Book*. Madison, WI: Medical Physics Publishing, 1997.

Peart O: *Lange Q&A: Mammography Examination*, 2nd ed. New York: McGraw-Hill, 2008.

Wagner JR, Wight EK: *Mammography Exam Review*. Philadelphia: Lippincott Williams & Wilkins, 2007.

COMPUTED TOMOGRAPHY

Blanck C: *Understanding Helical Scanning*. Baltimore, MD: Williams & Wilkins, 1998.

Phlipot-Scroggins D, Reddinger W Jr, Carlton R, Shappell A: *Lippincott's Computed Tomography Review*. Philadelphia: JB Lippincott, 1995.

Romans LE: *Computed Tomography for Technologists: A Comprehensive Text*. Baltimore, MD: Williams & Wilkins, 2010.

Seeram E: *Computed Tomography: Physical Principles, Clinical Applications, and Quality Control*, 3rd ed. Philadelphia: WB Saunders, 2008.

RADIOBIOLOGY AND RADIATION PROTECTION

American College of Radiology: *Radiation Risk: A primer*. Reston, VA: ACR, 1996.

Bushong SC: *Radiation Protection*. New York: McGraw-Hill, 1998.

Hall EJ, Giaccia AJ: *Radiobiology for the Radiologist*, 6th ed. Philadelphia: Lippincott Williams & Wilkins, 2005.

National Council on Radiation Protection and Measurements (NCRP) Report No. 147. Structural Shielding for Medical X-Ray Imaging Facilities. Bethesda, MD: NCRP, 2004.

Seeram E: *Radiation Protection*. Philadelphia: Lippincott, 1997.

Statkiewicz Sherer MA, Visconti PJ, Ritenour ER: *Radiation Protection in Medical Radiography*, 6th ed. St Louis: Mosby, 2010.

Wagner LK, Lester RG, Saldana LR: *Exposure of the Pregnant Patient to Diagnostic Radiations: A Guide to Medical Management*, 2nd ed. Madison, WI: Medical Physics Publishing, 1997.

About the Authors

Walter Huda studied Physics at Corpus Christi College, Oxford University, in the United Kingdom, followed by a doctorate degree in Medical Physics at the Royal Postgraduate Medical School (Hammersmith Hospital) at the University of London. From 1976 to 1981, Dr. Huda worked as a physicist at Amersham International, a commercial company specializing in radioactive products. In 1982, Dr. Huda moved to the Manitoba Cancer Treatment and Research Foundation in Winnipeg, MB, Canada, where he worked as a medical physicist in the fields of diagnostic imaging and medical radiation dosimetry. Dr. Huda has worked at the University of Florida, Gainesville, FL (1990 to 1997), SUNY Upstate Medical University at Syracuse (1997 to 2007), and the Medical College of South Carolina (MUSC) in Charleston, SC (2007 to present). His research interests are in medical imaging and radiation dosimetry. He has published one other book[1], approximately 200 scientific papers, and is board certified by the Canadian College of Physicists in Medicine and by the American Board of Medical Physics.

Dr. Huda has extensive experience in teaching x-ray physics, including to physicists, radiology residents, and x-ray technologists. Dr. Huda also offers review courses in North America directed at residents and other medical practitioners in Boston, Chicago, Ottawa, and Charleston, attracting over 400 attendees each year.

Kerry Greene-Donnelly holds a Master of Business Administration degree from SUNY Oswego, a Bachelor of Professional Studies degree in Health Service Management from SUNY Institute of Technology at Utica/Rome, and an Associate in Applied Science degree in Medical Radiography from SUNY Health Science Center at Syracuse. Kerry has 16 years of professional experience, with 11 of those years teaching in the Department of Medical Imaging Sciences at SUNY Upstate Medical University Syracuse. Kerry continues to work clinically, consulting on accreditation and CT protocol development.

Kerry teaches a variety of courses including: fundamentals of imaging, fundamentals of computed tomography, quality management, management principles, and imaging in radiation oncology, and coordinates computed tomography clinical rotations. Kerry is nationally certified in the following modalities: Radiography, Mammography, Computed Tomography, and Quality Management. Kerry participates in several professional societies: American Society of Radiologic Technologists (ASRT), Central New York Society of Radiologic Technologists, Western New York Health Physics Society, and the Upstate New York chapter of the American Association of Physicists in Medicine.

---

[1] Huda W: *Review of Radiologic Physics*, 3rd edition. Philadelphia: Lippincott Williams & Wilkins, 2010.

CPSIA information can be obtained at www.ICGtesting.com
Printed in the USA
238633LV00002B/1/P